S0-AEW-037

THE BOOK OF
SHADOWS™

The Mage Players Guide

Queen of Pattern

THE MAGE

THE TOWER

LUNA

The Sourcebook for Players and Storytellers of Mage

Credits

Written by: Emrey Barnes, Bill Bridges, Steve Brown, Phil Brucato, Brian Campbell, Sam Chupp, Beth Fischi, Don Frew, Dan Greenberg, William Hale, Harry Heckel, Sam Inabinet, Darren McKeeman, Judith A. McLaughlin, Jim Moore, Kevin Murphy, John R. Robey, Kathleen Ryan, Steve Wieck, Ehrik Winters, Teeuwynn Woodruff

Additional Material: Bob Asselin, James Estes, Andrew Greenberg, James Medley, Mark Rein•Hagen, Ryk Strong

Developed by: Phil Brucato

Edited by: Brian Campbell

Art Director: Richard Thomas

Layout and Typesetting: Aileen E. Miles

Art: James Crabtree, Scott Johnson, Matt Korteling, Robert MacNeill, Dan Smith, Joshua Gabriel Timbrook, Lawrence Allen Williams, Jeff Wright

Front Cover Art: Larry Schnelli

Front and Back Cover Design: Larry Schnelli

**4598 STONEGATE IND. BLVD.
STONE MTN., GA 30083
U.S.A.**

**WHITE WOLF
GAME STUDIO**

© 1993 by White Wolf. All rights reserved. Reproduction without written permission of the publisher is expressly denied, except for the purpose of reviews. **Mage The Ascension, Vampire The Masquerade, Werewolf The Apocalypse** and **The Book of Shadows: The Mage Players Guide** are trademarks of the White Wolf Game Studio. All names, titles, characters and text herein are copyrights of White Wolf unless otherwise noted.

Covenant, Mythic Europe, Regio, Cult of Mercury, Mistridge, Certamen, and Troupe Play are trademarks of Wizards of the Coast , Inc., are from the *Ars Magica*™ game, and are used with permission. *Ars Magica* is a trademark of Wizards of the Coast, Inc.

The mention or reference to any companies or products in these pages is not a challenge to the trademarks or copyrights concerned.

Due to mature subject matter, reader discretion is advised. **Printed in Canada**

Special Thanks to:

Rebecca "Rat Worship" **Shaeffer**, for knowing how to get Rob and Brian hot.

Louvie "Bungee" **Locklear**, for the reason she need not buy beers in Biloxi.

Lyndi "Bimbo" **Hathaway-McKeeman**, for her fan club's alternative to root canal surgery.

Richard "Not the Skinner" **Haight**, for not being the guy you love to Haight.

Mike "Exorcist" **Krause**, for battling the Devil in GOD.

Mark "Spitz" **Rein•Hagen**, for making a big splash at M.O.C.

Danny "Fabio Fan" **Landers**, for spilling the beans on Ken's secret obsession.

Wes "HoJo" **Harris**, for being the slickest *gaijin* at the Mafia party.

Jim "Recruiting Sergeant" **Townsend**, for finding new ways to pay the rent.

Oh Soon (Kim) "Welcome to the Jungle" **Shropshire**, for waltzing in where GOD fears to tread.

Sam "Comfy Chair" **Chupp**, for bringing pagan joy to Mouseville.

THE BOOK OF SHADOWS™

The Mage Players Guide

Contents

Prelude: Behind the Wall

By Kathleen Ryan

This is an elegant house. Its patrons claim it is the finest in the state, if not the nation, and solidly, if sordidly, endorse it. They describe the furnishings as perfect, the talents of the employees as exquisite and the arrangements as painfully discreet. Perhaps these things are true. Certainly the operation is so refined as to make unnecessary any blackmail. The mayor counts the madam among his closest friends.

The police never raid this house.

On the ground floor is a restaurant as famous and as respectable as any other. Amanda slinks deliberately across the main salon, drifting slowly closer to her target's table. Out of the corner of her eye, she sees him, sees the wineglass in his flaccid hand. Twice the magick has misfired, twice this man has escaped, all unwittingly. A clumsy waiter dropped the first tainted glass; a drunken diner stole the second. Though new to her powers, already Amanda has come to distrust coincidence, and ice settles in her spine. She longs to search these vacuous faces for the enemy, to fight directly the half-suspected opposition... she curses this clumsy approach even as she neutralizes the poison of the second glass. A knife, she feels, is so much more final.

She reaches the table just as a noisy party of seven crowds past in the other direction. Jostled, Amanda leans against the table for support, smiles vaguely as the murmured apologies begin. One satin-gloved hand moves a fraction of an inch...

"Jane, darling! Is it really you?" One of the passing diners, a handsome Asian gentleman in a tuxedo, takes her firmly by the shoulders. The pressure is light, but her hands are immobilized.

"Do I know you?" She searches his face. Never in her life has she used "Jane" as an alias, but this gives her time for a moment's thought.

"I'll be so hurt if you don't remember, you know." No. It makes no difference whether this man is her enemy or not. Her adversary doubtless watches, and this is her last chance.

"How could I ever forget?" As she kisses him, she shifts space behind her, loses herself to the twisting, raw-silk feel of reality in the room, lifts the branching futures out of their random order and reweaves them around the plate before her target. Food poisoning. She holds her control a moment longer, recoils from the shock of countermagick, satisfied that her adversary's attention is held there. Only then does she flick the wholly mundane poison into the wineglass.

The gentleman in her embrace has cold eyes now, and there is steel beneath his pleasant tones. He takes her arm, and there is steel in the gun that presses against her ribs. The diners see only the smiles, hear only the airy chatter of old lovers; most turn back to their meals before Amanda and her captor disappear through the shadowed doors at the rear of the salon. She must play this scenario out helplessly to give the poison time to work.

They halt by a closed door on a top floor of the old brick hotel. He knocks just once.

"All's fair. I've got her."

"What?"

"Wait a minute."

"Kill the lights. What she can't see... damn it, hurry up."

Trapped in this gilded hallway, Amanda simply waits, wonders if perhaps he will kill her, wonders if she should be afraid... wonders at her own delight. She has done what she came here to do. The kill was right, and it was hers, and it was good. The feeling convinces the young Euthanatos of the worth of her Path in ways the Old Man's teaching never has. As the door opens, she fights a smile.

They trip her up, hold her down, take her knives and trinkets and cuff her. Then someone slams her into an armchair, and the questions begin again.

"Who are you?" It's the "gentleman's" voice, but rougher, and all steel now.

"Who are *you*?" Amanda answers back, nearly laughing.

"Answer me. Who are you?"

"Why do you want to know?" she asks, ready to play the game for hours.

"Michael?"

"I'm not touching her." This voice is very low, rumbling across the room like a tiny earthquake. "She reeks of it. We should kill her and leave. Now."

"Michael, we need to know," says another. The voice is thin and reedy and is soon lost in the pitch-black darkness.

An exasperated sigh fills the room. Amanda feels movement behind her and a curved blade at her throat. The ice fear returns, and her muscles tighten against her will.

"Who are you, and who do you work for?" the "gentleman" asks again.

"Jane Carter. I'm free lance." With a start, she realizes the name she picks out of thin air is the same name he had called her. But even in the wash of memory, she speaks carefully, trying to hold her throat as still as possible, hoping the lies will pass by him.

"That's better. And why are— " He stops as the door slams open.

The tiny silhouette in the doorway stands poised for an instant, uncertain, and then fumbles for the light switch.

"He's dead," says the shadow, and the overhead light reveals her: a small girl with an elfin pointed chin, honey-dark skin and flinty, flashy eyes. Her movements are sharp and light, and her every gesture sends her short brown locks twitching around her face. Behind her stands a sleekly muscled man with a gray fedora and a dark blue suit. He eyes the child— if child she is— uncomfortably, and scratches at his shirt collar as he speaks.

"Well, not yet, actually. But— "

"But I saw the ambulance people, and they're all from Cerberus. Her people. She's that old guy's new apprentice, just with her hair changed and her face made up. She's practically an Adept. She got him, David. You missed it." The girl looks past the man in the tuxedo to Amanda. "It was the wine, wasn't it?"

"Yes." Amanda's voice is steady, but her glance darts around the room looking for exits, for holes in the cage closed round her. There are no windows, and only one door that she can see. Her gaze settles on her captor, David, trying to gauge his reaction, but by then, his face shows nothing. Slowly, she tries to move her neck far enough to see the man behind her, but the blade presses close, warningly.

"And you missed it, David."

"I'm sorry." He sits down on the edge of the bed, tries to catch her eyes. "But what —"

"Why did you do it?" The girl advances on Amanda. "Why? What gives you the right to come here and do this?" Her face is bleached with anger, and tears of fury stream down it like rain.

"His life was already over. I only ended it." But even relying on the new rock-hard core of certainty in her heart, she finds it difficult to face down this accuser.

"How do you know? You're just a student like the rest of us. How do you *know?*"

"He withered everything he touched... his corruption was—"

"Do you know that? Or did they tell you that? Your people only destroy things, and they never give any real reasons. They never give anything back or ask anybody else if what they destroy is important. Now he's dead." Amanda stares, unsure and shaken, and finds nothing to say.

The blade leaves her throat, and she sees its owner for the first time as he crosses to the girl's side. In silence, the swarthy, disheveled teenager puts one hand very gently on her shoulder and speaks to her quietly. The man with the gray fedora stands near them like an old friend at a funeral, guarding the mourners from further grief. David, watching all three, clears his throat.

"Well." He turns to Amanda. "Look... I also think that motherfu…" He hesitates, looking at his youngest colleague— "...that man you've just... recycled... was a waste of... spit. But we needed that bastard downstairs alive and where he was, so that his wife's lover would stop the Wellesley Parks development bill from reaching the State Senate. But no one ever consults us in these matters. Obviously." He rises quickly to his feet. "Shit."

"Xia?" The little girl turns to him. "You said the ambulance was already here? We need to move. That bastard will be D.O.A. or worse. The police will be slow to show up at Anne's place, and Big Brother is probably already on the way. Thank God Anne hates computers… oh, hello, Anne."

A statuesque blonde in evening dress and elaborate, sophisticated makeup comes striding through the door, clutching a sheaf of papers in one hand and a fountain pen in the other. David flushes, but turns and addresses her brightly. "Thank God you hate computers."

"That's not the only thing I hate." She speaks quickly and quietly, but her clipped, near-monotone only lends the words greater bite. "What kind of shit are you trying to pull here, Cho? They're carting one of my customers, one of my *upstairs* customers, away, and all Marilyn can say is that you and this bitch practically fell on him ten minutes before the convulsions started."

"I'm sorry, Anne. We tried to stop it, I swear, but I'll explain later."

"I don't want later, I want now. Before the Black Hats and Mirrorshades show up."

David Cho turns to his prisoner. "Jane —"

"Amanda." She doesn't know why she says it.

"Amanda. What was your exit route?"

"Cho! Have you heard a single damn thing I've said to you?" Still ignored, the blonde throws her papers at him.

"I…" Amanda hesitates in the wash of fury radiating from the older woman. "I was just going to walk out before he collapsed. It's a relatively slow poison."

"That's no good." He frowns, closes his eyes for a moment. "They'll be slowest around the back. I think we can use the laundry exit... I'll need the keys to the needle gate, Anne."

"Forget it. I need you here if I'm going to have the cops in this place."

"Anne. Please. You know it won't just be the cops."

And, as Amanda watches, the woman's face darkens, new lines revealing themselves in the shadows around her eyes. One side of her mouth grimaces, as if she were lost in some painful memory. When she speaks, she seems older... but the young assassin finds it to be a strange improvement.

"All right. Take them. But this is for the kid. Not you."

He nods. "But I'll recruit you yet, Anne darling. Choirboy, get the cuffs off of Lucretia Borgia here." A calm-eyed, grayish man appears in the far corner and walks toward her. "And you, Amanda, behave yourself, or we may forget how principled we are."

The gray man bends over her with the key and holds her wrists gently to unlock her bonds.

"Hold still," he whispers, "if you please. And may I suggest that you do nothing whatsoever to provoke my friend Michael, there."

"Why do you care?" she says, as Anne harangues David and David addresses the others.

"I, in the singular sense, of course, feel that in time we shall all be both less and more than we now permit and that these disparate portions of ourselves shall no longer oppose each other." He helps her to her feet.

"What?"

"We of the Traditions are allies, are we not? Even on the edge of ruin, we acknowledge the darkness that is our common foe." He reaches into his charcoal-colored coat and brings forth her foci and a further brace of knives, which he hands to her. "You can use these, can you not?"

"Yes."

"Then follow close behind us, and may We who are the One bless our common venture."

And from each in the room there came the same mumbled response.

"Amen."

Introduction

Tell me a tale, a parable, an illumination. Speak to me of
truths hidden in metaphor and secrets glimpsed behind a fleeting
image. Give me a hard crust of fantasy to nibble on. It's so much
more palatable than the dry waybread of conventional wisdom.

Astonish me.

— Hapsburg, Orphan Seer

A Book of Shadows is a road map to enlightenment, a journal of progress upon the Path of magick. In it, the practitioner charts her journey from initiation to understanding by using anecdotes, tales, lessons, rites and reflections. **The Book of Shadows: The Mage Players Guide** is no Book of Shadows in the truest sense, but it will hopefully provide some guidance and inspiration to **Mage** players and Storytellers alike.

There are few easy answers within these pages, but many possibilities. Much of the information contained herein takes the form of stories, parables imparting truth as seen from many different points of view. Some of these tales may raise more questions than they answer, but for **Mage**, this is only appropriate. If reality is malleable, then there are many truths from which to choose. Solid answers limit possibility.

A Reflection: What is a Mage?

Through stereotypes and popular misconceptions, the nature of a mage has been reduced to spell-casting and lab-tinkering. The *methods* of some mages have been perceived as the *meaning* behind their practices. Before we begin, let's take a look at the essence behind the facade.

The Mage

Each mage is, to himself or herself, a hero in the truest sense of the word, stepping out from the mass of humanity to follow an elevated Path. This is as true of the Technocracy and Nephandi as it is for the wizards of the Traditions; each faction simply follows a different Path towards a different goal. Many along the way get sidetracked and wander down the road of hubris, the fatal pride that comes with insight into the truth and power beyond mortal vision.

The mage does not simply cast magick spells; he or she *becomes* magick personified, transcending the boundaries of what is believed possible. A mage— any true mage— alters reality by simply becoming aware.

The Vision

The different mage factions perceive their place in the larger whole differently. For the Traditions, that Path includes gathering all the souls of humanity, all the Avatars of humanity, and leading them towards some common goal (about which they all disagree). To the Technocracy, the Path of the common good involves making reality safe for the Masses— controlled, protected and guided by the Technocracy's higher vision. The Nephandi, it is rumored, seek to polarize light and darkness into their purest forms so that the strongest might overcome the weakest and bring unification through conquest; the Marauders, some believe, seek to shape all creation into a dynamic ball of endless possibilities. Each mage has a vision; the Ascension War revolves around these different goals and the means to achieve them.

The Path

Some mages speak of the guiding forces behind the Paths; many see these forces as cosmological entities, while others view them as forces of existence, scientific principles or shifting essences of never-ending creation. Many spend lifetimes trying to define these forces, while others just chuck the whole deal and simply struggle for survival or strive for power. Nevertheless, each individual, whether mage or mortal, has occasional glimpses of the Big Picture. Mages are simply closer to grasping the "answer" (assuming that there is one). Through this insight, all mages are *dynamic*, guiding creation forward just by existing. Magick powers are only a side-effect of this condition.

The War

To the calmer mind, each Path assumes some function in the balance of creation. Most mages, however, are anything but calm. With enlightenment comes the certainty that each chosen road to Ascension is the only right one; with this certainty comes conflict, sometimes subtle, often deadly.

Conflict is dynamic; without struggle, creation stagnates. The intensity of the Ascension War, however, grinds mages and Sleepers alike beneath a Wheel gone wild. Each faction holds to its vision with a determination that rends the fabric of creation's Tapestry and crushes the souls of everyone involved. Now the balance is lost; the Wheel wobbles, the Tapestry frays. Welcome to the World of Darkness.

A Guide: How to Use this Book

The Book of Shadows is broken down into Books instead of chapters. Each Book contains material of interest to **Mage** players:

Book One: The Gifts of Awakening— Traits

This Book includes new Abilities, Archetypes and Backgrounds, plus Merits and Flaws, an optional spice for **Mage** characters.

Book Two: Faces of Magick— Portraits

This Book details the various mage factions through their own eyes and presents the lost Tradition of the Ahl-i-Batin.

Book Three: The Book of Rules — Systems

In this Book, **Mage** players and Storytellers will find new rules for foci, talismans, study points, familiars, child mages and the Akashic art of Do, as well as a quick-and-dirty system for magick and clarification of many gray areas of the **Mage** rules.

Book Four: The Magick Toybox — Equipment

The Book presents a collection of rotes, talismans and more mundane equipment for the well-equipped **Mage** character.

Book Five: The Fragile Path — Parables

This series of tales illuminates aspects of the Path of the mage: Seekings, Quintessence, the mentor/apprentice relationship, two opposing views of the end of the Mythic

Age and the rise of the Technocracy, and more. Unlike simple essays, these parables illustrate **Mage** in action and flesh out the world of the Awakened through the experiences of the mage.

Book Six: Guiding Words — Council

Words of wisdom to **Mage** players and Storytellers alike.

A Momentary Dash of Reason

Though many aspects of the game are rooted in real-world beliefs and metaphysics, **Mage** is a game. It's fiction. Period. You won't find lost secrets of arcane lore or authentic portrayals of occult doctrine here. Hopefully, your troupe will find entertainment mixed with food for thought in your **Mage** chronicle; we at White Wolf would like to inspire roleplayers to expand their horizons beyond the dungeon-crawl, but that's as far as it goes. **Mage** is a game. That's all.

Enter freely and of your own will. Enjoy.

Book One: Gifts of Awakening

Compensate me
Animate me
Complicate me
Elevate me
— Rush, "Animate"

This Book contains Traits for **Mage** characters: new Abilities and Backgrounds, as well as a new Trait category, Merits and Flaws. These Traits may be used to build new characters or to spice up existing ones, with the Storyteller's approval.

An important distinction separates mages from their "partners" in the World of Darkness: mages are mortal. They bleed. They age. They die easily compared to regenerating Garou or immortal Kindred. Without powerful combat magicks, mages must rely on their savvy, cleverness and esoteric knowledge to survive head-to-head encounters with other Awakened. A range of Abilities, coupled with good sense and wise use of magick, enable mages to compete with the many forces arrayed, more often than not, against them.

The usual rules for character creation still apply in regard to these offerings. Many of these Merits, Flaws and Abilities originated in **Werewolf** or **Vampire**, although many have been reworked to apply to mages. Storytellers and players should feel free to allow or disallow any or all of these Traits in their games.

New Abilities

With no words, with no song
You can dance the dream with your body on
And this curve, is your smile
And this cross, is your heart
And this line, is your path
— Kate Bush, "The Red Shoes"

The following are new Abilities you can use in any Storyteller game. They describe some of the limitless abilities your character can take and can help define your character. Some of these Abilities may seem less significant and useful than the more general abilities described in **Mage**. Some are sub-categories of more general abilities. For example, you might want to make a character roll Dexterity + Athletics when firing a bow rather than introducing the Archery skill. It is up to the Storyteller whether any of the Abilities listed here can be purchased.

Talents

Artistic Expression

You have the talent to produce works of art in various media. You can produce saleable works of two- or three-dimensional art and understand something of the technical aspects of paintings and sketches. You are able to sketch a reasonably accurate rendition of a place or person.

• **Novice:** Your work is simple, seen as charmingly naive by some and as amateurish by others.

•• **Practiced:** Your work could win prizes at local art society shows.

••• **Competent:** You could get a showing in a minor gallery.

•••• **Expert:** Your work is widely admired, and galleries contact you about exhibitions. You are invited to teach at local art colleges.

••••• **Master:** You are acknowledged as a driving force in contemporary art. Your work commands enormous prices and is found in art museums as well as commercial galleries and private collections.

Possessed by: Artists, Commercial Illustrators, Cartoonists, Police Artists, Forgers, Woodworkers, Theatre and Movie Set Builders, Special Effects Technicians, Model Makers

Specialties: Oils, Watercolors, Mixed Media, Charcoal, Sketching, Caricature, Lighting Artist, Impressionist, Photo-Realism, Abstract, Miniatures, Stone, Resin, Wood, Metals, Classical, Kinetic, Models, Decoration

Blatancy

You specialize in doing vulgar magick in plain sight and having Sleepers accept it. You may be a stage magician with a large following or a faith healer who prepares the faithful to accept miracles. Or you may just appear to be so weird and outlandish that compared to yourself, the things you do are mundane. This Talent can be combined with Manipulation to make Sleepers view vulgar magick as coincidental. Note that this Talent only works under the right circumstances; throwing fireballs down Main Street would be considered vulgar no matter what the cover might be.

• **Novice:** It's amazing how you pull gold bricks out of people's ears. How do you do that trick?

•• **Practiced:** Only a weirdo would tape rubber bat wings to a cat and throw it out the window. Good thing it landed okay. Someone should call the Humane Society.

••• **Competent:** The giant robot in your garage is really neat, and the kids love watching it walk around when you hook up the rubber brain in the jar. Would you consider letting the school use it for their Haunted House?

•••• **Expert:** Mrs. Wilson is on the roof again with her broomstick. It's really sad how you've gotten since her husband died. Poor woman. I think she really thinks she's a witch. But would you explain to the children that what we saw was just the wind and that we did not see her flying?

••••• **Master:** I'm a toad! Cool! Give me another hit of that stuff, man. This trip is really funky.

Possessed by: Stage Magicians, Neighborhood Weirdoes, Hermits, Crazy People, Gurus, Party Animals, Nannies

Specialties: Gadgets, Conjuring Tricks, Religious Miracles, Drug Trips

Carousing

This is the ability to have a good time at a party or other social occasion while making sure others around you also have a good time. It involves a mixture of eating, good cheer, and drinking without making a fool out of yourself. On a successful roll of Manipulation + Carousing, the character can make a lasting good impression on everyone around him; this can be helpful if the mage is trying to make friends, garner information or distract the attendees while his cabal rifles through the coat room. The difficulty of the roll depends on the social event: three or less for a house party with a buffet, seven or more for a sit-down dinner.

• **Novice:** Good ol' Uncle Bill
•• **Practiced:** Jake the Frat Rat
••• **Competent:** James Bond
•••• **Expert:** The Three Musketeers
••••• **Master:** Bluto in "Animal House"

Possessed by: Actors, Dilettantes, College Students, Vampires

Specialties: Sexual Innuendo, Bon Mots, Lewd Jokes, Drinking, Exaggeration, Anecdotes

Diplomacy

You have the ability to handle negotiations. Even when handling touchy subjects, you are able to get results without ruffling too many feathers. You are skilled at mediating disputes and discussing delicate subjects. You get along with others without overt manipulation and without letting your own aims fall by the wayside. This Ability involves a knowledge of the formal rules of give-and-take, as well as the official cultural rules of conduct and politeness.

• **Novice:** You can iron out schoolyard disputes.

•• **Practiced:** Friends ask you to deal with things for them.

••• **Competent:** You could shine in management or personnel.

•••• **Expert:** You could be a professional union negotiator or ombudsman.

••••• **Master:** You can defuse nearly any situation, from an industrial dispute to a religious war.

Possessed by: Schoolteachers, Union Negotiators, Politicians, Tycoons, Diplomats, Personnel Officers, Counselors

Specialties: Mediation, Negotiation, Etiquette, International Relations, Industry, Personal Relationships, Tact

Fortune Telling

You may or may not have the gift to tell accurate fortunes, but you can make people believe you do. This Ability may prove useful as a plot device, a means for the character to earn money, or a good cover for Time magick. While this Talent confers no magick in and of itself, it may add to your successes; for each two successes, reduce the difficulty of divination magick by 1.

• **Novice:** You are able to use one method of divination adequately and treat this Ability as a pastime.

•• **Practiced:** You can use one method of fortune telling well and can tell someone general information that will apply to her.

••• **Competent:** You know a lot about certain methods of fortune telling and can tell anyone detailed information that will be applicable.

•••• **Expert:** You are able to use multiple methods well and have a keen understanding of what people want to hear.

••••• **Master:** Gypsies take lessons from you.

Possessed by: Gypsies, Psychics, Professional Fortune Tellers, New Agers

Specialties: Tarot Cards, Prophecy, Romance, Death, Palmistry, I Ching, Goat Entrails

Instruction

You have a talent for passing on information and skills to others. You might have worked as a teacher, or as a Chantry Mentor. Either way, you can explain things and demonstrate techniques in such a way that anyone who listens to you can learn easily. You can teach any of your Skills or Knowledges to another character, but you can never raise a student's score above your own. For example, if you have three dots in Occult, you cannot teach someone enough to raise her Occult Knowledge to four dots.

For the time it takes to raise a student's skill, roll your Manipulation + Instruction against a difficulty of (11 minus the student's Intelligence). One roll may be made per month of teaching. The number of successes is the number of experience points the student can apply toward that skill. Example: Fabian Renalds is trying to teach Wyndi Blacksin the social intricacies of modern art (Culture Knowledge). Wyndi's pretty sharp (Intelligence 3), so the difficulty for Fabian's roll is 8.

A student may become too discouraged or distracted with other things to pay attention to his teacher. Therefore, the student may have to spend a Willpower point (at the Storyteller's discretion) to keep at his studies. Frequent interruptions can cost a student a number of Willpower points, or maybe they'll just prevent him from learning anything (in which case, the teacher might withdraw her services).

With the Storyteller's approval, a person can teach some Talents, such as Brawl or Dodge. In these cases, it is good to roleplay some of the training sessions. Get a few good licks in on the student and see if he learns anything from it. Talents such as Empathy or Alertness cannot be taught— they must be learned the hard way.

• **Novice:** You can take simple concepts (e.g. basic arithmetic) and present them in an interesting and digestible manner.

•• **Practiced:** You can teach moderately complex subjects (such as algebra) and make your lessons straightforward and interesting.

••• **Competent:** You can teach any subject of which you have Knowledge, up to high-school level subjects. You can make differential calculus sound like the simplest thing in the world.

•••• **Expert:** Learning from you is scarcely an effort. You could teach irrational-number theory or Sumerian cuneiform to almost anyone.

••••• **Master:** You are an inspiring teacher who bestows a touch of greatness on anyone who studies with you.

Possessed by: Mentors, Teachers, Do Masters, Professors, People from All Walks of Life

Specialties: Metaphysics, Tradition Practices, Customs and Laws, University, Skills, Knowledges

Interrogation

You are able to extract information from people by fair means or foul. Using a mixture of threats, trickery and persistent questioning, you ultimately unearth the truth. This is a common skill among the Men in Black.

- • **Novice:** Nosy neighbor
- •• **Practiced:** Movie cop
- ••• **Competent:** Talk-show host
- •••• **Expert:** Investigative journalist
- ••••• **Master:** Spymaster

Possessed by: Cops, Journalists, Secret Service Personnel, Inquisitors

Specialties: Good Cop/Bad Cop, Threats, Trickery, Moral Blackmail

Intrigue

You know the finer points of plotting and deal-making in the halls of power. You understand the practical use of power (in sometimes threatening but always non-confrontational ways) to achieve your own ends. This Talent also allows you to glean important facts about others in your social circle and separate truth from the endless amounts of false and useless gossip.

- • **Novice:** Wiseguy
- •• **Practiced:** Confidant
- ••• **Competent:** PAC lobbyist
- •••• **Expert:** Vampire
- ••••• **Master:** Big Wheel in Doissetep.

Possessed by: Chantry Masters, Technocracy Symposium Regulars

Specialties: Gossiping, Feigning Ignorance, Threats, Plotting, Rumormongering, Alliances, Betrayals

Mimicry

You have a versatile voice and can imitate accents, people and some other sounds. You can use this talent to entertain and deceive. With enough talent, almost any sort of sound can be created— the larynx is an amazingly flexible organ. This can be very useful when dealing with voice-keyed security systems or computers, but only if the practitioner is extremely skillful.

- • **Novice:** You can manage a few accents passably and do impressions of a couple of well-known personalities.
- •• **Practiced:** You can do a range of accents well enough to fool anyone but a native speaker and imitate a range of celebrities. You can do basic bird calls and some predatory animal sounds.
- ••• **Competent:** You could do celebrity impersonations on stage. You can pick up someone's vocal mannerisms by studying her for a couple of hours and imitate her well enough to fool anyone but a close friend. You can produce many mammal and bird sounds.

- •••• **Expert:** You can imitate a specific person well enough to fool someone on the phone, and pass as a native speaker in an accent close to your own. You can do a wide range of animal and technological noises.
- ••••• **Master:** You can imitate almost any accent, person, animal or noise.

Possessed by: Dreamspeakers, Cultists of Ecstasy, Hunters, Comedians, Men in Black, HIT Marks

Specialties: Accents, Celebrities, Birds and Animals, Mechanical Sounds, Vocal Impersonation

Scan

You are practiced at noticing small details and changes in the environment when you purposely look at or listen to what is going on around you. This Ability can only be used when you specifically say you are attempting to notice if anything is amiss. If you aren't concentrating, this Ability will do you no good.

- • **Novice:** If anyone notices police sirens, it's you.
- •• **Practiced:** The police should use your detective abilities.
- ••• **Competent:** The slightest motion draws your attention.
- •••• **Expert:** Nothing escapes your glance.
- ••••• **Master:** You can count the grains of salt on a pretzel— by taste.

Possessed by: Detectives, GIs, FBI Agents, Bodyguards, Night Watchmen

Specialties: Keeping Watch, Quick Scan, Listening, Smelling, Assassins

Scrounging

You have a knack for finding almost anything under almost any circumstances. The masters of your craft could find a hot spring at the North Pole or a mainframe computer in the heart of the Amazon Jungle, if necessary. In the city, you know where to find almost any kind of item or service— no questions asked. (It's amazing what you can find in dumpsters...)

- • **Novice:** You can find basic equipment and services, such as drugs, illegal weapons and hired thugs.
- •• **Practiced:** You can get hold of a vehicle, a forged passport or a skilled wiretapper.
- ••• **Competent:** You can find an aircraft and pilot or a hitman at an hour's notice.
- •••• **Expert:** You can find state-of-the-art military hardware, any vehicle you desire and services better imagined than described.
- ••••• **Master:** You could probably find a rent-controlled apartment overlooking Central Park for $100 a month.

Possessed by: Criminals, Intelligence Operatives, Entrepreneurs, Hollow Ones

Specialties: Illegal Goods, Vehicles, Services, Art, Technical Equipment, Magickal Tomes

Search

You know how best to go about looking for someone or something in a small area where you can concentrate your perceptions. You can search for anything from a lost ring in your bedroom to the assassin who might be hiding in your garden.

• **Novice:** You are good at finding lost items.

•• **Practiced:** Tell-tale signs (e.g. broken plants, footprints) are apparent to you.

••• **Competent:** You know where to look.

•••• **Expert:** Trained professionals defer to your expertise.

••••• **Master:** Sherlock Holmes was an amateur.

Possessed by: Detectives, Ingenious Servants, Policemen, Prison Guards, Men in Black

Specialties: Sounds, Woodwork, Small Objects, People, Concealed Doors

Seduction

You know how to lure, attract and command the attention of others in a sexual manner. By the way you hold yourself, how you look at someone and even by the tone of your voice, you are able to arouse and excite those upon whom you practice your wiles. Once you have fully seduced someone, he will be willing to do nearly anything for you.

• **Novice:** Teenager

•• **Practiced:** The "older woman"

••• **Competent:** Heartthrob

•••• **Expert:** Movie star

••••• **Master:** The envy of vampires everywhere

Possessed by: Thespians, Escorts, Cultists of Ecstasy, Good-for-Nothing Men, Strippers, Progenitor Glamour Traps

Specialties: Witty Conversation, Opening Lines, Innuendo, Alluring Looks

Sense Deception

Over the years, you have developed the ability to know instinctively when people are not telling you the truth or not telling you the whole truth. There is a way they look, a tone of voice, a movement of the eyes— you can't analyze it, but it's always there, and your instincts rarely let you down.

• **Novice:** Sometimes you can tell, but you still get suckered— though more rarely than the average person does.

•• **Practiced:** It takes a bit of skill to pull the wool over your eyes.

••• Competent: Anyone who can slip one past you is a highly skilled con artist.

•••• Expert: You could make a living screening people for security.

••••• Master: People whisper behind your back, and many are nervous talking to you. Your ability is almost supernatural.

Possessed by: Bodyguards, Reporters, Interrogators, Security Personnel, Detectives, Mothers

Specialties: Interviews, Investigative, Courtroom, Technical (Polygraphs)

Style

You may not have been born good-looking, or possessed of a natural charm, but you know how to dress and make the most of your appearance. Even if you are not physically attractive, heads turn because of your dress sense and style. Note that this Talent only applies to people's reactions to your appearance; once you get closer, it's up to you.

• Novice: Good taste

•• Practiced: Socialite

••• Competent: Celebrity

•••• Expert: Celebrity advisor

••••• Master: International model

Possessed by: Socialites, Celebrities, Fashion Professionals, the Gifted Few

Specialties: Classic, High Fashion, Street Fashion, Retro, Ethnic

Ventriloquism

You have the ability to throw your voice, making it appear to come from somewhere else. This talent can be used for deception as well as entertainment.

• Novice: You could do a ventriloquist act at a children's party.

•• Practiced: You could get a gig at a local amateur vaudeville club. You can make it seem like someone standing next to you spoke.

••• Competent: You could almost make a living from your talent, with occasional TV variety shows breaking up the round of cheap clubs and theaters. You can make it look like someone (or something) within five yards of you spoke.

•••• Expert: You could take your act to Vegas and headline TV specials of your own. You can make your voice seem to come from any spot within 30 feet of you.

••••• Master: Young hopefuls bombard you with questions, and *Variety* calls you the savior of a lost vaudeville art. You can make your voice seem to come from anywhere within earshot.

Possessed by: Entertainers, Con Artists, Pranksters, some Mediums

Specialties: Distance, Clarity, Dummy, Inanimate Object (e.g. radio)

Skills

Acrobatics

You are a trained tumbler and acrobat able to perform feats of agility far beyond the capabilities of an untrained character. For each success with this Skill, a character can ignore one Health Level of falling damage. For example, a character with two dots in Acrobatics can fall up to 10 feet without injury or would take only one Health Level of damage from a 15-foot fall. This skill may be paired with Dexterity to roll for leaps and other acrobatic feats.

• Novice: Grade school gym class

•• Practiced: High school jock

••• Competent: College team

•••• Expert: State champion

••••• Master: Olympic gold medalist

Possessed by: Professional Athletes, Jocks, Martial Artists, Dancers

Specialties: Sport, Martial Arts, Dance, Enhanced Jumping/Falling

Animal Training

You are able to train animals to obey commands and possibly perform tricks or other feats. Each species is a different specialty.

• Novice: Heel, Fetch, Sit, Stay

•• Practiced: Local shows

••• Competent: Champion sheep dogs

•••• Expert: Elite police dogs

••••• Master: Circus/stunt animals

Possessed by: Dog Handlers, Movie Animal Wranglers, Circus Animal Trainers, Marauders, Verbena

Specialties: Dog, Horse, Elephant, Seal, Dragon, Hellhound, Familiar

Archery

You know how to fire a bow, and may be able to do so with great proficiency. Bows fire wooden shafts, making them good weapons against vampires.

• Novice: High School Gym Practice

•• Practiced: Forest Bow Hunter

••• Competent: Medieval Ranger

•••• Expert: Will usually hit a bull's eye.

••••• Master: Robin Hood

Possessed by: Hunters, Dreamspeakers, Hobby Enthusiasts, Competitors, Medieval Recreationists, Beginning Zen Archers

Specialties: Arched Flight, Forests, Target, Hunting, Kyudo Technique, Crossbows, Primitive Archery, Moving Targets

Blind Fighting

Even when unable to see your foes, you can use your Brawl or Melee Abilities with a reduced penalty or no penalty. This Skill may also be of great use out of combat. It should be noted that this Skill does not grant any actual ability to see better in darkness. For each dot the character has in this Skill, reduce the difficulty for performing actions while blind by one. (Naturally, the difficulty can never be reduced below its unhindered equivalent.) This Skill does not add to Correspondence sensory effects.

•   **Novice:** You don't stub your toe in the dark.

••   **Practiced:** You can pinpoint the direction from which sounds come.

•••   **Competent:** You can fight and predict your enemies' locations at the same time.

••••   **Expert:** You can almost "feel" where your opponents are.

••••• **Master:** You possess an almost mystical sense— Zen and the Art of Spatial Awareness.

Possessed by: Ninja, Assassins, Do Masters, Spelunkers, Masters of Zen Archery

Specialties: Dodging, Punching, Indoors, Dueling, Multiple Foes

Camouflage

You can change your appearance through a mixture of clothing, makeup and movement, rendering you difficult to spot in a variety of different surroundings. This is not the ability to look like someone else, but simply to hide.

•   **Novice:** Boy Scout

••   **Practiced:** Infantry trooper

•••   **Competent:** Marine

••••   **Expert:** Special Forces

••••• **Master:** Ninja

Possessed by: Hunters, Military Personnel, Spies, Assassins, Poachers

Specialties: Woods, Mountains, Urban, Open Country, Arctic

Climbing

You can climb mountains and/or walls and seldom have any fear of falling. The technical skills of chimneying, spike-setting and rappelling are all well-known to you, although, depending on your skill, you may be good or indifferent at them. Remember, mountain climbing at night is far more difficult than a daylight climb unless you can see in the dark.

•   **Novice:** You can scale easy mountains or walls with handholds.

••   **Practiced:** You go on mountaineering vacations. You can climb heavily weathered stone or brick walls.

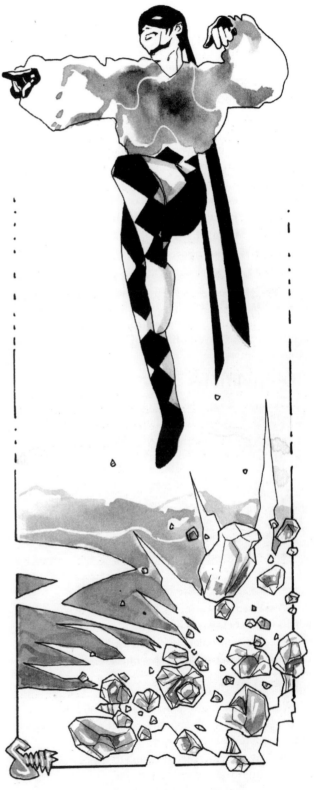

• • • Competent: You work in an "outdoor pursuits center" as a mountaineering instructor. You can climb moderately rough stone or brick walls.

• • • • Expert: You've done at least a couple of famous peaks. You can free-climb a fairly smooth stone or brick wall.

• • • • • Master: Everest and K2 are mild hikes. You could free-climb the World Trade Center.

Possessed by: Mountaineers, Burglars, Enthusiasts

Specialties: Cliffs, Hiking, Ice, Buildings, Free-Climbing, Rappelling

Crafts

With this Skill, you can master artisan techniques—woodworking, leather work, glassblowing, gemcutting, etc. You can make functional objects from various substances, with quality dependent on the successes you roll. Each type of material you can work must be bought as a separate specialty.

• Novice: High-school shop class

• • Practiced: Apartment handyman

• • • Competent: Professional

• • • • Expert: Specialist

• • • • • Master: Grand artisan

Possessed by: Craftsman, Renaissance-Faire Vendors, Hobbyists, Handymen

Specialties: Cooking, Carpentry, Blacksmithing, Leatherworking, Jewelry, Brewing/Distillery, Glassworking, Stonemasonry

Demolitions

You have a knowledge of explosives and demolitions that allows you to set off and build all types of bombs. You know how to handle nearly anything— dynamite, plastic explosive, nitroglycerin, black powder, blasting cord, even napalm. Additionally, you know the techniques for disarming explosives, which can come in very handy.

• Novice: Guy Fawkes

• • Practiced: Leroy Moody

• • • Competent: Underground Chemist

• • • • Expert: Blows up Technocracy Constructs for a living.

• • • • • Master: Bye-bye, Pentagon.

Possessed by: Terrorists, Police Bomb Squads, Armed Forces Personnel, Anarchists, War Chantry Cabals

Specialties: Dynamite, Plastic Explosive, Car Bombs, Disarmament, Detection, Forces Effects

Disguise

You can change your appearance— and even make yourself look like another specific person— through the use of clothes and makeup.

• Novice: Good enough to fool someone who knows neither you nor the person you're impersonating.

•• Practiced: Good enough to fool some of the people some of the time.

••• Competent: Good enough to fool some of the people most of the time.

•••• Expert: Good enough to fool most of the people most of the time.

••••• Master: Good enough to fool those nearest and dearest to you most of the time.

Possessed by: Actors, Spies, Undercover Cops, Criminals, Con Artists

Specialties: Specific Person, Type of Person, Conceal Own Identity

Dancing

You are a proficient dancer, and may perform socially or for the entertainment of others. You are familiar with most varieties of dance, but specialize in one particular style.

• Novice: You can manage a waltz at a wedding.

•• Practiced: You draw envious glances at weddings. You could perform on the local amateur stage.

••• Competent: You are the talk of the ball. You could perform on the local professional stage.

•••• Expert: People ask you to teach them. You could perform on TV.

••••• Master: Nijinsky, Fonteyn, Nureyev, Barishnikov, Astaire, Rogers, Kelley— and you.

Possessed by: Socialites, Pop Stars, Music Video Dancers, Ballet Dancers, Enthusiasts, Dreamspeakers

Specialties: Waltz, Jazz, Two-step, Foxtrot, Disco, Latin, Show, Ballet, Ethnic, Tribal, Ecstatic

Do

Do is the most basic and rudimentary of all martial arts forms. Taught and utilized by the Akashic Brotherhood, Do accesses the human body's ultimate potential. This skill is required to practice Do maneuvers. (See Book Three for more details about Do.) This is an exceptionally rare and powerful skill and can only be learned from an Akashic Brother. Beginning characters may not start with more than two dots in Do; higher levels may be purchased only with experience and training.

Ratings of knowledge in Do are usually noted as part of a person's name; each title is based upon a stratum of animals who possess the conceptual instincts of that rank of Do training. As the student advances, he eventually achieves the strata of humanity again. But this time, he has gained a knowledge of what the human body actually is and how to operate it to its ultimate potential. These names are only mentioned among members of the Akashic Brotherhood.

• Insect (grasshopper, gnat, worm, etc.): As an initiate in the teachings of Do, you can swing your arms and legs about with some efficiency.

•• Reptile (snake or lizard): When you become a true student of Do, you begin to become one with your body.

••• Four-Footed (tiger, leopard, horse, dragon, etc.): You have begun to specialize in a certain style of Do. You realize that there is a hidden potential inside of all men. You can sense an underlying current of energy beneath your physical form.

•••• Bipedal (monkey, ape, bear, etc.): As a Master, you can move your body through the simplest motion to any goal or exert a tremendous amount of force by drawing upon the design of the human body.

••••• True Humanity: Honored Master or Enlightened One. All things have strengths and weaknesses. All things are built and can be destroyed. The peaceful mind is more effective than the cluttered one, for it is easier to think than it is not to think.

Possessed by: Members of the Akashic Brotherhood, inspired Oriental Monastic Priests, highly advanced martial arts practitioners

Specialties: Punch, Kick, Throw, Dodge, External, Internal, etc.

Escapology

You are skilled in various techniques that enable you to escape from bonds and restraints. This skill is often used for entertainment, but can also be useful in real life.

• Novice: Children's party entertainer. Can escape from loose or poorly-tied bonds.

•• Practiced: Amateur entertainer. Can escape from fairly well-tied bonds.

••• Competent: Professional entertainer. Can escape from handcuffs and chains.

•••• Expert: Star. Can escape from a straitjacket.

••••• Master: Legend. Can escape from just about anything. You would feel safe tied in a sack underwater with a ticking time-bomb.

Possessed by: Entertainers, Spies, Special Forces, Amateurs, Pulp Detectives

Specialties: Magic Tricks, Ropes, Boxes, Locks, Underwater, Handcuffs, Showmanship, Arm Locks and Holds

Fast-Draw

This skill allows you to make a weapon ready almost instantly. By rolling Dexterity + Fast-Draw and getting three successes, you can draw a weapon and have it ready for use just as if it had been in your hand all along. The difficulty depends on how securely stowed the weapon was— a gun hidden in your underwear is harder to reach than one in a belt holster! This skill can be used with any weapon. When appropriate, the Fast-Draw score can be added to your Initiative roll.

• Novice: You have good reflexes.

•• Practiced: You're good, but not great.

••• Competent: You would have lasted a little while in the Old West. You could work Wild West shows. You are known among those who follow duels.

•••• Expert: Pretty fast. Your enemies are wary of your speed in drawing your ebon blade.

••••• Master: Greased lightning. You might have been able to take down Billy the Kid.

Possessed by: Knife-Fighters, Gunfighters, Martial Artists, Cops, Special Forces, Vigilantes.

Specialties: Knife, Pistol, Sword, Arrow, Rifle/Shotgun.

Fast-Talk

This Skill allows you to convince someone of something using a sincere expression and an avalanche of words rather than reasoned debate and logic. It's a surprisingly effective technique, provided that the mark has no time to think and does not have a Wits rating of four or more. The Storyteller should carefully judge whether this Skill is appropriate in a given situation, or whether it would be better to use some other Ability.

• Novice: Vacuum-cleaner salesman

•• Practiced: Used-car salesman

••• Competent: Professional con artist

•••• Expert: Teflon-coated politician

••••• Master: You could sell sand to the Saudis.

Possessed by: Salesmen, Con Artists, Politicians, Televangelists

Specialties: Sell, Confuse, Get Off the Hook, Convince

First Aid

This Skill allows a character to give basic medical attention to another character. It is not as comprehensive an Ability as the Medicine Knowledge, but it does allow for a basic grasp of all the practices of first aid, and, at higher levels, techniques known to paramedics. With sufficient skill, this can make vulgar healing appear coincidental.

• Novice: Mother of small children

•• Practiced: Boy Scout

••• Competent: Office safety representative

•••• Expert: School nurse

••••• Master: Paramedic

Possessed by: Mothers, Boy Scouts, Paramedics, Explorers, Outdoors Types

Specialties: CPR, Broken Bones, Artificial Respiration, Diagnosis, Terminology

Gambling

You are adept at one or more games of chance, and can play without too much risk of losing heavily. You can also increase your chances of winning without actually cheating.

• Novice: Saturday night poker with the boys

•• Practiced: A couple of weeks in Vegas each year

••• Competent: You are known in Vegas, Reno and Atlantic City.

•••• Expert: You make a living from this. Your mother despairs.

••••• Master: You have to be careful not to tell people your name.

Possessed by: Professional Gamblers, Amateur Gamblers

Specialties: Card Games, Dice Games, Roulette, One-Armed Bandits

Gunsmithing

You can repair firearms and produce ammunition for a variety of different guns. At high levels of skill, you can construct specialty ammunition, such as caseless, hollow-point, mercury-tipped or silver bullets. Given the time and the tools (and enough skill) you can build a gun from scratch— perhaps even one of your own design.

• Novice: Black powder and paper cartridges

•• Practiced: Cased standard ammunition

••• Competent: Magnum rounds

•••• Expert: Caseless and hollow-point rounds

••••• Master: You name it.

Possessed by: Gun Nuts, Survivalists, Cops, Serial Killers

Specialties: Black Powder Weapons, Field Repair, Invention, Magnum and Supercharged Ammunition, Specialty Ammunition

Heavy Weapons

You have the ability to operate heavy weapons of all varieties — anything from an M60 heavy machine gun to a Dragon anti-tank weapon. Additionally, your knowledge of the weapons includes an ability to repair them.

• Novice: Basic training

•• Practiced: Operator

••• Competent: Warrior

•••• Expert: Killer

••••• Master: Rambo

Possessed by: Mercenaries, Armed Forces Personnel, HIT Marks, SWAT Officers

Specialties: Desert, Jungle, Night Fighting, Friend from Foe, Loading

High Ritual

You know how to throw a party or gathering, anything from wild bacchanalia to a tear-filled memorial service. You know how to plan and choreograph the entire affair, down to the last item, making it an event to remember. Most people think High Ritual is musty robes and candles. It's not. High Ritual involves consummate showmanship, capturing the participants' attention and focusing their will, belief and emotion on the particular task at hand. A boring ritual makes for disinterested mages, which makes for sloppy magic. When High Ritual is done correctly, it looks artless, but it's really the highest form of art. Successful use of this Skill might reduce magickal difficulties by 1, or possibly more, in addition to any other modifiers, and could add to Social impressions as well.

- **Novice:** You can tastefully plan a wedding reception.
- •• **Practiced:** You give good parties and receive more acceptances than regrets when people R.S.V.P. The mood is high at events you hold, whatever that mood might be.
- ••• **Competent:** Your celebrations are becoming known, and not just in this world. Gatecrashers are a common occurrence.
- •••• **Expert:** When you choreograph the High Mass, angels appear in the choir loft, although they won't be visible to anyone but the gifted. Miracles may occur, and with far less trouble than they usually do.
- ••••• **Master:** Let the Wild Rumpus Start! When you give a revel, it is an affair of legend. You were probably responsible for Woodstock. What are you planning next?

Possessed by: Verbena, Caterers, Political Activists, Band Managers, Hollywood Producers, Elderly Matrons

Specialties: Weddings, Funerals, Religious Ceremonies, Hermetic Mysteries, Bacchanals, Outdoor Festivals

Hunting

You are skilled at finding and killing animals for food or sport. In familiar terrain, you are able to predict the type, number and likely location of food animals and know the best ways to find and kill them.

- • **Novice:** Weekender
- •• **Practiced:** Enthusiast or Trooper
- ••• **Competent:** Survivalist or Marine
- •••• **Expert:** Special Forces
- ••••• **Master:** You give pointers to werewolves.

Possessed by: Survivalists, Military Personnel, Pre-Industrial Societies, Outdoor Types, Dreamspeakers

Specialties: Temperate Forest, Jungle, Bush/Scrub, Mountain, Coast, Arctic, Desert

Hypnotism

You can place a subject into a trance and use hypnotism to gather information or treat psychiatric problems. To place a willing subject into trance, make an opposed roll of your Charisma + Hypnotism against the subject's Intelligence. (For an unwilling subject who is immobilized or Mind-magicked to comply, use Intelligence + Willpower). The number of successes indicates the depth of the trance and can be added to the your Hypnotism to roll for the success of tasks. For example, a hypnotist with Charisma 4 and Hypnotism 4 hypnotizes a willing subject with Intelligence 5. The hypnotist rolls 5 successes and the subject rolls 2—a total of 3 successes in the hypnotist's favor, indicating a fairly deep trance. The hypnotist can now roll seven dice (3 successes plus four dice from Hypnotism 4) to probe the subject's mind. Using this Skill successfully might reduce the difficulty of some Mind magicks by 1 or more, depending on the circumstances.

- • **Novice:** You do it to entertain occasionally.
- •• **Practiced:** You are a skilled amateur.
- ••• **Competent:** You can find some interesting secrets.
- •••• **Expert:** You can dig very deeply.
- ••••• **Master:** You can discover secrets from a subject's Past Lives.

Possessed by: Theurges, Entertainers, Holistic Healers, New Agers, Police Specialists, Psychiatrists

Specialties: Interrogation, Past-Life Regression, Hypnotherapy, Behavior Modification

Lockpicking

You are able to open locks without the correct key or the right combination. Though this Skill is certainly becoming more and more obsolete with all the new security devices in use, there are enough locks still around to make it worthwhile.

- • **Novice:** Simple mortise locks
- •• **Practiced:** Cylinder locks and basic security locks
- ••• **Competent:** Advanced security locks
- •••• **Expert:** Safes
- ••••• **Master:** Fort Knox

Possessed by: Burglars, Safecrackers, Spies, Locksmiths

Specialties: Key-Operated Locks, Combination Locks, Mag-Card Locks, Alarm Systems

Misdirection

Misdirection deals with distracting people from what you are trying to do. By making your subject focus his concentration elsewhere, you can steer him away from a subject of interest. The subject of interest could be anything from what you are doing to an object sitting in plain sight.

Masters of Do are able to utilize successes on Misdirection rolls to lower the difficulty on their next Do roll to strike the distracted target. The Do practitioner throws a feint or false blow. While the opponent is trying to Dodge or block that blow, the practitioner delivers the attack that he originally intended to utilize.

- • **Novice:** "Hey, your shoe lace is untied!"
- •• **Practiced:** You're real good at card tricks.
- ••• **Competent:** You can make a living at misdirecting people.
- •••• **Expert:** People give you things and then forget that they did.
- ••••• **Master:** Strangers forget that they ever met you.

Possessed by: Stage Magicians, Pickpockets, Con Men

Specialties: Theft, Concealment, Leading, Confusion

Pilot

You can operate a flying machine. Note that your skill limits the types of aircraft you can fly. A glider pilot (one dot) cannot fly a helicopter (requiring four dots).

- • **Novice:** Club member; hang gliders only
- •• **Practiced:** Club champion; gliders and small aircraft only
- ••• **Competent:** Professional or club instructor; commercial airplane license
- •••• **Expert:** Military or display pilot; helicopter, any type of commercial aircraft
- ••••• **Master:** Top Gun

Possessed by: Enthusiasts, Pilots, Military, Police

Specialties: Night Flying, Thermals, Dogfights, Long Distances, Takeoffs and Landings, Gliders, Helicopters, Light Planes, Corporate Jets, Commercial/Transport Jets, Fighter Jets, Vintage Planes, Autogyros, Blimps, Balloons, Hang Gliders, Microlights

Psychoanalysis

You are skilled in diagnosing and treating mental ailments without resorting to the use of behavior-altering drugs. During a session of analysis, you may roll Intelligence + Psychoanalysis (difficulty of the subject's Intelligence + 3). Keep track of your net successes; the Storyteller will decide how many successes are necessary to remove the illness. Even Freud couldn't cure people in a single session, so be patient! Note that it is possible to treat an unwilling patient this way, although the difficulty of so doing is equal to the subject's Willpower + 3.

- • **Novice:** A shoulder to cry on
- •• **Practiced:** Volunteer counselor
- ••• **Competent:** Professional counselor
- •••• **Expert:** Qualified psychoanalyst
- ••••• **Master:** Freud

Possessed by: Psychoanalysts, Holistic Healers, Good Listeners, Counselors, Parents, Teachers, Priests

Specialties: Freudian, Jungian, Humanist, Ericksonian, Holistic, Wiccan, Childhood, Psychosis, Neurosis, Self, Sympathy, Terminology, Research

Ride

You can climb onto a riding animal and stand a good chance of getting where you want to go without falling off, being thrown or having anything else unpleasant happen to you. When attempting something difficult, or when danger threatens, the Storyteller may require a Dexterity + Ride roll to avoid trouble. This Skill can also be combined with Mental Attributes to reflect your working knowledge of the relevant trappings and equipment.

- • **Novice:** Pony club member; dude ranch vacations
- •• **Practiced:** Pony club champion; weekend cowboy
- ••• **Competent:** Pony club instructor; professional cowboy
- •••• **Expert:** Showjumping champion; rodeo star
- ••••• **Master:** Stunt rider

Possessed by: Enthusiasts, Cowboys, Stunt Riders, members of pre-industrial societies

Specialties: Bareback, Horse, Mule, Camel, Elephant, Galloping, Tricks, No Hands

Singing

You can sing over a wide range and use a variety of styles and techniques. Singing is an extremely lucrative and popular Skill in the modern age. Though most singers are amateurs, some make enormous amounts of money.

- • **Novice:** You stand out when the family gathers around the piano.
- •• **Practiced:** You could get lead roles with local amateur societies or become a lead singer with a garage band.
- ••• **Competent:** You could get a choral part on the professional stage or get a recording contract.
- •••• **Expert:** You could get a lead on Broadway or a record on the charts.
- ••••• **Master:** They'll be playing your CDs 20 years from now.

Possessed by: Celestial Chorus Mages, Rock Musicians, Pop Stars, Opera Singers, Drunks

Specialties: Opera, Easy Listening, Ritual, Rock, Musicals

Speed Reading

Through practice, you have developed the ability to read and absorb large quantities of written material in a short time. This is especially useful when the character is doing research or checking for an obscure reference. It does not, however, reduce time needed to acquire the benefits of study points.

- • **Novice:** The *New York Times* in an hour
- •• **Practiced:** A novel in two to three hours
- ••• **Competent:** A textbook in two to three hours
- •••• **Expert:** A fat textbook in two to three hours
- ••••• **Master:** *War & Peace* in two to three hours

Possessed by: Academics, Literary Critics, Journalists, Researchers

Specialties: Technical, Fiction, Newspaper, Research, Cramming

Swimming

You can keep yourself afloat, at the very least. Normal swimming speed is 8 yards (plus Dexterity). A swimmer can increase his speed to 12 yards (plus Dexterity) if he is doing nothing else that turn. With Swimming skill, a character can try to swim faster than normal; roll Stamina + Swimming, difficulty 7, and add three yards to your swimming speed per success (one roll per turn).

- • **Novice:** You can swim.
- • • **Practiced:** You can swim fast, or for extended periods.
- • • • **Competent:** Instructor/Lifeguard
- • • • • **Expert:** Swim team
- • • • • • **Master:** Olympic gold

Possessed by: Athletes, Lifeguards, Scuba Divers and almost anyone else

Specialties: Racing, Distance, Sea, Survival, Lifesaving

Torture

You know how to inflict pain. Your ability is so precise as to be a science. You are capable of interrogating prisoners through torture and prolonging their suffering, keeping them barely alive— or undead.

- • **Novice:** You know how to hurt people in different ways.
- • • **Practiced:** You are good at causing extreme pain and can keep someone alive for interrogation purposes.
- • • • **Competent:** You are equal to a military torturer. You can create extremes of pain most people have never experienced.
- • • • • **Expert:** You are equal to a professional torturer. You are able to get almost any information you want out of your subject.
- • • • • • **Master:** You are an artist, a virtuoso of pain and suffering.

Possessed by: Military Interrogators, Prison Guards, Nephandi, Corrupt Euthanatos, Men in Black

Specialties: Exotic Methods, Life Magick Effects, Prolonging Life, Pain, Flagellation

Tracking

You can identify the trail of an animal or person and follow it under most conditions. The difficulty of such a feat varies according to the conditions— following fresh tracks in deep snow is easier than following week-old tracks across a concrete sidewalk!

- • **Novice:** Boy Scout
- • • **Practiced:** Eagle Scout
- • • • **Competent:** Hunter
- • • • • **Expert:** Native American guide
- • • • • • **Master:** You thought Samuel Haight was slow.

Possessed by: Hunters, Survivalists, Special Forces, Detectives

Specialties: Wolf, Deer, Rock, Urban, Identification

Traps

You know how to set various types of traps according to the type of game you want to catch.

- • **Novice:** Boy Scout
- • • **Practiced:** Weekend survivalist

- ●●● **Competent:** Outdoorsman
- ●●●● **Expert:** Mountain man
- ●●●●● **Master:** "Well done! And I thought dragons were extinct..."

Possessed by: Trappers, Special Forces, inhabitants of remote places

Specialties: Specific Species, Deadfalls, Pits

Knowledges

Alchemy

You are familiar with the writings of the classical and medieval alchemists, and you also have some practical experience. This Ability is indirectly related to the Knowledge of Chemistry, in a manner similar to the relationship between Astronomy and Astrology. You can interpret alchemical texts, and you understand the various symbols and ciphers used by the alchemists even when you find them in a non-alchemical context.

- ● **Novice:** A mere dabbler
- ●● **Practiced:** Apprentice, probably still dependent on a master for instruction
- ●●● **Competent:** Journeyman, capable of making your own way, but with a long road left to travel
- ●●●● **Expert:** Experienced alchemist, within reach of the greatest secrets
- ●●●●● **Master:** One of the true practitioners of the Craft of Alchemy.

Possessed by: Occultists, Scholars, some Scientists

Specialties: Transmutation, Cosmology, Lapis Philosophorum

Area Knowledge

You are familiar with an area— its landscape, history, inhabitants and Sleeper politics. This Knowledge will also provide a basic "who's who" for the areas around a Chantry or Construct.

- ● **Novice:** You know a fair amount for an outsider.
- ●● **Practiced:** You may have lived there for a year or two.
- ●●● **Competent:** You may have lived there for 5-10 years.
- ●●●● **Expert:** You're native born, and never left.
- ●●●●● **Master:** You know every stone, stream or building in the area.

Possessed by: Vigilantes, Guardians of the Sleepers, Men in Black, Cops

Specialties: History, Geography, Wildlife, Enemies, Politics, Transportation, Law

Astrology

You know how to compile and interpret a horoscope. Given the date and time (and, according to some systems, the place) of a person's birth, you can construct a personality profile and a set of predictions about the likely course of his life. Whether you actually believe these revelations is a matter of personal taste, but you can present them in a convincing and pleasing manner to those who *do* believe. This Knowledge does not confer any type of magickal ability.

- ● **Novice:** You merely dabble.
- ●● **Practiced:** Friends ask you to make horoscopes for them.
- ●●● **Competent:** You could run a small astrology business.
- ●●●● **Expert:** You could have a syndicated newspaper column.
- ●●●●● **Master:** You could work for celebrities and politicians.

Possessed by: Astrologers, Amateurs, Mystics, New Agers, Old Hippies

Specialties: Solar Horoscope, Ming Shu, Zu Wei

Chantry Politics

You know some of the ins and outs of Chantry alliances and relations— an important thing when acting as an emissary, seeking refuge or seeking access to rare texts or rotes. This Knowledge gives you a "scorecard" for the varied players in the convoluted world of the Chantry. Cranky Masters may be impressed with a newcomer who knows her way around; an agenda can be forwarded if one knows the right (or wrong) person to approach. A related but separate Knowledge, Construct Politics, works in a similar fashion for Technocracy strongholds. A Tradition mage who knows the power structure of a Construct would be a dangerous opponent. Note that the Chantry Politics Knowledge involves knowing people and factions; actually putting this knowledge to use involves other Abilities, such as Intrigue and Diplomacy.

- ● **Novice:** You know a few names and a few places.
- ●● **Practiced:** You're familiar with places you've visited.
- ●●● **Competent:** You know who's who and what's where.
- ●●●● **Expert:** "I know just the person you need! He's in the Bermuda Triangle right now..."
- ●●●●● **Master:** You're familiar with the pitfalls of Doissetep.

Possessed by: Masters, Ambassadors, Troublemakers, Spies

Specialties: Factions, Vices, Scandals, Secret Alliances, Wizards Behind the Curtain

Computer Hacking

The player must have at least two dots in Computer before purchasing this Knowledge. Hacking allows the computer user to break the rules. It is not a programming skill— that requires the Computer Knowledge. Hacking represents an imaginative faculty above and beyond the use of the programming codes. In the binary computer world of yes/no, hacking represents the little bit of genius that says, "Well... maybe."

Hacking is used instead of the Computer Knowledge when the user is breaking into other computer systems or trying to manipulate data in "real time." The Computer Ability is used for programming or other miscellaneous tasks. Hacking is used most often as a complementary Ability to Computer, but it can aid programming by allowing the character to work faster or to crack military codes that a normal programmer would not even be able to figure out. Rules for hacking can be found in Book Three.

- **Novice:** You are a computer geek who knows a few tricks, such as changing your grades in the university computer network.
- **Practiced:** You have great "luck" in guessing computer passwords.
- **Competent:** You thought your electric bill was too high last month, but you can fix that with a few keystrokes.
- **Expert:** Now that you have cracked the bank codes, which is it: Rio or Bermuda?
- **Master:** The European Community was pretty annoyed about that thermonuclear incident, but you know they can never trace it back to you.

Possessed by: Computer Geeks, CIA Operatives, Virtual Adepts

Specialties: Viruses, Data Retrieval, Networking, Magickal Protections, Telecommunications

Cryptography

You may skillfully compose and interpret codes and ciphers. You can construct a code that can only be cracked by someone who scores as many successes as you have dots in this Knowledge. You can also crack a code, rolling your Knowledge against a difficulty assigned by the Storyteller depending on the code's complexity.

- **Novice:** Grade-school spy fan
- **Practiced:** Word puzzle buff, military signals officer
- **Competent:** Intelligence officer
- **Expert:** Intelligence cipher specialist
- **Master:** James Bond

Possessed by: Spies, Puzzle Buffs, Military Signals Personnel

Specialties: Letter Shifts, Mathematical Encryption, Obscure Character Sets

Herbalism

You have a working knowledge of herbs and their properties, medicinal and otherwise. You can find and prepare herbs and know which herb or blend of herbs to use in any situation. This skill will also provide knowledge of the magical lore of plants.

- **Novice:** Read a book on it once.
- **Practiced:** Serious student.
- **Competent:** Local supplier.
- **Expert:** Author of books on herbalism.
- **Master:** Herbal doctor.

Possessed by: Verbena, Hermetic and Dreamspeaker Mages, Holistic Healers, New Agers, Wizened Old Women, Members of Traditional Cultures.

Specialties: Culinary, Medicinal, Poisonous, Narcotics, Hallucinogens, Spirit

History

You've studied the history of a specific area or period, and you understand what happened, when, why and who was involved. You also have a fair idea of social, political, economic and technological conditions in various past times and places. Note that in the case of ancient mages, this Knowledge relates only to times and places that are outside their direct experience. For instance, a mage born in Victorian London would rely on memory for knowledge of English history and culture, but would use History to uncover information about classical Greece, which was before his time, or about Czarist Russia, which was outside his experience.

- **Novice:** Amateur or high school
- **Practiced:** Enthusiast or college student
- **Competent:** Grad student or author
- **Expert:** Professor
- **Master:** Research fellow

Possessed by: Enthusiasts, Scholars, Mentors

Specialties: Political, Intellectual, Social, Economic, Technological, Classical, Medieval, Renaissance, Modern, Europe, Americas, Asia, Africa, Australia

Lore

You're familiar with the subcultures of the World of Darkness — the scoop on vampires, werewolves, the fey and your own kind. Each type of Lore must be purchased as a separate Knowledge; accurate dirt on the Camarilla won't tell you anything about the halls of Arcadia.

Much of your information will be second-hand, and thus suspect. It bears noting that the different "players" in the world-behind-the-scenes often have wildly inaccurate perceptions of each other. A mage, meeting a vampire, won't immediately ask "What clan are you, and where's your prince?" Likewise, a Technomancer will not immediately know the history of the Council of Nine. Mages have a lot to learn— many are lacking knowledge about their own Traditions.

This kind of knowledge will not be easy to come by— werewolves don't pass their secrets on to caern-robbers— and some knowledge can be actively harmful, especially Wyrm Lore. There really *are* some things man was not meant to know!

- • **Novice:** You've heard a few dubious tales.
- •• **Practiced:** You know a few accurate facts.
- ••• **Competent:** Familiar enough to hold an intelligent conversation.
- •••• **Expert:** You know a few things they'd rather you didn't know.
- ••••• **Master:** You know your subjects better than they know themselves. This can become a *real* problem!

Possessed by: Sages, War Cabals, Tale-Tellers, Research Assistants, Spies

Varieties: (Each one bought separately) Faerie, Forbidden Secrets, Garou, Ghosts, Kindred, Sabbat, Technocracy, Tradition, Wyrm, Camarilla

Poisons

You have a working knowledge of poisons, their effects and antidotes. You can analyze a poison to tell its origin, and can mix a poison or antidote given time and equipment. You must have at least one dot in Science to acquire this Knowledge.

- • **Novice:** Dabbler
- •• **Practiced:** Detective, Mystery Reader
- ••• **Competent:** Pharmacist, Mystery Writer
- •••• **Expert:** Forensic Scientist, Emergency-Room Doctor
- ••••• **Master:** Assassin

Possessed by: Progenitors, Euthanatos, Mystery Buffs, Detectives, Pharmacists, Medics, Assassins

Specialties: Venoms, Chemical Poisons, Plant-based Poisons, Analysis, Antidotes, Instant Poisons, Slow-build Poisons, Undetectable Poisons, Magickal Poisons

Psychology

You have a formal education in the science of human nature. You know the modern theories of emotion, cognitive development, personality, perception and learning. Though this is largely a scholarly understanding of the human psyche, it can be used practically to understand those around you.

- • **Novice:** High school
- •• **Practiced:** College student
- ••• **Competent:** Grad student
- •••• **Expert:** Professor
- ••••• **Master:** Theorist

Possessed by: Teachers, Researchers, Scientists, Counselors, Psychologists

Specialties: Behaviorism, Freudian, Jungian, Humanist, Developmental, Experimental, Animals

Science Specialties

The subtleties of science are many and varied, especially for the Technomancers who employ them. Characters who specialize in one type of science (Biology, Mathematics, Engineering, Cybernetics, etc.) more than others should simply take that Science as a separate Knowledge with specific applications outside of the more general body of knowledge that is represented by the Science Trait.

Because their magick depends on their belief in a certain paradigm, Technomancers must work their effects along certain 'theories' to get away with coincidental magick. Violating these paradigms might cause a failed Effect or even a Paradox Backlash. A successful Science roll could allow a Technomancer to "fast-cast" a theory on the spur of the moment, then explain the effect away in a ream of complex gibberish. The importance of belief, however, cannot be underestimated; magick is a function of your belief over the beliefs of those around you. A Technomancer shackled to a belief system must still adhere to that paradigm to work his magick. The greater your knowledge of a subject, the better your ability to work it to your desired ends.

- • **Novice:** A basic understanding of the concepts involved.
- •• **Practiced:** A working knowledge of the subject.
- ••• **Competent:** Good enough to bend the rules without breaking them.
- •••• **Expert:** Extensive and esoteric theories.
- ••••• **Master:** You know so much that you can prove anything you want within your chosen field.

Possessed by: Scientists, Technomancers, Research Technicians

Varieties: Astronomy, Biology, Genetics, Mathematics, Cybernetics, Metallurgy, Any Other Type of Specific Science

Secret Code Language

Many Traditions and Crafts have secret magic languages that only Adepts or better understand. The Verbena use the Language of Flowers, composing bouquets and nosegays whose component flowers and arrangements conceal hidden meanings— mullein, or hag taper, means "take courage," while nettle means "You are spiteful" and verbena means "You enchant me." The Akashic Brotherhood uses the Secrets Signs of the notorious Hung Society. Even the Celestial Chorus has its own method of swift, secret communication, citing Chapter and Verse from their holy books, the meanings of which are only readily apparent to those who have committed them to heart.

Fragments of these codes have leaked into the world of the Sleepers, and some basic meanings can be deciphered by those with the appropriate background. Upper class matrons understand bits of the Language of Flowers, and Asian street gangs know a few of the hand signs of the Hung Society.

Secret Codes are purchased like Linguistics, one per point in the Knowledge. Like Lore, this skill may be difficult to obtain. The codes are kept secret for a reason.

Possessed by: Verbena, Akashic Brotherhood, Spies, Celestial Chorus, Secret Societies, Homeless

Varieties: Language of Flowers, Hung Society, Chapter & Verse

Sign Language

Sign Language can be bought as a level in Linguistics. Not all sign languages are the same. You must declare each language separately. Ninja, deaf people, spies and many mage cabals have their own separate hand codes. These must generally be taught by a member of a select group; obtaining this training may range from easy to damn near impossible.

Stone Lore

You know the reputed properties of stones and all the magic inherent in them. You may use this knowledge in the creation of Talismans and fetishes and can assist with ritual magick.

- • **Novice:** You sell birthstones and psychic crystals.
- •• **Practiced:** You can match metals and stones to make amulets for most occasions.
- ••• **Competent:** You know your stones. Other mages come to you to get their rocks.
- •••• **Expert:** The Garou come to you to get rocks and metals. You talk to stones.
- ••••• **Master:** Not only do you talk to stones, but sometimes they talk back. You know all the powers of the minerals, and can identify the great jewels of legend.

Possessed by: New Agers, Jewelers, Alchemists, Dreamspeakers

Specialties: Planetary Influences, Jade Carving, Metals

Taxidermy

You can take an animal apart and preserve all the bits and pieces, not just the skins and heads. Your deer skins won't rot and your raven claws won't smell funny. Moreover, you can make sure newts' eyes will stay fresh for years.

- • **Novice:** The newts should freeze well.
- •• **Practiced:** Nobody will buy from you, but you should be able to cure a pelt or properly preserve a snake in formaldehyde.
- ••• **Competent:** Relatives who like animal heads nailed to their walls appreciate your presents. Others find your hobby distasteful because the animals don't look dead anymore. Of course, they don't look alive either.
- •••• **Expert:** You could get a job at the natural history museum. Old ladies who want their chihuahuas stuffed come to you, and the frog toes are as fresh as the day you got them.
- ••••• **Master:** You probably embalmed the Pharaohs in a past life. Your work looks like its going to get up and run off any second now.

Possessed by: Morticians, Hunters, Furriers, Sons of Ether, Serial Killers, High School Science Teachers

Specialties: Tanning, Embalming, Preserving, Trophies, Techniques of Frankenstein, Victims

Theology

Religion is a familiar aspect of human endeavor for you, and you fully understand its place in the world. At higher levels, this Knowledge imparts an appreciation for all religious beliefs, while individuals with less skill tend to view their own beliefs as intrinsically superior to any others. This, of course, varies with the individual. Possession of this Knowledge in no way requires personal belief in the tenets of any specific religion.

- • **Novice:** Participant
- •• **Practiced:** Altar boy
- ••• **Competent:** Priest
- •••• **Expert:** Professor
- ••••• **Master:** Theologian

Possessed by: Missionaries, Priests, Pastors, Nuns, Theologians, Atheists

Specialties: Women's Theology (often called Theaology), Comparative, Liberation, Agnosticism, Christian, Buddhist, Branch Davidian

Merits and Flaws

I will walk with my hands bound
I will walk with my face blood
I will walk with my shadow flag
Into your garden
Garden of stone
— Pearl Jam, "Garden"

Merits and Flaws are new character Traits that add color and flavor to your **Mage** chronicle. Merits provide characters with some benefit, while Flaws act to their detriment. Some of these Traits will have little effect on a game beyond a dash of style; others could unbalance a chronicle or completely change its direction. Powerful Merits or Flaws will shape a character's destiny and any relationships he or she has.

When you create a character in **Mage**, you are given 15 "freebie" points to assign to whatever Traits you like in order to give your character the finishing touches that make her unique. The optional system of Merits and Flaws expands on this idea and further allows you to personalize your character.

Merits may be purchased only with "freebie" points and only during character conception. Flaws provide additional freebies to spend, again, only during initial conception. A maximum of seven points of Flaws may be taken, limiting potential freebie points to a total of 22. Mangus Warhawk, for example, buys Dark Fate and Obsession, a total of seven points in Flaws. If he also chooses to buy Absent-Minded, he wouldn't gain any additional points, although he would add an interesting (and potentially dangerous) new quirk to his personality. Some Merits and Flaws have variable point costs; these Traits offer more options for character creation.

Merits and Flaws are provided to flesh out a character and add new story hooks and details, not to allow power-gamers to mini-max their characters into war-machines. Players should make sure that the Storyteller allows these options in the chronicle before creating characters based around these options. Each chronicle is individual and unique, so there is no telling what restrictions or changes the Storyteller has in mind. There is no right or wrong way, only ways that work for everyone concerned.

Psychological

These Merits and Flaws deal with the psychological makeup of your character, and may describe ideals, motivations or pathologies. Some psychological Flaws can be temporarily ignored by spending a Willpower point, and are so noted. If you possess such a Flaw and do not roleplay it when the Storyteller thinks you should, then she may tell you that you have spent a point of Willpower for the effort. Flaws cannot be conveniently ignored.

Code of Honor: (1 pt Merit)

You have a personal code of ethics to which you strictly adhere. You can automatically resist most temptations that would bring you in conflict with your code. When battling supernatural persuasion (Mind magick or vampiric Domination) that would make you violate your code, either you gain three extra dice to resist or your opponent's difficulties are increased by two (Storyteller's choice). You must construct your own personal code of honor in as much detail as you can, outlining the general rules of conduct by which you abide.

Higher Purpose: (1 pt Merit)

All mages have some vision of their Path, but you have a special commitment to it. Your chosen goal drives and directs you in everything. You do not concern yourself with petty matters and casual concerns, because your higher purpose is everything. Though you may sometimes be driven by this purpose and find yourself forced to behave in ways contrary to the needs of personal survival, it can also grant you great personal strength. You gain two extra dice on any roll that has something to do with this higher purpose. You need to decide what your higher purpose is. Make sure you talk it over with the Storyteller first. (If you have the Flaw: Driving Goal, listed below, you cannot take this Merit.)

Curiosity: (2 pt Flaw)

You are a naturally curious person and find mysteries of any sort irresistible. In most circumstances, you find that your curiosity easily overrides your common sense. To resist the temptation, make a Wits roll verses difficulty 5 for simple things like "I wonder what is in that cabinet?" Increase the difficulty up to 9 for things like "I'll just peek into the Progenitor lab— no one will know. What could possibly go wrong?"

Addiction: (1-3 pt Flaw)

You are addicted to any one of a variety of things. A one point Flaw would be a mild addiction to a easily attained substance, such as caffeine, nicotine or alcohol. A two point Flaw would be either a severe addiction to any easily-obtained substance or any "mild" drug, such as pain killers, sleeping pills or marijuana. A three point Addiction involves the heavy street drugs or hard-to-find drugs. The need for these drugs varies from once a day for some drugs to two to three times a day for others, depending on the strength of the drug and the addiction. If, for whatever reason, you are denied access to the drug, you lose the number of dice equal to the level of your addiction (one, two or three) until you receive your "fix." If you are deprived of the drugs for an extended length of time, you will be forced to make a Willpower check (difficulty of 4 for the first day, + 1 for each additional day). If you fail, you will forgo everything and forcibly go seeking the drug. This would be an easy way for you to be either controlled or forced to do favors for your supplier, especially if the drug is hard to obtain due to its rarity or price.

Compulsion: (1 pt Flaw)

You have a psychological compulsion of some sort, which can cause you a number of different problems. Your compulsion may be for cleanliness, perfection, bragging, stealing, gaming, exaggeration or just talking. A compulsion can be temporarily avoided at the cost of a Willpower point, but it is in effect at all other times.

Dark Secret: (1 pt Flaw)

You have some sort of secret that, if uncovered, would be of immense embarrassment to you and would make you a pariah among your peers. This can be anything from having murdered a Master to having once fallen to a Nephandi's temptations. While this secret weighs on your mind at all times, it will only surface in occasional stories. Otherwise, it will begin to lose its impact.

Intolerance: (1 pt Flaw)

You have an unreasoning dislike of a certain thing. This may be an animal, a class of person, a color, a situation or just about anything else. The difficulties of all dice rolls involving the subject are increased by two. Note that some dislikes may be too trivial to be reflected here— a dislike of *White Wolf Magazine* or tissue paper, for instance, will have little effect on play in most chronicles. The Storyteller is the final arbiter on what you can pick to dislike.

Nightmares: (1 pt Flaw)

You experience horrendous nightmares every time you sleep, and memories of them haunt you during your waking hours. Sometimes the nightmares are so bad they cause you to lose one die on all your actions for the next day (Storyteller's discretion). Some of the nightmares may be so intense that you mistake them for reality. A crafty Storyteller will be quick to take advantage of this. Conflict with your Avatar, Paradox, bad episodes of Quiet or even difficult Seekings may lie at the roots of these night terrors.

Phobia (Mild): (1 pt Flaw)

You have an overpowering fear of something. You instinctively and illogically retreat from and avoid the object of your fear. Common objects of phobias include certain animals, insects, crowds, open spaces, confined spaces and heights. You must make a Willpower roll whenever you encounter the object of your fear. The difficulty of this roll is determined by the Storyteller. If you fail the roll, you must retreat from the object.

Overconfident: (1 pt Flaw)

You have an exaggerated and unshakable opinion of your own worth and capabilities— you never hesitate to trust your abilities, even in situations where you risk defeat. Because your abilities may not be enough, such overconfidence can be very dangerous. When you do fail, you quickly find someone or something else to blame. If you are convincing enough, you can infect others with your overconfidence.

Shy: (1 pt Flaw)

You are distinctly ill at ease when dealing with people and try to avoid social situations whenever possible. The difficulties of all rolls concerned with social dealings are increased by one; the difficulties of any rolls made while you are the center of attention are increased by two. Don't expect your character to make a public speech.

Speech Impediment: (1 pt Flaw)

You have a stammer or some other speech impediment which hampers verbal communication. The difficulties of all relevant rolls are increased by two. Do not feel obliged to roleplay this impediment all the time, but in times of duress, or when dealing with outsiders, you should attempt to simulate it.

Sadism/Masochism: (2 pt Flaw)

You are excited either by causing pain or receiving it. In many situations, you will seek either to be hurt or hurt someone for your pleasure. For a masochist (someone who enjoys pain), your soak roll for actual physical damage is increased by one because you really want to feel the pain. A sadist (someone who likes to hurt others) must make a Willpower roll verses a 5 to stop combat (modified depending on how much you are into the attack and how much you are enjoying hurting the other person). If you fail, you are so caught up in the event that you are unaware of anything else happening around you.

Obsession: (2 point Flaw)

There is something you like, love or are fascinated by to the point where you often disregard common sense to cater to this drive. You react positively to anything related to your obsession, even if it's not in your best interests. For example, if you are obsessed with supernatural creatures, you will go out of your way to talk to and befriend vampires, werewolves and stranger things, and find out as much as you can about them, disregarding all warnings. If you are obsessed with Elvis, you have your house decorated with velvet paintings and annoy your friends with your constant talk about the King. You don't necessarily believe that Elvis is still alive, but you buy every supermarket tabloid that carries an article about him anyway. There are many other obsessions, including British Royalty, guns, knives, football, roleplaying games... you know the type.

Vengeance: (2 pt Flaw)

You have a score to settle— a cabal was wiped out, a friend was corrupted, a mentor was slain... whatever. You are obsessed with wreaking vengeance on the guilty party. Revenge is your first priority in all situations. The need for vengeance can only be overcome by spending Willpower points, and even then, it only temporarily subsides. Someday you may have your revenge, but the Storyteller won't make it easy.

Flashbacks: (3 pt Flaw)

You are prone to flashbacks if you are in either high-pressure situations or circumstances that are similar to the event that caused the flashback itself. The flashback does not have to be combat-oriented. Either positive or negative stimulation could result in a flashback episode. The repeated use of drugs has been proven to cause a wide range of hallucinations, and in the right circumstances, the mind could flashback to any one of them. Emotional anxiety and stress are the usual catalysts for the flashbacks to begin. Flashing back to a good and happy vision can be just as dangerous or distracting as suddenly flashing to being surrounded by demons. The flashbacks can be caused by almost any trauma— torture, extended combat or repeated drug experimentation. During the flashback, you are not aware of what is really around you. Even people speaking to you will be viewed as people or objects from the vision. You can mistake men for women, people for animals and even inanimate objects for people. To you, reality has shifted, and you are back there again.

Driving Goal: (3 pt Flaw)

You have a personal goal, which sometimes compels and directs you in startling ways. The goal is always limitless in depth, and you can never truly achieve it. It could be to eradicate the Technocracy or achieve total enlightenment. Because you must work toward your goal throughout the chronicle (though you can avoid it for short periods by spending Willpower), it will get you into trouble and may jeopardize other actions. Choose your driving goal carefully, as it will direct and focus everything your character does.

Hatred: (3 pt Flaw)

You have an unreasoning hatred of a certain thing. This hate is total and largely uncontrollable. You may hate a species of animal, a class of person, a color, a situation or just about anything else, and you constantly pursue opportunities to harm the hated object or to gain power over it.

Lifesaver: (3 Pt Flaw)

You believe that human life is a sacred gift and will not take a person's life except in the most extreme of circumstances. You may not ever willingly endanger the lives of innocents or in any way participate in a killing. You have no problems with killing animals (for the right reasons), and will kill evil and inhuman creatures to protect others if necessary. (Be very careful, however, with your definition of "evil"....) Senseless death in all forms repulses you, and you feel that those who perform murder should be punished and stopped.

Phobia (Severe): (3 pt Flaw)

You have an overpowering fear of something. Common objects of fear include certain animals, insects, crowds, open spaces, confined spaces, heights and so on. You must make a Willpower roll not to freak out when faced with the object of your fear. The difficulty depends on the circumstances. If you fail the roll, you must retreat in terror from the object of fear. If you score less than three successes, you will not approach it. The Storyteller has final say over which phobias are allowed in a chronicle.

Mental

These Merits and Flaws deal with the mind: its strengths, weaknesses and special capacities. The mind of a mage is a powerful weapon; quirks should be considered carefully.

Common Sense: (1 pt Merit)

You have a significant amount of practical, everyday wisdom. Whenever you are about to do something contrary to common sense, the Storyteller should alert you to how your potential action might violate practicality. This is an ideal Merit if you are a novice player because it allows you to receive advice from the Storyteller concerning what you can and cannot do, and (even more importantly) what you should and should not do.

Concentration: (1 pt Merit)

You have the ability to focus your mind and shut out any distractions or annoyances, above and beyond normal magely discipline. Any penalty to a difficulty or Dice Pool arising from a distraction or other inauspicious circumstance is limited to two dice, though no extra benefits are gained if only one penalty die is imposed.

Lightning Calculator: (1 pt Merit)

You have a natural affinity with numbers and a talent for mental arithmetic, making you a natural when working with computers or betting at the racetracks. The difficulties of all relevant rolls are decreased by two. Another possible use for this ability, assuming you have numbers on which to base your conclusions, is the ability to calculate the difficulty of certain tasks. In appropriate situations, you may ask the Storyteller to estimate the difficulty rating of a task you are about to perform. This Merit is common among the scientists of Iteration X and Virtual Adept hackers.

Eidetic Memory: (2 pt Merit)

You can remember things seen and heard with perfect detail. By gaining at least one success on an Intelligence + Alertness roll, you can recall any sight or sound accurately, even if you heard it or glanced at it only once (although the difficulty of such a feat would be high). Five successes enable you to recall an event perfectly: the Storyteller relates to you exactly what was seen or heard.

Prodigy: (2 pt Merit)

You were Awakened very early in your life and have not been subject to the problems of unlearning the cultural reality. Perhaps one or both of your parents were Awakened and sheltered you from the reality created by the Technomancers. As a result of this protection, you have an easier time grasping the most abstract Spheres of magick. You receive one extra die on rolls that relate to abstract ideas or magickal comprehension. Though you were Awakened at an early age, your actual training in magick probably began much later. (See the Flaw: Age)

Iron Will: (3 pt Merit)

When you are determined and your mind is set, nothing can divert you from your goals. You cannot be Dominated, nor can your mind be affected in any way by

Thaumaturgic rituals. Mages using mental attacks against you gain an additional + 3 to their difficulties if you are aware of them and resisting. However, the additional mental defense costs you one Willpower per turn. Even if you are unaware of them, mages seeking to magickally influence you add + 1 to their difficulties.

Self-Confident: (5 pt Merit)

When you spend a point of Willpower to gain an automatic success, your self-confidence may allow you to gain the benefit of that expenditure without actually losing the Willpower point. When you declare that you are using a point of Willpower and roll for successes, you do not lose the point of Willpower unless you fail. This will also prevent you from botching, but only if you declare that you are spending the Willpower point before you roll. This Merit may only be used when you need confidence in your abilities in order to succeed. You can use it only when the difficulty of your roll is six or higher. You may spend Willpower at other times; however, if the difficulty is five or less, the Merit: Self-Confidence will not help you.

Amnesia: (2 pt Flaw)

You are unable to remember anything about your past, yourself or your family. Your life is a blank slate. However, your past may someday come back to haunt you. (You can, if you wish, take up to five points of other Flaws without specifying what they are. The Storyteller can supply the

details. Over the course of the chronicle, you and your character will slowly discover them.)

Confused: (2 pt Flaw)

You are often confused, and the world seems to be a very distorted and twisted place. Sometimes you are simply unable to make sense of things. You need to roleplay this behavior all the time to a small degree, but your confusion becomes especially strong whenever stimuli surround you (such as when a number of different people talk all at once, or you enter a nightclub with loud pounding music). You may spend Willpower to override the effects of your confusion, but only temporarily.

Absent-Minded: (3 pt Flaw)

This Flaw may not be taken with the Merit: Concentration. Though you do not forget such things as Knowledges or Skills, you do forget such things as names, addresses and the last time you meditated. In order to remember anything more than your own name and the location of your Chantry, you need to make a Wits roll or, as a last resort, spend a Willpower point.

Awareness

These Merits and Flaws involve perception (or the lack thereof). Life magick may be used to repair some of these Flaws; characters doing so must buy off the Flaw with new points.

Acute Senses: (1 pt. Merit)

You have exceptionally sharp hearing, smell, vision or taste. The difficulties of all dice rolls that relate to the sense in question (e.g. Perception + Awareness to hear a faint noise, taste poison in food or see an oncoming attacker) are decreased by two. Combined with sensory Effects (first rank Effects), this Merit allows the mage to add an additional success to her die roll.

Color Blindness: (1 pt Flaw)

You can only see in black and white. Color means nothing to you, although you are sensitive to color density, which you perceive as shades of gray. Life 3 cannot fix this problem, as you can't truly conceive the true nature of color! Note: color blindness actually indicates an inability to distinguish between two colors, but we fudged a bit for the sake of playability.

Hard of Hearing: (1 pt Flaw)

Your hearing is defective. The difficulties of all dice rolls related to hearing are increased by two. You may not take Acute Hearing if you take this Flaw.

Bad Sight: (2 pt Flaw)

Your sight is defective. The difficulties of all dice rolls related to vision are increased by two. This Flaw is neither nearsightedness nor farsightedness— it is a minor form of blindness. The impairment is not correctable. Life 3 may correct this for a short time, but repairing the blindness permanently requires buying off the Flaw or tying the effect to a focus (goggles, a visor, etc.). You may not take Acute Vision if you take this Flaw.

Deaf: (4 pt Flaw)

You cannot hear sound, and automatically fail any rolls that require hearing.

Blind: (6 pt Flaw)

You automatically fail all dice rolls involving vision. You cannot see — the world of color and light is lost to you.

Aptitudes

These Merits and Flaws establish special capacities and abilities for your character, or modify the effects and powers of your character's other Traits.

Animal Magnetism: (1 pt Merit)

You are especially attractive to others. You receive a -2 to your difficulty on Seduction or Subterfuge rolls. However, this will aggravate others of your gender.

Ambidextrous: (1 pt Merit)

You have a high degree of off-hand dexterity and can perform tasks with the "wrong" hand at no penalty. The

normal penalty for using both hands at once to perform different tasks (e.g. fighting with a weapon in each hand) is at a +1 difficulty for the "right" hand and a +3 difficulty for the other hand.

Computer Aptitude: (1 pt Merit)

You have a natural affinity with computers, so the difficulties of all rolls to repair, construct or operate them are reduced by two. This is especially handy for Virtual Adepts and servants of Iteration X.

Crack Driver: (1 pt Merit)

You have a natural affinity with driving motorized wheeled vehicles, such as cars, 18-wheelers and even tractors. The difficulties of all rolls requiring risky or especially difficult driving maneuvers are reduced by two.

Mechanical Aptitude: (1 pt Merit)

You are naturally adept with all kinds of mechanical devices (note that this aptitude does not extend to electronic devices, such as computers). The difficulties of all dice rolls to understand, repair or operate any kind of mechanical device are reduced by two. However, this Merit doesn't help you drive any sort of vehicle.

Poison Resistance: (1 pt Merit)

You have, for some reason or another, become resistant to poisons. It could be that you are somehow naturally resistant or that you have spent years building up your resistance against all known types of poisons. Any time you need to make a soak roll against the effects of a poison or toxin, reduce your difficulty by 3.

Natural Linguist: (2 pt Merit)

You have a flair for languages. This Merit does not allow you to learn more languages than the number permitted by your Linguistics score, but you may add three dice to any Dice Pool involving languages (both written and spoken). This Merit is common among Order of Hermes mages and Gypsies.

Daredevil: (3 pt Merit)

You are good at taking risks, and are even better at surviving them. All difficulties are one less whenever you try something particularly dangerous, and you can ignore one botch result when you roll "ones" on such actions (you can cancel a single "one" that is rolled, as if you have an extra success).

Fast Learner: (3 pt Merit)

You learn very quickly, and pick up on new things faster than most do. You gain one extra experience point at the conclusion of each story (not each game session).

Perfect Balance: (3 pt Merit)

Your sense of balance has achieved great heights by constant training or inherited traits. It is very unlikely that you will ever fall during your life. You may trip, but you will always catch yourself before you fully lose your footing or handhold.

This Merit functions for such actions as tightrope walking, crossing ice and climbing mountain sides. All difficulties involving such feats are reduced by 3. It would take a lot to push or shove a character off his feet if he has this Merit. This is very appropriate for Akashic Brothers or Masters of Life magick.

Jack-Of-All-Trades: (5 pt Merit)

You have a large pool of miscellaneous skills and knowledge obtained through your extensive travels, the jobs you've held, or just all-around know-how. You automatically have one dot in all Skill and Knowledge Dice Pools. This is an illusory level, used only to simulate a wide range of abilities. If the character trains or spends experience in the Skill or Knowledge, he must pay the point cost for the first level a "second time" before raising the Skill or Knowledge to two dots.

Age: (1 pt Flaw)

You began your training in magick either very early in your life or very late. Maybe you were not discovered by anyone until you had already passed the usual age of students, but the Master, for whatever reason, chose to teach you anyway. Or perhaps something about you intrigued your masters so much that they began your studies very early (see the Prodigy Merit). This age difference will cause people to react to you differently. If you are older than the norm, they may either think that you are more skilled than you actually are (which could get you in over your head quickly) or think that you're a joke. If you're young, the older students may resent you or not take you seriously. ("You've got to be kidding. He's just a kid!") Increase the difficulty of your Social rolls by 1 to 3 depending on the circumstances of your situation or the individual you are confronting.

Supernatural

These Merits and Flaws are different kinds of supernatural benefits or detriments. Though rare, they are far more common among mages— who alter reality by their very presence— than among other beings. Because of the potential of these particular Traits, the Storyteller may not allow you to choose from this category— ask before you choose one. Furthermore, you should not select such Traits unless they firmly fit your character concept, and you can explain why your character possesses them. In general, we do not recommend that anyone have more than one or two supernatural Merits or Flaws— they should be strictly controlled by the Storyteller.

Past Life: (1-5 pt Merit)

The mage can remember one or more of her previous incarnations. This can be as simple as constant *deja vu* in places known to her past lives, or as complex as conscious, waking memories of being another person. In practical terms, this means that the mage, and therefore the player, knows slightly more about whatever situations the dead memories contain. The mage might know her way around the past life's hometown, or back away from her murderer without knowing why. This is a good Background for beginning players; the Storyteller can tell them that something they are about to do is stupid, dangerous, or both, because even if the character wouldn't logically know that, one of her past lives might. However, this Background cannot be used to 'remember' Abilities; the character still needs the Dream Background to do that.

The Storyteller can, and likely should, take the opportunity to flesh out one or more of these past selves with the player. Unless the memory is very detailed, the character, and probably the player, isn't likely to know everything about that past. In fact, this half-and-half recollection is a rich source of story ideas, particularly if any of the past lives were Awakened themselves. This is fairly common for those with "old souls" and powerful Avatars.

• **One point**—*Deja vu* memories of one life

• **Two points**— Dreamy, vague memories of one life, with deja vu from several lives

• **Three points**— Vague memories of several lives and one or two well-remembered impressions from one life

• **Four points**— Several well-remembered impressions from many lives

• **Five points**— A clear but broken thread of memories back to the Mythic Age and beyond...

True Love: (1 pt Merit)

You have discovered, and possibly lost (at least temporarily) a true love. Nonetheless, this love provides joy in a torrid existence usually devoid of such enlightened emotions. Whenever you are suffering, in danger, or dejected, the thought of your true love is enough to give you the strength to persevere. In game terms, this love allows you to succeed automatically on any Willpower roll, but only when you are actively striving to protect or come closer to your true love. Also, the power of your love may be powerful enough to protect you from other supernatural forces (Storyteller's discretion). However, your true love may also be a hindrance and require aid (or even rescue) from time to time. Be forewarned: this is a most exacting Merit to play over the course of a chronicle.

Medium: (2 pt Merit)

You possess the natural affinity to sense and hear spirits, ghosts and shades. Though you cannot see them, you feel their presence and are able to speak with them when they are in the vicinity. It is even possible for you to summon them (through pleading and cajoling) to your presence. Spirits will not simply aid you or give you advice for free— they will always want something in return. Mages with both this Merit and the Spirit Sphere reduce the difficulties of Spirit magick by two. Combining the Medium Merit with the Spirit Magnet Merit will make your life exceedingly interesting and problematic.

Danger Sense: (2 pt Merit)

You have a sixth sense that warns you of danger. When you are in danger, the Storyteller should make a secret roll against your Perception + Alertness; the difficulty depends on the remoteness of the danger. If the roll succeeds, the Storyteller tells you that you have a sense of foreboding. Multiple successes may refine the feeling and give an indication of direction, distance or nature. This Merit is more reliable and specific than rank one sensing effects; the two can be combined to create an even more potent warning system.

Faerie Affinity: (2 pt Merit)

Your presence does not frighten faeries; indeed, it attracts them, and you are naturally attuned to their ways. You may even share some small amount of faerie blood. Friendly fey *might* allow you to meditate at their circle once in a while (though gods only know what effect this might have in the long run…).

Spirit Mentor: (3 pt Merit)

You have a ghostly companion and guide. This spirit is able to employ a number of minor powers when it really struggles to exert itself (see Haunted, below), but for the most part, its benefit to you is through the advice it can give. This ghost is the incorporeal spirit of someone who was once living, perhaps even someone particularly famous or wise. The Storyteller will create the ghost character, but will not reveal to you its full powers and potencies. Mentors of this sort are not true Mentors of magick, but might give special insights into aspects of Sleeper life that mages have missed or forgotten. (Further ideas for this Merit can be obtained from **Wraith**.)

Werewolf/Vampire Companion: (3 pt Merit)

You have a friend and ally who just happens to be a werewolf or vampire. Though you may call upon this being in time of need, she also has the right to call upon you (after all, you *are* friends). Neither your kind nor hers appreciate such a relationship; while mages deal with the other Awakened often, all sides share a healthy distrust of each other.

Your friend will not become a walking Quintessence battery for greedy mages. Such relationships often end badly.... The Storyteller will create the character in question, and will not reveal its full powers and potencies.

Luck: (3 pt Merit)

You were born lucky: your Avatar guides your steps, or maybe the Devil looks after his own. Either way, you can repeat three failed non-magickal rolls per story. Only one repeat attempt may be made on any single roll.

Twin Souls: (4 point Merit)

Your Avatar has been fragmented and has a "soulmate" equal in power to your own Avatar and similar in Essence, Nature and Demeanor. This fragment may be possessed by your physical twin (brother or sister, identical or otherwise), a look-alike, another mage, or a complete stranger—possibly even a Sleeper. When in physical contact with your soulmate (or spiritual contact, for actions in the Umbra), the two may share Quintessence and use magick as one (if both are mages), taking the highest ratings in Arete and Spheres while gaining an additional measure of Quintessence equal to the strength of either individual. The parts are greater than the whole. This joint pool must be replenished through meditation in a Node, like a regular pool of Quintessence. Paradox points gained from joint spells are not split, however, and each twin gains the same amount of Paradox.

With only one level of Correspondence, you will always know where your soulmate is; with one dot in Life, you'll know his state of health; with one rank in Mind, you may share thoughts. If one soulmate dies, the other must make a Willpower roll, difficulty 8, to avoid following you due to psychic shock. She must wait also until her soulmate's reincarnation before the power may again be shared. Soulmates are not just walking Merits and must be presented and run as characters, preferably by different players in a group. Also note that you do not have to get along with your soulmate... Twin souls are distinct and separate individuals, not just tag-team powerhouses, and Storytellers should feel free to take over one half of a pair being played as one mind with two bodies.

Unbondable: (4 pt Merit)

You are immune to being Blood Bound. No matter how much vampire blood you drink, you will never be Bound to one. This is exceedingly rare among mortals, and the Merit should be carefully considered by Storytellers before it is allowed into the game.

Spark of Life: (5 point Merit)

The vitality of Life flows within you with preternatural strength. This lifeforce is so strong, in fact, that all non-aggravated wounds heal as if they were one wound level less; if you are Injured, you will heal in three days what others heal in a week. If you are Hurt, you heal in only one day. Bruises disappear in an hour.

If in perfect health yourself, you may share your vitality with others through the power of your touch. Anyone you assist recovers at your accelerated rate, but if the person is badly mauled or crippled, she will require months of constant bedside nursing. If the possessor of this gift is proficient in the Sphere of Life, he may heal aggravated wounds as if they were non-aggravated. All difficulties with Life magic for the purpose of healing, creation, growth or positive change (repairing congenital defects, for example) are at -2 when the touch is used. The mage's supernatural vitality aids the effect. Verbena consider this merit to be the mark of a born healer, while the Sons of Ether think it is a recessive, albeit desirable, mutation.

On the downside, your blood is particularly tasty to vampires, being twice as potent as most mortals, and you regenerate on top of it. Vampires have names for people like you — "Cornucopia," "Big Gulp," or simply "Mine!"

Sphere Natural: (5 pt. Merit)

You are able to utilize one of the Spheres of magick with a greater degree of ease than other mages. In a previous incarnation, you were extremely proficient in one of the Spheres — so much so that your Avatar has managed to draw a small portion of that knowledge through into this lifetime.

Select a Sphere; when spending experience points to gain levels in that Sphere, you pay three-quarter of the normal cost. This Sphere must be declared during character conception. Of course, this Merit may only be purchased once.

Guardian Angel: (6 pt. Merit)

Someone or something watches over you and protects you from harm. You have no idea who or what it is, but you have an idea that someone is looking out for you. In times of great need, you may be supernaturally protected. However, one can never count upon a guardian angel . The Storyteller must decide why you are being watched and what is watching you (not necessarily an angel, despite the name).

Avatar Companion: (7 pt. Merit)

You are in a cycle of reincarntion. However, every time your corporeal form is reestablished, your Avatar has to start its path back several paces. The world is a new place once again, and even the Awakening can not bring back the Knowledges the Avatar stored within a previous incarnation. The strange thing about your passages through the birth-death-rebirth cycle comes from the fact that your Avatar has another lesser Avatar connected to it. This fragment also enters the reincarnation cycle, follows your Avatar through each incarnation, and often retains memories of its previous incarnation.

This companion will fight by the side of your Avatar until death. For many companions, there is no real reason to do this; the Avatar companion knows, however, that her place in the way of things is to follow alongside your Avatar and do just that.

The Storyteller creates and controls this other being in whatever form it may take. Like other companion Merits, this is a background benefit, not an opportunity to get two characters for the price of one.

True Faith: (7 pt. Merit)

You have a deep-seated faith in and love for God, or whatever name you choose to call the Almighty. You begin the game with one point of Faith (a Trait with a range of 1-10). This Faith provides you with an inner strength and comfort that continues to support you when all else betrays you. This Merit is most common among members of the Celestial Chorus. Although other factions may possess Faith, Technomancers of any kind may not (and Faith in Kibo does not count!).

Your Faith adds to Willpower rolls, giving +1 to the Dice Pool for each point in Faith. It does not affect magick use in any way, but may allow for some other form of outside intervention (see, for example, Guardian Angel or Luck). Certain types of mage may, at the Storyteller's discretion, reduce any Paradox gained around Sleepers if those Sleepers share the mage's faith (in effect, performing miracles before the faithful). The exact supernatural effects of Faith, if any, are completely up to the Storyteller, although it will typically repel vampires. (Basically, the mage must make a Faith roll against a difficulty of the vampire's Willpower to repel him. For more rules, see **Vampire Players Guide, pg.** 30, or **Hunters Hunted**, pp. 64-66.) It will certainly vary from person to person, and will almost never be obvious— some of the most saintly people have never performed a miracle greater than managing to ease the suffering an injured soul. The nature of any miracles you do perform will usually be tied to your own Nature, and you may never realize that you have been aided by a force beyond yourself.

An additional benefit of True Faith is innate countermagick. This effect will *not* work for mages (theories about the reason for this vary), but can add a dangerous wrinkle to fanatical witch-hunters or enemy Acolytes. Each point of True Faith grants one die worth of countermagick. A mage, therefore, facing a hunter with 5 points of True Faith stands a slim chance of sending powerful effects against him.

True Faith is a rare attribute in this day and age. No one may start the game with more than one Faith point. Additional points are only awarded at the Storyteller's discretion, based on appropriate behavior and deeds.

Spirit Magnet: (3-7 pt Merit or 2-6 pt Flaw)

Spirits congregate at location in the Umbra that parallels your position in the Realm. You do not know of their presence unless you possess the first Rank of the Spirit Sphere or have been alerted by others that do. Spirits are there because they like being around the Quintessence that forms your physical body's Pattern or your Avatar. These spirits often fight amongst themselves for various reasons— the spirits are enemies, they all want to be around the character's heart or brain, they want to protect the character, they want to kill the character, etc.

Some of these spirits might remain within the Spirit Realms in areas that correlate with the physical space that makes up a mage's Pattern in the physical world. (Some areas in the Spirit Realms correlate to physical locations.) These spirits affect the behavior and appearance of the character. If there are evil spirits within the character's "spirit" form, the character will slowly be twisted into doing evil acts unless the proper procedures are taken to remove these blights from the character's Avatar. If good spirits possess the "spirit" form, they will be likely to help the character out in appropriate situations. Also note that there is a distinction between spirits and wraiths.

• If the Spirit Magnet is a Merit, benign spirits will flock about the Umbra in area (of the Penumbra) that correlates to the character's physical location. They will do what they can to alert the character to dangers within the Umbra. If the character is about to unknowingly perform an act that is "evil," the spirits will do their best to alert the character of that fact. If these spirits are destroyed, others will soon arrive to take their place.

• If the Spiritual Magnet is a Flaw, malignant spirits battle over the same location. They seek to taint the character with evil thoughts and pollute the Umbra about the location. Evil spirits will often taunt characters and try to annoy the mage at the worst of times. Other mages will notice this, and no amount of magicks will keep these spirits away for long.

The number of freebie points spent or gained affects the level of spirit involvement with the character and other spirits within the Umbra. For more information on the Umbra, see Book Three of this tome, **Umbra: The Velvet Shadow** or **Werewolf: The Apocalypse, Second Edition**.

Strangeness: (1 pt. Flaw)

Reality is slightly stranger for you. Once per game session, the Storyteller will choose one of your Spheres, pick an Effect at random and roll for a bizarre coincidental effect. If the roll succeeds, something unusual involving the Sphere will happen for no apparent reason. For instance, Mind 3 could result in a mage getting a visit from a telepathic dog, picking up Mexican radio stations in his head or hearing stray thoughts from a passing serial killer.

If the roll fails, the strangeness passes. If the roll botches, Paradox descends on the mage, pushing him a little closer towards Quiet. This Flaw can alter the tone of a campaign; therefore, allowing a character to take it should require the approval of not only the Storyteller, but also the other players in the group.

Throwback: (1-5 pt. Flaw)

One or more of your past lives still affects you... badly. Their fears come back to haunt you in your dreams, and you have flashbacks of their worst memories (such as their death, or, even worse, a personality that encroaches on your own). For bad dreams or flashbacks, take one to two points depending on the severity of the condition and how much it will affect your studies or performance in dangerous situations. For a "roommate in your head," take three points (whether you know he exists or not). For the package deal and a truly miserable existence, take 5 points, but expect the Storyteller to take every opportunity to use these against you. This Flaw can be "worked off" during the course of play, but only with difficulty.

Echoes: (1-5 pt. Flaw)

The beliefs of the unawakened affect you more strongly than they do most mages. Depending on where you are at any given time, the superstitious beliefs of the Sleepers around you can actually become your reality. The severity of the Echoes differs from mage to mage— for some, there is only minor inconvenience, but for others, the situation can be deadly. In some cases, the beliefs of the Sleepers can be beneficial, but they are most often harmful in some way.

• **Very minor:** While you are not truly affected by the Echoes, you have an affect on the nature of reality in the area. For example, milk may sour in your presence, or bread does not rise while you are in a kitchen. (1 pt)

• **Mild:** Echoes of this level can be an inconvenience, sometimes physically and sometimes mentally. For example, dogs have a tendency to growl when you are around; you could be physically incapable of entering a person's home without permission (anyone at all can invite you in, it need not be the owner of the property); horses break into a hard sweat when you are nearby. (2 pts.)

• **Noticeable:** The flaws are easily noticed by those with a trained eye. You are easily distracted by religious symbols of any nature; you develop a sudden allergy to salt; your hair moves opposite the breeze. (3 pts.)

• **Distracting:** You have trouble concentrating when people act a certain way around you, and people of a superstitious nature will not trust you without the aid of magick. You may be affected by the "evil eye"; anyone casting this gesture in your direction is unaffected by your powers; certain herbs and home remedies have the same affect on you; you cast no shadow, or your shadow moves of its own volition. (4 pts.)

• **Powerful:** You are still able to alter reality, but you are now susceptible to the whims of the collective unconscious. Also, you now affect reality without trying. The beliefs of the area where you are currently located can grant you extra powers and cause you physical changes. You might not sink in water, you float; physically touching the ground can cause you pain; those who are "psychically aware" are thrown into convulsions in your presence and often speak in tongues. (5 pts)

Cursed: (1–5 pt Flaw)

You have been cursed by someone or something with supernatural or magical powers. This curse is specific and detailed. It cannot be dispelled without extreme effort, and it can be life-threatening. Some examples follow:

• If you pass on a secret that was told to you, your betrayal will later harm you in some way. (1 pt.)

• You stutter uncontrollably when you try to describe what you have seen or heard. (2 pt.)

• Tools often break or malfunction when you attempt to use them. (3 pts.)

• You are doomed to make enemies of those to whom you become most attached (so whatever you do, don't get too close to the other characters!). (4 pts.)

• Every one of your accomplishments or achievements will eventually, inevitably, become soiled and fail in some way. (5 pts.)

Magical Prohibition or Imperative: (2–7 point Flaw)

There is something you must or must not do, and your life, your luck, your magic and perhaps your very soul depends on it. It may be something that has always been upon you, a *geas* prophesied by druids at your birth, a sacred oath or vow you swore, or a promise or bargain you made, and Someone (with a capital S) witnessed it and is going to hold you to it. If you disobey, the consequences are dire, if not deadly.

For example, Dominic De Woolfe is forbidden to ever harm a wolf, the totem shape chosen by his Avatar. A crazed Nephandi discovers this and pulls a rabid wolf out of his hat. Dominic then has the choice of violating his *geas* or getting bitten by a rabid wolf. He chooses to shoot both the wolf and the Nephandi, and, as a result, his Avatar deserts him, leaving him a mortal without the ability to do magic.

Characters may have several magical prohibitions or imperatives, and these may come into conflict. In Celtic myth, Cuchulainn had the *geasa* to "Never refuse hospitality" and "Never eat dog meat." Three hags once offered him roast dog for dinner, and Cuchulainn died soon after. Consequently, most mages keep their magical prohibitions and imperatives secret, lest they be used against them by enemy mages. Perversely, *geasa* curses and sacred oaths are also marks of great status among certain Traditions, espe-

cially the Verbena and Dreamspeakers, who accord status to mages with such Flaws as if each were extra points of Destiny. Simply put, unimportant people don't have *geasa* or family curses.

Storytellers should examine each prohibition or imperative and assign a point value to it, as well as to the punishment for violating it. Easily avoided circumstances, such as "Never break bread with a red-haired man," are worth 1 point, while more common, or difficult, things, such as "Stop and pet every cat you see," are worth 2 points, and particularly drastic or dangerous circumstances, such as "Never back down from a fight," are worth 3 (or more) points. Consequences are worth points as well. Automatically botching the next major spell you do is worth 1 point, having bad luck for the rest of your life is worth 2, losing all your friends and worldly possessions is worth 3, dying is worth 4, and being deserted by your Avatar is worth 5. Characters and Storytellers may come up with variants of these.

Traditionally, there is very little that may be done about *geasa*, which are simply facets of one's Destiny, and curses are devilishly hard to lift (and the Flaw must be bought off if they are). Characters who accidentally violate them may attempt to atone for their crime, fixing whatever they did wrong. A witch who has vowed to never eat any red meat, and then suddenly finds ham in her pea soup, might be able to atone for the trespass by fasting and sending checks to PETA. However, if a mage violates an oath willingly and with full knowledge — and survives — he becomes an oathbreaker, one of the foulest epithets among the Traditions. Oathbreakers are psychically marked. It is virtually impossible for them to find a tutor or any sort of aid. Some Traditions, notably the Order of Hermes and the Verbena, kill them on sight, numbering them among the Nephandi, whose dark paths of power are the only ones left open to them.

Characters who wish to begin as oathbreakers should take Dark Fate or some Curse, as well as the Flaw: Oathbreaker, worth 4 points.

The Bard's Tongue: (1 point Flaw)

You speak the truth, uncannily so. Things you say tend to come true. This is not a facility for blessing or cursing, or an Effect that can be ruled by any conscious control (use Time 3 instead). However, at least once per story, an uncomfortable truth regarding any current situation will appear in your head and come out your lips. To avoid speaking prophecy, the owner of this 'gift' must expend a Willpower point and take a wound level from the strain of resisting (especially if he bites a hole in his tongue).

Primal Marks: (2 point Flaw)

You have an Avatar of the Primordial essence— some totem or god of legend. If the totem spirit is an animal, you strongly resemble what one would look like in human form, so much that people who don't even know you call you

"Bear," "Moose" or "Raven." If the Avatar is some well known god or hero, you look just like people would expect him to, including any particular deformities (though you do get extra points for those). You look the part so much that anyone can guess your nature at a glance, and there is some danger in that, especially if your Avatar has legendary enemies (and most do). Your Avatar will also require you to protect its species if it is an animal, or finish up its unfinished agenda if it is some god or hero.

Haunted: (3 pt Flaw)

You are haunted by a ghost that only you (and Mediums) can see and hear. It actively dislikes you and enjoys making your life miserable by insulting, berating and distracting you, especially when you need to keep your cool. It also has a number of minor powers it can use against you (once per story for each power): hiding small objects; bringing a "chill" over others, making them very ill at ease with you; causing a loud buzzing in your ear or the ears of others; moving a small object such as a knife or pen; breaking a fragile item such as a bottle or mirror; tripping you; or making eerie noises, such as chains rattling. Yelling at the ghost can sometimes drive it away, but it will confuse those who are around you. The Storyteller will likely personify the ghost in order to make things all the more frustrating for you. (More ideas for this Flaw can be obtained from **Wraith**.)

Sphere Inept: (5 pt. Flaw)

You are unable to utilize the magicks of one of the Spheres. This is not due to the fact that you have not yet been trained in the particular Sphere of magick. You are denied access to this Sphere because your Avatar has been 'crippled' in some way. No matter how much time you spend trying to correct the problem, you are unable to remedy it. You will be forever disconnected from the mystic Sphere selected. Discovering the cause of this 'injury' might become a character's long-term goal. Perhaps some sort of 'penance' could be found to eventually buy this Flaw off. This effect could have been generated by the mage being put through a lesser Gilgul in a previous incarnation. The Sphere of Ineptitude must be declared during character conception.

Psychic Vampire: (5 point Flaw)

The spark of Life is dying within you and must be continually fed from outside forces. You are a psychic vampire. Plants and insect life wither or die in your presence as you feed on their energies, and any person you touch for more than an hour will suffer one non-aggravated Health Level as you siphon away his life. Those already injured (including those whose Bruised Health Level has been sucked away) will not heal while in your presence. You can still be in the same building without harming someone, but sharing a bed is not possible unless you want the other person to slowly die. If you do not feed the emptiness within yourself at least once a day, you will begin to die. The rate at which you take wounds follows the progression for natural healing in reverse: you take a Health Level after one day, a second in three days, a third in a week, a fourth in a month, and, finally, one wound every three months.

Mages with this Flaw who possess the Sphere of Life have a -2 on all difficulties with Effects designed to damage, stunt, destroy or corrupt a living thing when the healing touch is used. For each Health Level done in this matter, however, a Health Level caused to the mage as the result of life-energy starvation may be healed, or, if the mage has not gone without, the dying flame may be sated for an additional hour per Level done. While a psychic vampire is bloated with Life energies, he will not automatically cause death and injury to those around him. The Verbena and the Celestial Chorus both find this Flaw to be a mark of extreme evil, best dealt with by the extermination of the one possessing it, while the Nephandi actively recruit those with this dark blessing. On the plus side, vampires find your blood completely lacking in sustenance.

Dark Fate: (5 pt Flaw)

You are doomed to experience a most horrible demise or, worse, suffer eternal agony. No matter what you do, someday you will be out of the picture. In the end, all your efforts, your struggles and your dreams will come to naught. Your fate is certain, and there is nothing you can do about it. Even more ghastly, you have partial knowledge of this, for you occasionally have visions of your fate— and they are most disturbing. The malaise these visions inspire in you can only be overcome through the use of Willpower, and the malaise will return after each vision. At some point in the chronicle, you will indeed face your fate, but when and how is completely up to the Storyteller. Though you can't do anything about your fate, you can still attempt to reach some goal before it occurs, or at least try to make sure that your friends are not destroyed as well. This is a difficult Flaw to roleplay; though it may seem as if it takes away all free will, we have found that, ironically, it grants freedom. Combining this Flaw with the Destiny Background is very appropriate— Elric and Vanyel are classic literary examples.

Mage Ties

These Merits and Flaws deal with the place, position and status of a character within mage society. These need not only apply to Tradition mages; the Technocracy and Nephandi (and perhaps even the Marauders) have internal politics with which they must contend.

Boon: (1-3 pt Merit)

A Master owes you a favor because of something either you or your Mentor once did for him. The extent of the boon owed to you depends on how many points you spend.

One point would indicate a relatively minor boon, while three points would indicate that the Master probably owes you his life.

Prestigious Mentor: (1 pt Merit)

Your Mentor had or has great Status among your Tradition, and this has accorded you a peculiar honor. Most treat you respectfully as a result, while some have only contempt for you, believing you to be nothing compared to them. This prestige could greatly aid you when dealing with elders acquainted with your Mentor. Indeed, your Mentor's contacts may actually approach you at some point offering aid. Although your Mentor might no longer have contact with you, the simple fact of your apprenticeship has marked you forever.

Reputation: (2 pt Merit)

You have a good reputation among the mages of your Tradition. This may be your own reputation, or it may be derived from your Mentor. Add three dice to any Dice Pools involving social dealings with others of your Chantry or Tradition. A character with this Merit may not take the Flaw: Notoriety.

Enemy: (1-5 pt Flaw)

You have an enemy, or perhaps a group of enemies. Someone wants to harm you. The value of the Flaw determines how powerful these enemies are. The most powerful enemies (Masters or elder vampires) would be five point Flaws, while someone nearer to your own power would be worth only one point. You must decide who your enemy is and how you earned such enmity in the first place.

Infamous Mentor: (1 pt Flaw)

Your Mentor was, and perhaps still is, distrusted and disliked by many of your fellow mages. As a result, you are distrusted and disliked as well. This is a heavy load, and one not easily shed.

Insane Mentor: (1 pt Flaw)

Your Mentor has completely lost his grip on consensual reality, and has become lost in Quiet or dangerously insane. Any wrong committed by your Mentor may affect your reputation, and some of your Mentor's dangerous schemes may somehow involve you. This Flaw does not apply to Marauders.

Mentor's Resentment: (1 pt Flaw)

Your Mentor dislikes you and wishes you ill. Given the smallest opportunity, your Mentor will seek to do you harm, and may even attack you if provoked. Your Mentor's friends will also work against you. Good luck!

Twisted Apprenticeship: (1 pt Flaw)

Your Mentor was quite malevolent and taught you all the wrong things about mage society. Your concepts of Chantry politics are all wrong, and your faulty beliefs are likely to get you into a great deal of trouble. Over time, after many hard lessons, you can overcome this bad start (the Storyteller will tell you when). But until then, you will continue to believe what you were first told, no matter how others try to "trick" you into thinking otherwise.

Diabolical Mentor: (2 pt Flaw)

Your Mentor is engaged in acts that could cause a tremendous uproar. She could be wantonly ignoring Protocols, causing havoc with vulgar magick and Paradox, dealing with Nephandi or torturing captured Technomancers. Plenty of folks are after your Mentor's hide, and your skin may be tarred with the same brush.

Notoriety: (3 pt Flaw)

You have a bad reputation among your peers; perhaps you violated the Protocols once too often, or belong to an unpopular Chantry. There is a two dice penalty to all dice rolls for social dealings with associated mages. A character with this Flaw may not take the Merit: Reputation.

Sleeper Society

These Merits and Flaws deal with the influence, power and station of a character among the Sleepers. Some of them correspond very closely to certain Background Traits (such as Influence and Resources), while others simply elaborate and expand upon them. The Backgrounds give you more creative freedom, while the Merits provide you with exact details of what you possess.

Such Influence is common among the upper ranks of the Technocracy, but Tradition mages and even Nephandi may share it. Mages with their fingers embedded too deeply in these pies may find themselves crossing swords with vampires, who exert a constant influence on the lives of the mortals around them.

Black Market Ties: (1-5 pt Merit)

You have special ties to the underground shopping network, ties that help you acquire hard-to-find equipment. This Merit adds +1 die per point to your Streetwise roll when trying, for instance, to obtain black market weaponry. Difficulties for such rolls are left up to the Storyteller (typically 7 or higher). The point cost reflects how "connected" you may be. The Storyteller may allow you to use your Black Market connections during the game to provide you with needed or useful equipment. Such connections will not simply hand you whatever you want — such things don't come cheap! It is up to the Storyteller to determine the quantity, quality and availability of the equipment. He may feel free to disallow it entirely if such connections would unbalance the game.

- **One point**— Small items: ammo, low-clearance ID badges, good software
- **Two points**— Average items: guns, hi-tech software, special ammo
- **Three points**— Fancy items: antique cars, explosives, automatic weapons
- **Four points**— Hefty items: heavy weapons, high-security IDs or access codes
- **Five points**— "Yeah, right. Maybe next game.": hi-tech military weapons, high explosives, military vehicles

Judicial Ties: (2 pt Merit)

You have both influence over and contacts in the justice system. You know most of the judges as well as the attorneys in the prosecutor's department, and can affect the progress of various cases and trials with limited difficulty. Though it is difficult to intervene in a case, you can influence it in one direction or another. These ties can also make it easy to acquire search warrants.

Mansion: (3 pt Merit)

You own a large mansion— a home with 25 or more rooms— as well as the surrounding estate. The servants, if you have any, are provided for if you choose this Merit, although they cannot be used as Acolytes (Allies) unless you purchase the appropriate Background. The mansion is assumed to have the most current electronic security available and a fence around the perimeter, but has no ties to Nodes or Horizon Realms (see the Chantry Background for such a place). While the mansion can be in as poor or as good a shape as you wish, the more inhabited it appears to be, the more attention it will garner. A ghost house won't attract IRS audits, but it may attract police scrutiny if bands of strange kids hang out there.

Media Ties: (2 pt Merit)

You have both influence over and contacts in the local media. You can suppress and create news stories (though not always with 100 percent efficiency; journalists are an unruly bunch) and you have access to the files and gossip of the staffs of newspapers and TV stations. Common among agents of the N.W.O. and Virtual Adepts.

Nightclub: (2 pt Merit)

You own a moderate-sized nightclub, perhaps one of the hottest nightspots in the city. This club brings in enough money to support you in moderate luxury ($1000 a month, but it can grow), but more important than the money is the prestige. You may use the nightclub as your Chantry, or you may simply hang out there. The name of the nightclub, its style, design and its regular patrons are all up to you. Variations on this theme could include: a restaurant, theater, comedy club, sports arena or retail store.

Church Ties: (3 pt Merit)

You have influence and contacts in some local churches, and have the means to create protest rallies, help the needy or raise money. The more you use your ties, of course, the greater your risk of being discovered. This is appropriate for the Celestial Chorus and, perversely, the Nephandi.

Corporate Ties: (3 pt Merit)

You have both influence over and contacts in the local corporate community. You understand the dynamics of money in the city and have links with all the major players. In times of need, you can cause all sorts of financial mayhem, and can raise considerable amounts of money (in the form of loans) in a very short period of time. Common among Technomancers, and almost obligatory in the Syndicate.

Entertainment Ties: (3 pt Merit)

You have a degree of fame and influence in the local entertainment scene (music, theatre, dance, S.C.A., etc.). Either you own or manage a good venue or site or you have some notoriety among both peers and fans. You can exert this influence to ferret out information, or buy favors. This is especially useful when searching for Acolytes or attempting unsubtle magick under the right circumstances ("But he's a stage magician! He's always doing stuff like that.").

The Book of Shadows: The Mage Players Guide

For 5 points, this fame can become nationwide (Is David Copperfield really working for the Order of Hermes?).

Police Ties: (3 pt Merit)

You have both influence over and contacts in the local police department. You can, with a single phone call, cause an APB to be issued. However, the more often you use your ties with the police department, the weaker they become, and the more attention you attract toward yourself. Your influence is not solid (that can be achieved only through game play), and it can let you down at times.

Political Ties: (3 pt Merit)

You have both influence over and contacts among the politicians and bureaucrats of the city. In times of need, you can shut off the power and water to a building or neighborhood, and can unleash many different means of harassment against your enemies. The more you use your political ties, the weaker they become: Total control can only be achieved through game play. Syndicate and N.W.O. mages often have this Merit.

Underworld Ties: (3 pt Merit)

You have both influence over and contacts in the local Mafia and organized street gangs. This provides you with limited access to large numbers of "soldiers," as well as extensive links to the underworld of crime. The more often you use your ties with the criminal element, the weaker they grow.

Corporation CEO: (5 pt Merit)

You have a particular influence and sway over a major corporation and associated companies, just as if you were its chief executive officer. Indeed, you might have owned this company before your Awakening, and you have retained your control. Through this corporation, you know much that takes place in the corporate community and have the means to wage economic warfare. This Merit provides you with some informal Allies and Resources, the exact extent of which are determined by the Storyteller. This is a Common Merit for Technocracy higher-ups.

Ward: (3 pt Flaw)

You are devoted to the protection of a Sleeper. You may describe your ward, though the Storyteller will actually create her. This character may be a friend or relative from your pre-Awakened days, or just a good friend. Acolytes do not count as Wards, as they "pay their own way." Wards have a talent for getting caught up in the action of stories, and they're frequent targets of a character's enemies.

Hunted: (4 pt Flaw)

Vampires and werewolves are not the only Awakened who need to fear fanatical witch-hunters (see "The Rule of Shade" in Book Three). You have somehow attracted the interest of some Sleeper agency (perhaps controlled by the Technocracy or Nephandi) or individual who now seeks your destruction. This hunter is beyond reason and has some form of power, influence or authority that puts you at a disadvantage. Your friends, family and associates are likewise endangered. Sooner or later, this Flaw will result in a confrontation. The resolution should not be an easy one.

Physical

These Merits and Flaws deal with your health and physical makeup. Life 3 can recreate these Merits or fix these Flaws to a degree, but the limitations of the **Better Body** Effect apply.

Double-Jointed: (1 pt Merit)

You are unusually supple. Reduce the difficulty of any Dexterity roll involving body flexibility by two. Squeezing through a tiny space is one example of a use for this Merit.

Huge Size: (4 pt Merit)

You are abnormally large in size, possibly over seven feet tall and 400 pounds in weight. You therefore have one additional Health Level, and are able to suffer more harm before you are incapacitated. Treat this as an extra Health Level, with no penalties to rolls.

Allergic: (1-4 pt Flaw)

You are allergic to some substance — pollen, animal fur, alcohol, chocolate, etc. For one point, you get hives, sneeze or become dizzy upon prolonged contact with your bane; for two points, you swell up uncomfortably in the affected area, reducing all Dice Pools by one; for three points, your reaction actually incapacitates you, reducing appropriate Dice Pools by three. If the substance is really common in your chronicle, add an additional point to this Flaw.

Asthma: (1 pt Flaw)

You have difficulty performing strenuous tasks because you cannot breathe properly. With asthma, your lungs only pull in a fraction of the air that normal lungs require. Any time that you exert yourself, you must make a Stamina roll against difficulty of 6 or be unable to perform any action on the next round while you catch your breath.

Short: (1 pt Flaw)

You are well below average height, and have trouble seeing over high objects and moving quickly. You suffer a two dice penalty to all pursuit rolls, and you and the Storyteller should make sure your height is taken into account in all situations. In some circumstances, this will give you a concealment bonus.

Disfigured: (2 pt Flaw)

A hideous disfigurement makes you ugly and easy to notice or remember. You therefore have a zero Appearance. Common among the Nephandi and some particularly bizarre Technomancers.

Child: (3 pt Flaw)

You were a small child at the time of your Awakening (see "Child Mages" in Book Three). You may be precocious, but you're still just a kid. You have the Flaw: Short (see above), and find it difficult to be taken seriously by others (two dice penalty to all relevant rolls). Additionally, you may be subject to parental control, curfews and child labor and truancy laws. Few clubs will admit you, because you are "underage."

Deformity: (3 pt Flaw)

You have some kind of deformity — a misshapen limb, a hunchback or whatever— that affects your interactions with others and may inconvenience you physically. The difficulties of all dice rolls related to physical appearance are raised by two. Your deformity will also raise the difficulty of some Dexterity rolls by two, depending on the type of deformity you possess.

Lame: (3 pt Flaw)

Your legs are injured or otherwise prevented from working effectively. You suffer a two dice penalty to all dice rolls related to movement. A character may not take this Flaw along with the Merit: Double-Jointed.

One Arm: (3 pt Flaw)

You have only one arm — choose which, or determine randomly at character creation. This could be a battle scar, birth defect or other form of injury. It is assumed that you are accustomed to using your remaining hand, so you suffer no off-hand penalty. However, you do suffer a two dice penalty to any Dice Pool where two hands would normally be needed to perform a task. A character may not take this Flaw along with the Merit: Ambidextrous.

Mute: (4 pt Flaw)

Your vocal apparatus does not function, and you cannot speak at all. You can communicate through other means — typically writing, Mind magick or signing.

Paraplegic: (6 pt Flaw)

You can hardly move without assistance, such as a pair of crutches or a wheelchair. Even then it can be painful and cumbersome to do so. The Storyteller and you should take care to roleplay this Flaw correctly, no matter how difficult it makes things. A character may not take this Flaw along with the Merit: Double-Jointed.

New Backgrounds

Before enlightenment,
Carrying water and chopping wood.
After enlightenment,
Carrying water and chopping wood.
— Anonymous Zen Proverb

These Backgrounds may give a chronicle a bit of flavor. Some modifications to the Talisman Background are provided in Book Three. As always, the suitability of these Backgrounds will depend on your Chronicle.

Chantry

This background can work two ways: with a straight-forward rating of the player's Chantry strength, or in tandem with the optional point-based system described in Appendix Two of **The Book of Chantries.** Note that the Chantry Background differs from the Node Background, which refers to the amount of additional Quintessence the players' cabal may access on its own.

If the rating equals the Chantry's strength, the character belongs to an existing Chantry, sharing in its duties, politics and wars. This membership is proportionate to the character's rank; a beginning mage from Doissetep may have powerful friends, but is still a beginning mage and sits very low on the Chantry totem pole. This can be a mixed blessing, as low-ranking mages from high-caliber Chantries tend to get stuck with grunt work, deadly enemies and cranky superiors. Storytellers are advised to play this up to counterbalance the benefits of Chantry membership. Weaker Chantries will demand less from their members than powerful ones.

All cabal members must belong to the same Chantry if this Background is chosen by more than one member, unless the cabal has been formed specifically through an alliance of Chantries (which is possible). Player characters with Chantry membership can call upon a degree of help, find certain information, or pull a bit of weight with other mages, but are subject to Chantry laws (called covenants)

and the whims of their masters. This choice can provide any number of story possibilities, but can be a pain as well.

If the characters are pooling their Chantry Background points, the characters may build the Chantry themselves using the creation rules referred to above. For simplicity, the Storyteller may compare the total of the cabal's points against the table below:

Pitifully Weak Chantry	10-20 Creation Points
Weak Chantry	20-30 Creation Points
Average Chantry	30-50 Creation Points
Strong Chantry	50-70 Creation Points
Powerful Chantry	70-100 Creation Points
Overwhelmingly Powerful Chantry	100+ Creation Points

If the characters build the Chantry, they run it. This assures both independence and a never-ending stream of headaches; maintenance, internal and external politics, and possible discovery by outside parties. Players are referred to **The Book of Chantries** for details on Chantry construction, workings and membership. Characters need not have this Background to belong to a Chantry, but it should be bought if that Chantry plays an important part in the chronicle.

• 1 Creation Point, or membership in a pitiful Chantry (the Nightmare Theatre)

•• 2 Creation Points, or a small Chantry (the Sepulcher)

••• 3 Creation Points, or a strong Chantry (the Lodge of the Gray Squirrel)

•••• 4 Creation Points, or a powerful Chantry (the House of Helekar)

••••• 5 Creation Points, or an overwhelmingly powerful Chantry (Doissetep)

Familiar

Mages with this Background have a familiar, an intelligent creature of spirit-made-matter which is magically bonded to the mage. But just as the familiar is bonded to the mage, so too is the mage bonded to the familiar. The relationship between a mage and her familiar varies widely, but the relationship itself is an extremely powerful tie (see the rules for familiars in Book Three).

The familiars of different Traditions tend to vary in form. The familiars of Verbena are often cat-creatures, while the familiars of the Dreamspeakers are more often eagles, hawks, other birds or snakes. The Sons of Ether imbue golems with the spirits of familiars, while some Hollow Ones have been known to take sewer rats or stray dogs as familiars. The Virtual Adepts, it is said, even make familiars out of their computers!

Regardless of their form, familiars provide their mages with information and even abilities beyond those the mage can attain alone. The exact nature of these powers varies with the familiar. In return, familiars feed on the mage's Quintessence. The strength of the familiar determines both the amount of power and information it can confer to the mage and the amount of Prime energy it must be fed weekly. If it does not receive sufficient "food," the familiar may become disgruntled and leave. If a familiar breaks its bond, that mage loses all the benefits the familiar con-ferred. A mage whose familiar dies immediately loses an amount of Quintessence equal to twice the power level of their familiar, as well as all the abilities conferred by the familiar.

Mages with this Background are assumed to have already called their familiar or to have used the Life Effect: **Imbue Flesh** to create one.

• Familiar can eat one point of Paradox per month. Familiar has access to a few pieces of information. Requires one point of Quintessence per week.

•• Familiar can eat one point of Paradox every other week and has access to noteworthy pieces of information. Requires two points of Quintessence per week.

••• Familiar can eat one point of Paradox per week, knows a great deal about Esoteric subjects and is considered equivalent to a one dot Mentor. Requires three points of Quintessence per week.

•••• Familiar can eat two points of Paradox per week and is considered a two dot Mentor for study purposes. Requires four points of Quintessence per week.

••••• Familiar can eat one point of Paradox per day and has a vast wealth of information, equivalent to a three dot Mentor. Requires five points of Quintessence per week.

Resources

Mages can get their hands on money in a variety of ways. Many Virtual Adepts siphon funds from bank accounts; Celestial Chorus mages or Acolytes may "pass the hat" and coincidentally end up with more money than one would think possible; Hollow Ones and Cultists of Ecstasy often use Mind magick to beg; Technocracy research associates wrangle over funding for their special projects. Some mages even conjure money "as needed" by using vulgar magick. All of these methods work, and all have a common drawback: sooner or later, someone wonders where these mages get all their money.

"Someone" can take many forms—IRS agents, N.W.O. snoops, Paradox Spirits, citizens' watchdog groups or just plain thugs. These parties will, when they discover a mage's monetary indiscretions, seek to part that mage from his funds by one means or another. Thus, while magickally augmenting one's income works once in a while, it's a good idea to have more mundane Resources at hand.

This Trait describes your financial resources or access to such resources. These Resources are not completely liquid assets, but you can often sell them to gain money. It may take weeks or even months to do so, depending on how much needs to be sold. It may even represent your regular "haul" from one or more of the methods described above.

This Trait assumes that the character gains a basic allowance each month appropriate to the level of Resources. The source of this income must be detailed, however, as it could easily "dry up" depending on the circumstances of the chronicle.

• Small savings: You have an apartment and perhaps a motorcycle. If liquidated, you would have $1000 in cash. Allowance of $500 a month.

•• Middle class: You have an apartment or condominium. If liquidated, you would have $8,000 in cash. Allowance of $1200 a month.

••• Large savings: You own a house (or at least have some equity). If liquidated, you would have $50,000 in cash. Allowance of $3000 a month.

•••• Well-off: You own a large house, or perhaps a dilapidated country manor. If liquidated, you would have $500,000 in cash. Allowance of $9000 a month.

••••• Fantastically rich: You are easily a millionaire many times over. If liquidated, you would have at least $5,000,000 in cash. Allowance of $30,000 a month.

Sanctum

"Sanctum" is a general term for a place where a mage "sets" reality to her paradigm, shaping it to her will. This Background provides a safe place to experiment — a spot protected against mundane intrusions or, to a degree, Paradox. Sanctums are not Horizon Realms or Chantries. They exist in consensual reality, although they have some

amount of privacy and protection. Sanctums can vary from dungeons filled with weird science contraptions to a Verbena's cottage still room, from uptown apartments filled with alchemical and academic regalia to out-of-the-way chapels frequented by believing Sleepers.

Sanctums contain many of the bulkier foci that a mage might use— cauldrons, summoning circles, alchemy gear or clone tanks. These foci serve a duel purpose: assisting the mage with her work and helping her maintain the integrity of the Sanctum. This stock of foci can be rather unusual— herbs, devices, offerings, ancestral bones, hallucinogens and special musical instruments are a few examples.

Setting up a Sanctum requires some prep time. The mage selects a suitable place, stocks it and enacts her will upon it in some fashion. Dreamspeakers may perform a spirit-summoning rite; Ecstasy Cultists might share a visionquest; a Verbena might cast protective wards, while a Batini might pray Allah's blessings on the place. New mages can inherit a Sanctum from their mentors or share a communal circle. The details should be decided by the Storyteller and players.

Because the mage has "set" the reality within a Sanctum to coincide with her own beliefs, magick often considered vulgar is considered coincidental in a mage's chosen Sanctum. This allows her to roll her straight Arete when using magick, regardless of its "vulgarity." Paradox is likewise figured as if an effect cast in the Sanctum were coincidental. Sanctums also reduce magick difficulties if a mage takes her time, grant a temporary point of Arcane within the Sanctum, and make some helpful skills possible (see pp. 111-112 for the rules on magick and Abilities). These effects last indefinitely, so long as the mage periodi-cally "re-sets" the room's paradigm. Though these benefits apply only inside the Sanctum, fighting a mage on her home ground is a dangerous task.

Many esoteric supplies can be kept or grown in a Sanctum— potions, minerals and metallic ores, animal components (raven's claws, rabbit pelts, goldfish and white mice), musty tomes, strange bubbling serums or whatever fits. The source of these components can be anything from a classic witch's garden to a junior high school science lab "gifted" by student discoveries. Mages of all types sharpen their concentration with proper "trappings." These usually depend on the type of Sanctum.

Sanctums may only encompass a room or two— no more than 200 square feet or so. Different Traditions are at a -1 to use each other's "workspace" due to minor paradigm differences. Some mages may not use others' Sanctums at all — a Son of Ether won't have much use for an ancestral burial mound. Sanctums are rated by their stock of supplies, their effect on magick roll difficulties, and the Arcane the owner gains when "home".

•   Barely adequate stock: no reductions for difficulties, although the owner's magick is all coincidental here. One point of Arcane.

••   Small stock; difficulties reduced by 1. Two points of Arcane.

•••   Average stock; difficulties -2. Three points of Arcane.

••••   Good stock; difficulties -3. Four points of Arcane.

•••••   Excellent stock; difficulties -4. Five points of Arcane.

Book Two: Faces of Magick

Morality is not a simple set of rules. It's a very complex struggle of conflicting patterns of values.
— Robert Pirsig, *Lila*

 Look into the soul of the mage, and you will see a Path: a destiny and paradigm that guides his steps, beliefs and actions. Vampires follow the dictates of survival in a soulless existence because they know they are immortal and damned. A vampire either fights the Beast within or rides it to destruction. Werewolves are gallantly doomed from birth to battle teeth-to-throat with an unstoppable foe. The mage is different: he makes his own destiny. Though guided by an Avatar, Mentor and circumstances, the mage steps out from the mass of Sleepers and sets out to shape reality by force of knowledge, hand and will.

Each Path is a lonely road; we are born alone and we die alone. The mage, with his insight of the Big Picture, stands more alone than most of us. There are so many foes, inside and out, and so many choices, temptations and failures. For security and survival, most mages join some sort of fellowship— a Tradition or Convention sharing some common ground with the mage himself. Predictably, these Paths disagree; many see worldwide Ascension as the day when their chosen group wins out over the others. A few see Ascension as unity, a future where all Paths become one. Neither option seems to be approaching anytime soon.

In the spirit world, many say, there is a rough correspondence to the Triat: the Weaver (Stasis), the Wyld (Dynamism) and the Wyrm (Entropy). Whether this Triat represents physical beings or metaphysical concepts could be debated at great length. In any case, the strongest mage factions seem to correspond to this Triat: the Technocracy to the Weaver, the Marauders to the Wyld and the Nephandi to the Wyrm, with the Traditions treading a middle Path between them all. Perhaps it's this middle road that leads to ultimate Ascension. The world may never know.

The Traditions

The Akashic Brotherhood

Seekers of Perfection

And there we have it; the whole thing; caste, karma, the wheel of rebirth and escape from it; an association of the moon with the cycle of death and birth, and of the solar door with release; disciples of secular piety (sacrificial rites, almsgiving, etc.) as the means to a favorable birth, as well as to a pleasant heavenly sojourn among the fathers, and, on the other hand, disciplines of austerity practiced in the forest, as the means to release.

— Joseph Campbell, *The Masks of God: Oriental Mythology*

The Disciple, Fall Breeze, sat in lotus position before the Chantry's two Pedagogues:

Sitting motionless in meditative posture, Gentle Mountain's mind locked deeply into inner tranquillity and the flowing currents of Quintessence.

Raging Eagle's muscular form glided subtly through an ornate kata. His focus marked locations just within reach of his lashing limbs that moved quicker than the eye could see.

"What is the way to Ascension?" The question bubbled up into Fall Breeze's meditating mind.

"Perfection of the mind." The thoughts of Gentle Mountain, hummed in her head.

"Perfection of the body." Raging Eagle spoke the words in slow distinct syllables. His body seemed to fly with his leaping kicks to the high arched roof.

"Is it both ways? Is it two ways at once? Is that the secret?" She tried to center herself, but the questions kept bubbling up from her subconscious.

For centuries, the Akashic Brotherhood has been broken down into several schools of thought. The primary schools being those of the development of the mind and the development of the body. Perfection of human nature is the key to both. Peace of being achieved by understanding of the form and limitations of each. One must understand the self in order to understand the Cosmic All and one's place within it.

"There are as many ways to Ascension as there are people who have Ascended." Gentle Mountain's logic fit snugly into Fall Breeze's psyche. It made so much truth that it hurt her brain.

"In repeated incarnations, we slowly work our Avatars forward toward Ascension." Raging Eagle's kicking and punching continued. Now it seemed as though three or four images of him darted about the dais.

"How do I attain it?" She cursed and tried again to clear all thoughts from her mind.

"Ascension is not a possession." Raging Eagle blew out twenty candles nearly three meters away with a sweeping kick.

"But how does one achieve it? Why aspire to find it if we travel toward it naturally?" Fall Breeze lips slowly mouthed the words, but her thoughts projected from her mind with greater clarity. She could contain her need for answers no longer.

"Forge the body into that which it was meant to be. Link into the primal forces of the Pattern and focus it through you. Become the higher being you are." Raging Eagle leapt in a mighty flying kick to transverse the length of the training hall from the dais to the far confining wall and kicked a stone statue twice his size into smoke-like dust before recoiling back to land with one leg still poised in the air.

"It is the will of your mind." Gentle Mountain's thoughts rolled out to encompass Fall Breeze. It felt like the old man's mind was within her. Like he was her. Like he was everything. She knew that Gentle Mountain was right; there was no doubting that fact. *"You must think within your mind into a single point; thus, the human mind encompasses the Cosmic All."*

With great power comes great responsibility. Hubris gets in the way of many. Such individuals are fuel for the Ascension War— fodder for the cosmic cycle. The goal of the Akashic Brotherhood is personal Ascension. Be pure in mind. Remember that meditation and being is the method to achieve enlightenment and, through enlightenment, Ascension. Do not be distracted by the need to battle. Do not hesitate to destroy those who block your Way or impede the Flow.

"Understanding the world? Feeling separate from it? Lost to the Umbra? Becoming a Sleeper to think about it never again?

"No one knows. Few of those who Ascend return. Those that managed to do so can never last long in the Realm. Once the form has reached saturation with Quintessence, the physical Pattern begins to dissolve. It can no longer find representation in this plane of existence, for it is too big to fit." Raging Eagle's voice seemed to be spoken so that the words would reach Fall Breeze's ears and hers alone.

"Such power transcends the rationale that makes up what we sense."

There is a greater truth that the Akashic Brotherhood seeks. It can not be found in learned study or hours of teaching. The goal can only be shown by example. The individual must look deep within himself and summon up the strength and sight to find what it is to *be*. The act of trying to *do* continually gets in the way of this. The process is natural and must occur with intense concentration until it can be naturally occurring. Like a river bed directs the flow of water, so should the Avatar of the mage learn to direct Prime.

"Peace of mind. Obtain the Balance. Feel the intense euphoria of the Pure Ones rushing through you. Being transcends space and time. It is everywhere and always."

"How do I achieve this?" Her mind raced. Through her mental link with Gentle Mountain, she watched her body flood with the Quintessence that made up the Patterns that established the Realm.

"Are we not your teachers?" The words and thoughts paused. "This you must achieve by yourself. We can only lead you through the foothills.

"You must scale the mountain alone. Only through one's own strength of being can Ascension be achieved."

"Perfect the body in order for the mind to have its proper place. If the body is weak, it draws down the vitality of the brain. Ruin your brain, and you will ruin your mind."

Fall Breeze felt her link to Gentle Mountain slipping away.

"The goal is to perfect the body, but, since this requires thought, the mind must train itself to concentrate its will into the tightest of points. You must not think about it. Allow your mind to find its own way. Be. The Avatar is the guide."

Fall Breeze grasped at their thoughts and words, but her mind was still slipping.

"The body must remain limber. One must focus to purify the body of poisons and foreign matter."

Fall Breeze adjusted her posture and leaned into the teachings with her mind.

"Pick away extraneous thoughts. Concentration is the key." Raging Eagle locked his body into a steady stance. His feet remained still, but his form began to slide along the brick work until he had transversed the room. With a mighty leap, he was back upon the dais.

"Open your eyes to what is called 'Ascension'."

"Attune to the All, and the All will see through you. Be your most efficient state. Lean into it. What are you trying to achieve? Be; do not do."

The Akashic Brotherhood applies basic principles one at a time. A group of ideas may be related to an individual. That individual must decide which idea is most important, finding the principle upon which her Avatar must focus.

Questioning by the student is an important part of this process; people can not truly learn what they are not interested in. Purification and practice of the Do with strict adherence to directions given by a Mentor are necessary to grasp complete comprehension.

Fall Breeze felt her thoughts drifting to happy times; she concentrated into the Flow.

"Never give up the path or leave learning to a one view perspective of existence. Expand your senses."

"Cleanse the body. Be as you must to purify. Without this, you will never reach Ascension."

"The body should be free of the pollutants that the beast-men call the Wyrm. Be not corrupt. Be true to yourself. Cleanse yourself of that which sickens you. Your mind, body and spirit must run clean as the cold, clear mountain streams."

"Gain harmony in your heart. The rest will follow. All things fall into their appropriate place in time."

"Project yourself from the fires that kindle deeply within you. Fuel it and make it grow. Built it up until your Pattern is consumed."

"Slow down." The sudden flood of information rushed too rapidly through Fall Breeze's mind.

"Go to town and beg for some rice."

Who had said that? Her thoughts fractured. She sat in the empty temple once again. Her eyes blinked in the darkness. She shook her arms and straightened her spine.

The members of Akashic Brotherhood have always lead monastic lifestyles. Meditation takes place in temples, and, during states of intense mediation, Mentors "appear" to students either through use of the Sphere of Mind or via the Correspondence or Time Sphere. This withdrawn state lends to the Brothers' peace of mind. Through the use of the Second Rank of the Sphere of the Mind, it is easy for a Brother to discern true teaching from false.

Slowly Fall Breeze left the temple. A simple bow showed her respect as she pulled cloth shoes onto callused feet. She strapped on her outer travelling clothes with her sash and walked away from the tree-lined mountain side.

The small village at the bottom of the hill— that would be the place where she would find rice — and with rice would come another day to seek Ascension.

Celestial Chorus

Keepers of the Faith

Harmonies unheard create the harmonies we hear and wake the soul to the consciousness of beauty, showing it the one essence in another kind; for the measures of our music are not arbitrary, but are determined by the Principle whose labor is to dominate matter and bring pattern into being.

— Plotinus

Brother Randall Dexter knelt to examine the young woman. She had been badly beaten, and Dexter could detect a severe concussion and several broken bones. She would most likely die without immediate attention. Dexter glanced toward the mouth of the alley in which the woman lay. Seeing no one, he quietly began to sing. Running his hands lightly over the woman's body, he healed the worst of her injuries. He stood as she slowly regained consciousness.

The Celestial Chorus remains haunted by its past. Although it has had a long history of guiding and protecting the Sleepers, it is all too often remembered for its involvement in the Inquisition. Unfortunately, a few extreme members of the Celestial Chorus used the Inquisition to ferret out and punish mages who were guilty of having beliefs or philosophies that these zealots deemed incorrect.

Other Traditions like to forget that the Sleepers were ultimately responsible for the atrocities of the Inquisition and place the blame on the Celestial Chorus. While the Chorus— like all Traditions— has always contained its contingent of zealots, the majority of its members are more concerned with the hand of mercy than with the fist of discipline. The Chorus' detractors all too easily ignore the good that the Chorus has done.

More than any other Tradition, the Celestial Chorus is concerned with the well-being of the Sleepers: the goal of the Chorus is to help usher all toward Ascension. While many mages live cloistered lives of song-filled meditation, many others serve the Sleepers in a variety of manners. Some do so through vigilance against the many evils in the Tapestry— the Kindred, the Nephandi, the Technocracy, even some Sleepers. Others serve the Sleepers by tending to those in need: ministering to innocent victims in war zones, helping the homeless, junkies and other lost souls of urban blight, or merely travelling from place to place and assisting Sleepers as they can. The missionaries become important parts of the local community, sources of spiritual strength, solace and encouragement. They are never known as mages, of course, and are seen in more mundane terms: the doctor at a local clinic, the missionary, the parish priest, the social worker.

R.M.

"How are you feeling, Miss?" Dexter asked.

The woman put her hand to her head, wincing. Her response was limited to a low groan. Dexter took her arm and helped her stand. He recognized her from the streets: another hooker. They had even spoken on occasion. She was probably beaten by her john for some imagined offense. Maybe she was yet another victim of a trick turned bad.

"They're comin' for you, brother," the woman said. "They set you up. Get outta here while you can." She leaned against Dexter for support. She looked around, frightened, confused, and still dazed. Slowly at first, and then more strongly, Dexter realized that he had been drawn into a trap with a bait he could not ignore.

The squealing of car tires caused Dexter to turn quickly to the mouth of the alley: an immense black Cadillac blocked his exit. "Men in Black?" Dexter thought, confused. Four men stepped out, indeed in black, but not the soulless uniforms of the Technocracy: instead they wore leathers and overcoats and reached for weapons beneath their coats. He had seen these men before too: enforcers for a local criminal whose drug and prostitution business had been suffering due to Dexter's presence in the community.

Mages tend to make enemies easily, but few Traditions other than the Celestial Chorus garner enemies merely by helping people. Certainly, members of the Chorus who feel called to battle against the myriad evils of the universe are likely to establish a roster of enemies. However, even those who minister to helpless Sleepers are likely to attract undue attention. While injudicious use of magick attracts the Technocracy, of course, the well-intentioned activities of some Chorus members also attracts the attention of Sleepers who profit from the suffering of others: drug pushers, pimps, crime lords and others.

The thugs raced down the alley, apparently interested in taking Dexter alive. Dexter contemplated a fight. He could best the Sleeper thugs easily with even coincidental magick. But the woman's presence created an obvious problem. She was likely to be caught in any crossfire that ensued, and he was not willing to take the risk. She was obviously expendable enough for the thugs to beat her and use her as bait. He doubted that they'd show any concern for her safety now.

He withdrew a tiny silver orb from a jacket pocket, then hurled it to the ground. Smoke began to pour out from the broken shell, obscuring him from the four men. Grabbing the woman around her waist, he began to ascend the wall of one of the buildings enclosing the alley. He hoped the woman was still too addled to fully realize what was happening as they scaled the building more quickly than could be possible. Dexter felt the cold mist of Paradox settle into him as he defied reality. He hated it when that happened, but he had no choice at the moment.

The Celestial Chorus has produced its share of militant crusaders, and few Chorus members are totally without some combat training. Martyrdom is not uncommon as a trait in the Celestial Chorus, but those who fall in battle tend to take their enemies with them. While certain zealots may be willing to sacrifice Sleepers for the greater good, most Chorus members will not endanger the innocents they are sworn to guide and protect. Cowards are rare among the Chorus, but the Tradition avoids conflict whenever possible. Likewise, even the more peaceful members of the Chorus can be brave fighters when necessary.

Dexter gained the roof with his squirming package. He had only a matter of minutes before the thugs began searching the area. This was no time to be gentle: he deftly pressed on the woman's carotid, and she fell into limp unconsciousness. He shifted his perceptions to a nearby shelter for battered women, a number of blocks away. Seeing that the alley behind it was empty, he stepped into it.

He banged on the rear door of the shelter. It opened partially, and a woman's familiar face peered out through the chained opening. "Dex! What the hell happened?"

"No time now, Sandra," Dexter hissed. "Open up!" The door closed momentarily as the chains were undone, and then it reopened. Sandra gestured Dexter and his charge in, and closed the thick door behind them, locking it. Dexter carefully deposited the woman on one of the many cots that filled the small room.

"How'd you find this one?" his friend asked, examining the woman. Dexter merely shrugged. The less said, the better. Sandra had accepted that a long time ago. She had learned to love her friend for his selflessness and allow him his many enigmas. He'd answer when he was ready.

Members of the Chorus tend to gather a flock wherever they go. The mage and her flock have a reciprocal relationship: while the flock usually depends upon the mage for guidance and solace, the mage must sometimes call upon her flock for assistance. Most of the mage's flock will not know of the mage's true nature; they just see her as a dynamic, dedicated individual. Sometimes, if the mage has learned to trust someone enough, she will share her secret.

They were in a private office on the second floor of the shelter. "Will you be all right?" Sandra asked. Dexter was glancing down at the street through the blinds. He shrugged. There was no way the thugs would guess he was here, but he didn't want to endanger anyone else, just in case.

"Will SHE be all right?" he responded.

"The usual," Sandra shrugged. "We'll clean her up, give her a place to stay, and hope she keeps off the streets. Chances are, in a few months, she'll be turning tricks again." Sandra looked closely at her friend and said, "You never can tell, of course. Maybe you just changed her life, the way you changed

mine." *Sandra smiled warmly, looking nothing like the homeless drug addict that Dex had befriended five years go.*

Many members of the Chorus feel that even one life saved, one spirit nurtured, is worth any amount of personal risk and self-sacrifice. Some Chorus members may take vows of abstinence and poverty, but this is hardly a rule. Other Chorus members will still engage in sexual activity and maintain an interest in financial matters. Even then, it is often with an understanding of the ephemeral nature of money and sexual satisfaction. Even those that remain unattached to any one person are never lonely: they are surrounded by a caring and loving flock, as well as the memories of their personal successes and the fire of their commitment.

Dexter sat alone in the office, his feet on a coffee table. He leaned his head back and closed his eyes. "What to do?" he wondered. He had been here less than a year, and he'd already seen a change in the community. People's faces seemed brightened by hope, and the streets seemed a little less grim than before. Unfortunately, he was starting to attract enemies. He knew from experience that enemies could be ignored or avoided for only so long. It was time for action.

He fondled the cross at his neck, fingering the small blazing sun in the center of the cross. Silently, he issued a supplication to the One. Should he take the war back to his enemies? He could easily defeat one crimelord, but did he want to deal with an army of brainless thugs? Was it worth the risk of possibly alerting the Technocracy? Should he just leave, let his flock languish and drift back away from Ascension after he had brought them so far?

Many commonly interpret the Celestial Chorus as a religion of its own. Rather, it is a shared meta-belief: all religions are manifestations of the One, and as all creation came from the One, all creation ultimately belongs in the One again. While the Chorus has been predominantly Christian for centuries, it contains members from a number of religious traditions. Likewise, a multitude of factions exist within the Chorus; a long-standing point of debate is whether the One should be perceived as male, female, neither or both. Regardless, most within the Chorus believe that all gods are masks of the One, and all they can really do is discuss the masks. The One defies true comprehension.

Dexter sighed. He had gained too much just to leave now and abandon his people. He knew his life would not be easy if he took this path. He could have chosen a life of contemplative solitude in a remote Chantry, but this was his Destiny. The Nephandi-slayers think their job is tough…

The Cult of Ecstasy

Revelers in Dream

The Grateful Dead are the best answer today to the atom bomb.

— Joseph Campbell, "Ritual and Rapture"

Jank strode through the dark, dank tunnel, past sector numbers stenciled on the peeling paint of the cinderblock walls. He stepped off the musty concrete floor of the stadium hallway and emerged in paradise. The bright sunlight flashed an explosion of bright, prismatic colors before his eyes, as lithe, supple, dancing bodies in lavish tie-dyed clothes swirled and ebbed before him. Fine traceries of smoke floated delicately on the air. Graceful patchouli and musky hemp. And the music— the sacred music enfolded him like a blessed womb and drew him forward into the gathering.

The esoteric purpose of the Cult of Ecstasy is secretly encoded into their name. The word "ecstasy" comes from the Greek phrase "ex stasis," or "out of stasis." This Tradition was founded to literally break out of Static Reality through exploration of all aspects of human potential. Their mission is simple, but easily misunderstood: if Static Reality is enforced by restricting possibilities, it is the duty of all ex-stasis mages to explore other paths. They confront, head-on, what the rest of the world fears— the shadows of the inner landscape.

Many other Traditions see the Cult as an irresponsible mob of self-obsessed sensualists who require favored "vices" to perform magick. In truth, they are a force of freedom and consciousness in a world of enslaved Sleepers, liberators who utilize the powerful and forbidden tools of illumination. The Cult of Ecstasy continually and unhesitatingly offers opportunities for breakthrough to a suspicious and ungrateful world, gleefully casting their magickal pearls before swine. They live true to the credo that they neither force nor prevent the Awakening in others. In their heretical deviation from the political, social and personal orthodoxies of their times (orthodoxies that constitute the true "Political Correctness"), the Cult of Ecstasy has contributed more to the collective Awakening of mankind than any other Tradition.

In the midst of the undulating paradise, Jank sensed a rigid interruption. Someone was not having fun. He knew who they were before he saw them: two men in ill-fitting poly-blend suits that were several years too old and several inches too tight. Their distended power bellies protruded over belts cut with extra notches, and their arms were crossed and folded over their chests, as if to protect their hearts from the outpouring of love from the swaying crowd. Their mouths frowned, and their eyes smoldered. They were the self-appointed yet unwitting guardians of static reality, foot soldiers in the trenches of the reality wars— in a word, cops. Jank noted with sly amusement his momentary pity for the men, who scowled when they met his gaze. After all, they were village-burning grunts in their own personal Vietnam against substance abuse. They had put their bodies on the line in a war they could never win but could not stop fighting. He indulged the moment of pity, marked their location, and moved on into the warm, pulsing, inviting crowd.

The Cult of Ecstasy has confounded mages of the Technocracy time and time again throughout their colorful history. Like tricksters, they shatter seemingly monolithic paradigms from within. Though they have lost many battles to the Technocratic juggernaut, they have also infiltrated the institutions that are the cornerstones of static reality, then chipped away from the inside. When holy warriors forced swordpoint conversions from the pagan worshippers of Pan and Dionysus, the Cult of Ecstasy simply went underground within the Church. They covertly encouraged sacramental debauchery, ecstatic worship and the greatest heresy—Goddess worship— through the establishment of the Cult of the Virgin. Though the Church managed to de-sexualize their priests, twisting remaining sexual interests into perversions, the flames of Cult of Ecstasy freedom continue to burn brightly in global liberation theology.

Jank moved through the delirious crowd, drawn by a warm and welcoming presence. His body rippled against theirs, and he lost himself in the sensation — brushing here, touching there, and fully embracing another before moving on toward the welcoming presence. He saw her hair first — a gentle golden storm that appeared to move in slow motion, blurring into her simple white gown. She moved with abandon and grace, a vision of lush sensuality and exquisite power in the warm afternoon sunlight. Jank's eyes unfocused as his other senses rushed up to bring him far more potent and urgent information. He smelled her, and knew that her name was Maura, and that she was freshly Awakened. They smiled together, and coiling, serpentine energy rose the full length of Jank's spine.

They danced barefoot on the grass, circling closer and closer together. They grew oblivious to the fresh, tender bodies that danced near them and sometimes caressed them as they passed. Jank drew up the lace hem of Maura's dress and pulled her toward him. They moved as one to the music that was now indistinguishable from their entwined bodies. For a moment, Jank's rational mind returned to him, and he noted with interest that he was suddenly wearing a condom. "What a coincidence," his observer mind noted, "that even in my fugue state, I decided to not rely on coincidence alone. Remarkable." And then he went under again, overtaken by the rapture.

Virtually all members of the Cult of Ecstasy access the consciousness- altering portions of their minds and exalt their spirits through explorations of physicality. Through dance, food, theatre and sexual delight, they celebrate the union of their sacred physical beings with the sacred transcendence of eternity. The Technocracy has gained great power and robbed mankind of one of the greatest sources of potential for Awakening by demonizing sexuality. The Cult of Ecstasy serves as a reminder to a frightened, sexually-repressed populace that free-flowing sexual energy is always a healing force, and that sexual energy is only made damaging by binding it up, cutting it off or bringing it where it is not welcome.

Convention mages have propagandized that the Cult of Ecstasy sanctions all forms of sex. Much to more "conventional" mages' disgust, this includes "deviant" practices as well — domination, body alteration, S&M and others. Many Cultists acknowledge the thin line between pleasure and pain and see a transcendental Path through both. True to their credo, however, the Cult of Ecstasy does not sanction forced sex. Rape, molestation and pederasty are even more reprehensible to Cultists than to the populace at large; these perversions violate the sanctity of a person's inner self and defile what should be divine. Sadly, too many outside the Cult see all forms of sex as dirty and everything as perversion.

The Cult's phenomenal success in unleashing the sexual revolution of the 60's and 70's began to trigger mass Awakenings across the globe, causing the Technocracy to retaliate with drastic efforts to make sex fearsome and deadly. The Cult of Ecstasy perseveres, however, and actively seeks a solution to the AIDS crisis that stands between mankind and mass Awakening.

Jank and Maura finished their reverie, and sank peacefully to the grass of the stadium. They lay in silence, breathing deeply in the twilight. Gentle clouds of smoke floated past them, the warm, familiar smell awakening delicate visions that twinkled at the edge of their perceptions. Jank smiled at the power of the contact high; with his Awakened sensitivities and Time mastery, there was no need to actually smoke dope anymore. He looked over at Maura and peered deeply into the young mage's spirit. The warm, wet power in her surged impatiently, like a young dragon. The pair nestled in each other's arms, and felt the world breathe with them as the stars began to break through the darkening sky.

The most powerful lie told to discredit the Cult of Ecstasy is that they use and advocate the use of all drugs. The truth is more elaborate, and does not reduce well to simpleminded sloganeering. The Cult of Ecstasy advocates personal responsibility in consciousness-alteration, rejecting the notion that anyone should be allowed to restrict the choices of others. They do not, however, feel that all drugs are created equal.

Most members of the Cult respect psychedelics — revered by mankind for centuries as sacred materials — but reject tranquilizers, stimulants and prescription drugs that mask illness without curing it. They refer to psychedelics as "opening up" or "running toward" drugs, believing that judicious use of psychedelics can impel humans toward great revelation, insight and joy. Alcohol, nicotine, barbiturates and cocaine, however, are called "closing down" or "running away" drugs, because they numb the valuable pain and joy that are such essential parts of life.

The Cult of Ecstasy is, however, divided over the use of synthetic psychedelics like LSD. Some embrace them as more potent versions of natural hallucinogens, but others feel that only "natural" drugs really create truly natural breakthroughs. Most Ecstatic mages realize that the power of the mind unleashed requires a steady hand, and frown on careless tripping.

Because both natural and unnatural psychadelics have such great power, the forces of order have manipulated political and military institutions to suppress the "running toward" drugs, even in traditional religious settings, while flooding the market with "running away" drugs, even resorting to using the Technomancer-influenced CIA to import vast quantities cocaine into the U.S. Many Cultists fear that the Progenitors have a finger in the drug pie, and that they use their own chemical compounds to further enslave the Sleepers.

Jank floated blissfully through the deep pools of longing, drawing power and soothing old wounds. Gradually, a long, low vibration hummed through him. He responded to it on a cellular level, and moved toward it like a child to a mother's breast. The vibration brought him back up toward the surface, and he emerged in the stadium again. The Dead were playing "Ripple," and it raised him up out of the pools of longing and into the air, like a colorful balloon on a string. He sailed high into the air, and saw the crowd below as a swirling, shifting mandala of healing energy. Maura was there as well, using her roiling power to fuel the living mandala that pulsed to the music. A boundless presence surrounded and engulfed them. "Ripple in still water…"

The Cult of Ecstasy reveres music above all forms of consciousness exploration, though even they scarcely understand the magickal effects of music. Music seems to defy clear categorization. Some members theorize that music is part of the fundamental vibration that summoned reality and life into being. Perhaps understanding the chords and rests of music will bring an intuitive understanding of the chords and rests of Universe. Perhaps these sacred harmonies hold the keys to Ascension.

The Technocracy's mages have no real way to stop music, though they've enjoyed some success with commercializing music to banality. They have, however, failed badly at removing transcendent music from the hands of Sleepers, let alone mages. Clumsy attempts to ban performers and put warning labels on recordings usually crash and burn, though recent attempts have been more successful. Most Cult of Ecstasy members take full advantage of the legality and availability of

music and become musicians or avid music lovers. Many employ music and dance as foci for their magick. Although they rarely agree about which music affords the greatest potential for Ascension, the fiercely independent Cult of Ecstasy members put aside their differences to enjoy music together in blessed silence.

This openness to all forms of sensation exposes the dark side of the Tradition. Sensual transcendence opens the floodgates to the passions. Hate, fury, greed, lust beyond reason or respect — these are passions, too, and the Cultists of Ecstasy are perhaps more vulnerable than most mages to the bestial side of their natures. Addiction to a transcendental state becomes a plague to the Cultists as well; some forget how to function without artificially-boosted senses or become obsessed with new forms of stimulation. Strange as it may seem, self-discipline is more important to Ecstatic mages than to nearly any other Tradition. To lose it is to become all that the Tradition despises.

An explosion of laughter drew Jank's attention to the two plainclothes police officers as they staggered and reeled under visions beyond their comprehension. Deadheads pointed and laughed, but Jank's heart froze at the desperate terror etched across the faces of the suddenly-tripping cops. Jank turned to Maura: "Stop it."

She merely watched the cops dance, her face cold. "Why?" she replied. "They're just a couple of pigs. I know their type; they love to push people around." She turned her attention back to the cops; "Have a little sunshine, boys."

"It's not right," Jank replied. "Knock it off."

"Why? They were just hassling those guys over there. They would hassle us, too. I'm not hurting them, just giving them something to think about."

Jank took her wrist; "Stop it. Please." His voice was polite but firm. "Some folks can never see past their blinders. Maybe some never should. But they need to come that decision on their own. Ascension is a caress, not a club. The flip side of freedom is responsibility. Let 'em go."

Maura dropped the mind-fugue, allowing the officers the benefit of their own blindness. "Thank you," Jank said as he released her wrist.

"I didn't mean anything by it," Maura insisted, looking at Jank nervously, fearing further disapproval.

He smiled and took both her hands in his. "I'm sure you didn't, but you have to be careful." He gestured around the gathering, encompassing the revelry about them; "Here's a world of great beauty and splendor. The more I see it, the more I love it. The more I love it, the more I see it. The more I see the beauty and love the splendor, the more the world becomes beautiful and splendid. Do you see it? In one moment, I can stop the world and remake it, and not all the powers of hell can stop me. Trust, young one— trust and exalt. You mirror the excellence of the universe, and the world in turn mirrors your trust and exaltation."

She ruffled his hair; "You're kinda cute yourself, you bum!" They embraced, fell together laughing and lost themselves in the song.

The Dreamspeakers

Primal Dancers

The power of the world always works in circles, and everything tries to be round.
— Black Elk, *Black Elk Speaks*

Annalise walked in the footsteps of her own dreams this night. She danced in the arms of the Earth Mother. Her companions beat their callused palms against the well-oiled drums whose pounding rhythms spiraled Annalise downwards into the wellspring of her own spirit-soul. As the pounding of the drums increased, the shaman, Laughing Eagle, placed a small drum in Annalise's hands.

"Join your dreams with ours, Annalise. The rhythms of Gaia are the rhythms of your heartbeat, the rhythms of your own imaginings."

Dreamspeakers conceive of the world as an entity in which each piece, from the smallest pebble to the largest whale, has a part. The conglomerate of matter and life combine to create the unity most often referred to as Gaia or the All-Mother. Their rituals often involve music and drumming. The Dreamspeakers feel the rhythmic pulsing of drums is most conducive to guiding the mind and body into a state in which true enlightenment may occur. In such an enlightened state, everything from healing to contemplating the nature of the universe is easier to accomplish.

Looking down, Annalise could see her footprints in the sand of the beach. Even as she made the footprints, they shifted and transformed. One filled with water and swirled into nothingness, while another quickly became home to a small crab. Still another revealed the pearlescent beauty of a conch shell.

"We each act in concert with the world, Annalise. The Reality of the Technomancers is a sterile one destined to die a lonely death, ours is the Reality of Gaia. We have always been and we always will be. We know that our power, our true beauty, comes in our connection to the All. By ourselves, we are less than the tiniest grain of sand, a lone drumbeat, but in opening ourselves to the universe, we are everything. We are the All-Mother and the turtle and the earth beneath our feet." Mother Umbala's proud tones were a counterpoint to the pounding rhythms that now coursed through Annalise, body and soul.

There is some debate about the true consciousness of Gaia, but all Dreamspeakers believe in the fundamental connection that each living being has to every other being, and that the dance of life is greater than the sum of its parts.

The craft of the Dreamspeakers is perhaps the most ancient of all the Traditions. Its roots are found deep in the primal essence of all living creatures, their lizard-brains, their souls. Such power, though perhaps raw and primitive in comparison to others, has deep connections to all aspects of Reality. It is the World Tree of the Traditions, and the Dreamspeakers are at home climbing in its branches and digging among its roots.

Mother Umbala pushed Annalise's head under the waves, and she could feel her body pushed this way and that by the swirling tides. Time moved by her in a forever-moment as Annalise tasted salt and sand on her tongue. Mother Umbala's hands were gone from Annalise's head, and she seemed suddenly to be in deep water. Trying to swim, Annalise could not seem to find the surface. As she felt her lungs greedily take in the last of her oxygen, Annalise acknowledged the awesome power of the All and opened her mouth to let the water take her — and found herself lying in a foot of water.

Placing the drum back in Annalise's hands, Mother Umbala said; "You are cleansed and made ready to take on the name of Dreamspeaker!"

The Dreamspeakers believe the reality created by the Technomancers is the main cause of the divisive dichotomy between mind and body, science and nature. In order to begin healing this rift in new Dreamspeakers, the Tradition requires a ritual death of the divided self and the subsequent rebirth of the whole. This cleansing journey of death and rebirth also gives the young Dreamspeaker her first true contact with the primal pool of power made up of the dreams, the lives, the souls of all life. Even Gaia's body is part of this collective, her stones and dirt, water and air all belong to this pool. From this great pool of Being, the Dreamspeakers draw their power and their knowledge. All living beings are connected to this pool, and their combined dreams, fears and knowledge come from and contribute to the pool. The Dreamspeakers see it as both their right and responsibility to draw upon the power therein.

As Annalise arose and spun in the circle made up of Dreamspeakers, the circle of earth, air and sky, she could feel her senses filling with the heady power of Gaia. Her drum, like all of Reality, stretched out taut and strong, and Annalise knew she could play Reality as easily as she did her drum.

"So long as you remain a part of the Tapestry that is Gaia, so long as you take part in the great dance of life and death and rebirth, so long as you freely give back that power which Gaia grants, you can play in the fields of the All-Mother," Laughing

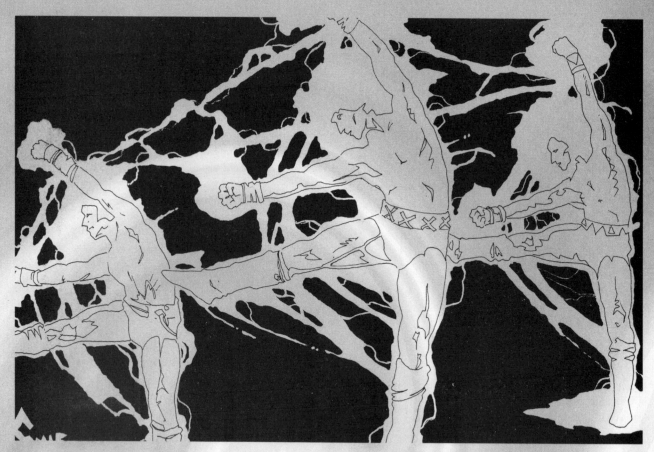

Eagle intoned over the orchestra of drums and surf and calling birds. *"But always hold on to the rhythms of Gaia, lest you become intoxicated with your gifts and spurn your Mother's embrace. Just as the beat you play on the drum in your hand would turn sour should the wood warp or the strings break, so would your magick warp into dust and death if you were to deny your connection to the rest of the universe. A drummer cannot play without her drum."*

The power of the Dreamspeakers' magick arises from their acknowledgment of the intricate connections between all living beings. It is the ability to channel the energies of the world that brings magick. Without this acknowledgment, Dreamspeakers feel their power would at best leave them, and at worse act as a cancer on Gaia, breaking up the connections that keep her whole. As part of this acknowledgment, the Tradition is made up of mages from a variety of cultures and backgrounds. Witch doctors, pagans, shamans and ecologists, among others, are all part of this diverse Tradition. Dreamspeakers acknowledge that different paths are necessary to represent the entirety of the world's energies. In the interweaving of minds viewing the world from different angles of perception, the truth of the whole can be seen. With just one viewpoint, one sees only part of the truth. Understanding part of the truth can be far more dangerous than understanding nothing of the truth at all.

"Body and mind come together to create something greater than either concept by itself. In the wedding of the two lies greatness. To denigrate one is to denigrate all. Do not lose yourself in either, Annalise," added Mother Umbala as she kissed the newborn Dreamspeaker. *"Come, we have dwelt overlong in the realms of the spirit this night! Anyone up for pizza?"*

Euthanatos

Menders of the Wheel

Is something wrong, she said.
Of course there is.
You're still alive, she said.
Oh, but do I deserve to be?
Is that the Question?
And if so, if so,
Who answers, who answers?
—Pearl Jam, "Alive"

Stan Edwards stared at his old high school chum lying in the hospital bed and frowned; "How're you doing, Jack?" Jack could not respond. He'd been in a coma for the last five weeks, and his doctors said that his chances of recovery with even part of his mental facilities intact were negligible. Jack Anderson, star quarterback in college and high school alike, had learned at last that he was not indestructible. Not bullet-proof. Part of Stan's mind refused what had to be done, but his beliefs were strong enough to override his emotions. Stan focused his will, pulled his power into a tight fist in his mind, and released that power at his friend. Jack's heart stuttered briefly and simply gave way to the entropy within.

Many of the Traditions frown upon the actions of the Euthanatos. The Euthanatos do not care. They hold steady in the belief that death is not the end of life, simply another beginning in an endless cycle. Death is a necessary aspect of life, more necessary for some than it is for others.

Sometimes the duties of providing the Good Death bore down heavily upon Stan's shoulders, a crushing weight that was perfectly capable of driving a weak man to his knees. Stan was not often weak, but today he felt the need for release. At times like this, he could easily see suicide as a viable option. Contrary to what the other mages in his Chantry thought, Stan felt the loss of his friend's life as strongly as anyone would. Jack was dead. Even knowing that Jack would be reincarnated, Stan missed him horribly.

The Euthanatos believe that they know when a person's time to die is at hand, often before the person knows it himself. From time to time, they assist those whose need to die is stronger than their will to live. This duty is considered an honor, one of the foundations of the Euthanatos philosophy. Alas, most of the people that the Tradition helps along the path to reincarnation do not go willingly. In many cases, the Euthanatos act as judge and executioner against the more corrupt individuals they encounter. Karmic balance, they believe, provides new opportunities, new

options for those who have been forced to go in the wrong direction in life. To the Euthanatos, it is simply better to get the foolish moving on to their next life as soon as possible.

Stan wandered the darkest alleys in town, leaving himself vulnerable, an open invitation to the more predatory members of the unawakened. One of the town's Kindred came too close for his liking, but was driven away with only a look. Before an hour had passed, Stan was assaulted by a young group of would-be muggers. Their deaths were more rewarding than Jack's had been. Jack's death had been a mercy killing; the gutter-scums' deaths were a welcome necessity.

The Euthanatos are often seen as grim and unforgiving, and to most people, that assessment is fully accurate. But the Euthanatos are simply dedicated to a lifestyle that often requires them to kill even those that are close to them. They hope that the next life will provide better options for their loved ones. The Euthanatos are as susceptible to the loss of a loved one or close relative as anyone else; there is no guarantee that the freshly released soul will reincarnate near the mage who has brought about destruction, no guarantee that said soul will forgive the one who ended its previous life.

Most Euthanatos choose not to have close friends at all, as a protective maneuver against the traumas caused by the death of someone close. Like nearly everyone else, the Euthanatos prefer not to suffer the loss of a friend. These mages fully understand the pain they cause whenever they must kill another. For every person who dies, others among the living will likely mourn that person's loss. Few among the Euthanatos enjoy killing, necessary though it is for dynamic change.

Jack thought back to his First Death, the time he spent wandering the realms of the dead before coming home. He shunted suicidal thoughts aside and went on his way. Death would come when the time was right; he would not force himself to die. Besides, best to allow the others of the Chantry to decide when his time had come.

Stan walked in silence for several hours, pausing only to shove fuel into the mouth of his Incarnation, his physical form. He felt no hunger, but realized that food was important. Stan had learned the hard way that the body needed proper care. He still suffered nightmares of his last death and had no desire to repeat the process.

The Euthanatos are also unique in that they do not fear death. Most have already experienced death before, during their initiation. Death literally holds no secrets for the Euthanatos; they have come to know it intimately and to understand its workings and functions. Death is a means to

an end for the Euthanatos, a useful tool in the restructuring of the world. As often as not, the Euthanatos will kill their own when the time has come, certain that their comrades will return to them when the time is right. Most Euthanatos have brief flashes from their previous lives, and many are certain that their Avatars have been with the Euthanatos in previous lives. There are no doubters of this belief among the Tradition. Even the few who do not have access to their previous lives' memories suffer from deja vu more frequently than any among the unawakened.

For reasons they still have not discovered completely, the Euthanatos have gained the enmity of the werewolves. The only viable hypothesis they have run across is that their proximity to death has left them "Wyrm-corrupted" in the eyes of the Garou. Oddly enough, this negative reaction is removed with every death a Euthanatos mage endures, coming back to bother them only after they have started on the path of stalking those ready for death. Generally speaking, however, the Euthanatos do their best to avoid the Garou.

The wraiths howled. Stan ignored them. In time, even the restless dead would understand the ways of the Good Death. Meanwhile, the Euthanatos mostly left them to their own devices. Playing with the dead was left to the Giovanni and the Samedi. Thinking of his Tradition's vampiric counterparts, Stan allowed himself to smile, stepping faster and walking towards the home of his friend, Dawson. What he needed was a good debate, and Dawson was always willing to argue the responsibilities of death-dealers.

Euthanatos do not dabble in necromancy, finding the idea of stopping a spirit from following its course to be vulgar. They do not, however, condemn others who do perform the darker arts. They simply see necromancers as being something like backwater cousins— slow, but with their hearts in the right place. Ascension is a personal thing, and each mage must learn at her own pace. They especially enjoy conversations with the Giovanni and Samedi vampires, finding the discussions of eternal life versus the following of reincarnation principles a fascinating subject. Rumors abound that the three groups have actually made a pact, allowing for information exchanges between them. None are willing to confirm or deny the accusations.

Dawson opened the door to his haven after the very first knock. Without a word, he gestured for Stan to enter, guiding him to a comfortable chair in his offices. Stan talked of his troubles in the night, and Dawson listened as he always did, nodding and making comments when necessary. Of all the vampires he had met in his lives, only the Samedi seemed to understand where he was coming from with his beliefs. Again he

offered to assist the Samedi in experiencing death, and again, Dawson politely declined, explaining that when the time was right, he would come to Stan. "My work among the Kindred is not yet finished. There are many among them who do not understand the need for the work we share. Someone must teach them."

While utterly fascinated by the concept of vampirism, most Euthanatos are leery of risking the Embrace. There is a strong belief that the Embrace would destroy the connection a mage has to his Avatar, and very few are willing to risk the loss of their power for something as petty as immortality. Still, many Euthanatos take comfort in the knowledge that the Samedi follow similar beliefs, and are perfectly willing to destroy vampires who have not realized when the time is right for death.

After leaving Dawson's place, Stan wandered again, weaving slowly towards the Chantry. None of his associates spoke to him; one look at the black cowl he drew upon entering the building made his desire to mourn in silence obvious to all who saw him. As the sun finally rose, Stan allowed the cold heavy dread of his loss to escape. Jack was gone and now, in his own room, and with none save the other members of his Tradition to hear, he could mourn. Let the other Traditions say that he and his had no heart, let them all claim that the Euthanatos were cold and heartless. They would never understand the weight of his responsibilities, at least not in this Incarnation.

The Order of Hermes

Masters of the Art

We cannot live by power, and a culture that seeks to live by it becomes brutal and sterile. But we can die without it.
— Max Lerner

Its hard to fight an enemy who has outposts in your head.

— Sally Kempton

Like sentinels, the walls stand, eternally watching, eternally indifferent. Likewise, I stand facing a flat, featureless panel and shiver as the prison's chill penetrates my skin. The wall at my back curves slightly, a half-embrace. At times, I think clearly; at other times, I question my sanity. Often, a strong, clear voice comes to me, speaking the appalling truth. Appalling, yes; but if truth, how do I dare reject it?

YOU ARE RIGHT— IF YOUR AVATAR SPEAKS THE TRUTH— HOW CAN YOU REJECT IT?

Yet why does something feel wrong when I speak to you? Am I not imprisoned? Why cant I leave if I like?

THE SAME QUESTIONS AGAIN AND AGAIN. DO YOU NOT REMEMBER? THE ANSWER IS ALWAYS THE SAME: YOU SOUGHT THE TRUTH THROUGH REVELATION, AND YOU WILL NOT LEAVE UNTIL YOU FIND IT.

Yes, I remember.

As Order of Hermes mages grow more experienced, they often willingly enter a state akin to the Seeking, which they term "The Revelation." During this time, they are particularly vulnerable to Mind and Spirit magick. They open themselves fully to their Avatars in order to learn more about reality. The great danger of this practice is that, on occasion, Technomancers detect the questing mage, capture her, and subject her to "reeducation." Mages captured in this fashion are often brainwashed by Technomancers posing as the mage's own Avatar.

GOOD. NOW LET US RETURN TO THE BEGINNING. WHAT IS YOUR NAME?

Me llamo diez y tres. I am number 13. The tarot card of Death and Rebirth.

WHY IS THIS YOUR NAME?

I am dying and being reborn.

AND YOUR MISSION, YOUR PURPOSE?

To study and to know. To bring humanity to the Ascension fated by the stars. Yet, even as I think this, I see a man and a woman, like figures animated from a Goya painting, larger than life. On their backs they carry heavy burdens, bundles dotted with arcane symbols of Life and Spirit. They clamber up a steep, rocky hill. As they ascend, their packs grow larger and more symbols appear on the dark cloth, one by one, like stars in the night sky. They ascend further; the symbols of spirit and life wriggle and squirm on the cloth, thrashing like worms in the rain, transforming— I cant make it out, but then I see: they melt into the symbols of Entropy and Death. The man and woman collapse beneath their writhing burdens and slide down the slope into a muddy ditch. There they decay and disappear like salt into water.

In theory, Order of Hermes mages hold that they serve humanity by resisting the Technocracy, studying arcane lore and transforming that lore into everyday reality. In practice, they have become so entwined in political intrigue within their own Chantries that Technomancers have to come knocking down their doors before they remember their stated mission. Even if they work to change reality in humanity's favor, most cabals disagree on policy, and often thwart each other's efforts. On the positive side, Order of Hermes may work hindsightedly, but when they fall, they typically take more than their share of Technomancers down with them.

HAVE YOU ATTAINED ASCENSION?

Of course not.

BUT YOU BELIEVE ASCENSION EXISTS AND IS ATTAINABLE. WHY DO YOU BELIEVE THIS, 13?

Because others in the Order have attained it.

The Order of Hermes, because it sees itself as the oldest and most renowned of the Traditions, has deluded itself into thinking it can spread rumors of its members' attainments without eliciting the scorn of the other Traditions. While its claims that more Oracles originated in their Tradition than any other Tradition are likely true (simply because their Tradition is so ancient), rumors of Ascended Order of Hermes mages are the products of too many mages sinking into Quiet.

HAVE YOU SEEN EVIDENCE OF THIS?

No scientific evidence.

A MATHEMATICIAN, ARE YOU NOT? HOW CAN THIS BE THAT YOU BELIEVE IN SUCH A THEORY WITHOUT A SCRAP OF EVIDENCE?

It is a benevolent mission, to seek Ascension. (The image of a decaying man and woman, mud-spattered and lying in a forgotten ditch, resurfaces.) Even if it is doomed to failure, it is a far better cause than the Technocracy's dark, worthless goals. Our cause is good: we seek the power that will allow us to defeat the Technocracy.

WHAT POWER IS THAT?

A complex admixture of factors: political, financial, magickal. Our cabal, as you know, feels that the best place for our reality to gain a foothold is in universities and schools. If we can gradually make our views academically feasible, then they will propagated throughout the educational system, from tenured professors down to elementary school students. A whole generation of students will believe, and they will pass this knowledge on to the next generation.

The Order of Hermes feels that the best way to control Nodes and ley lines, which will ultimately determine who wins the struggle over consensual reality, is to have financial and political control over the areas in which they appear. Consequently, many Order of Hermes mages have used their magick to become wealthy or politically prominent. Other Traditions look skeptically upon this practice as an excuse for greed and other vices. A significant percentage of Order of Hermes mages are university professors or other kinds of educators. They feel that education is one of the best forms of control, and that it can be directed via the financial and political pressures their Hermetic colleagues can bring to bear. Unfortunately, the Technocracy is savvy to these tactics, and, to date, has successfully undermined the reputations of all such "pioneers" of reality.

Do you truly think it possible that your views will be accepted?

It is possible. Probably the best way is to have them accepted as "science," a form of science long abandoned, but only now revealing its hidden worth. The sciences of numerology and of Forms would, of course, have to be renamed. But they could appear and spread under the guise of complex mathematical formulae and breakthroughs in physics.

Is that not accepting the Technomancer's paradigms?

Perhaps, perhaps. But there are those of the Order who align themselves with Marauders just to break out of the pervasive paradigms of the Technocracy, only to find themselves committing acts just as perverse. Personally, I find the slower, safer, more traditional route more appealing.

All Tradition mages, if they think about it, eventually find themselves in a quandary: if they use magick with coincidental effect, they are not working to change humanity's view of reality and thus are further stabilizing the Technocracy-controlled consensual reality. If they attempt to break out of the Conventions' paradigm by ignoring coincidental effect, they kill themselves, only to accomplish the Technocracy's ends. Order of Hermes mages, some of them recalling the Mythic Age before the current

paradigm took hold, wish to return the modern world to its magickal roots. To do so, some have searched for allies in odd places, and some have even made alliances with Marauders and faeries. A very few Order of Hermes mages are rumored to have learned magick from these sources; there are even rumors that there is an undiscovered Sphere to which these factions have access. However, most mages of this Tradition believe that the middle road is the safest and, though plodding, will someday enable them to reshape reality without risking the lives or sanity of its members.

Do you believe that the Traditions should work together to this end?

Of course; who wouldn't? But it is rare that we do. How can we work together when we do not agree on our goals? Even the most basic goal — Ascension — is a fundamental source of disagreement.

How do you see it?

It is a state of pure understanding.

Omniscience?

No, because it is not also a state of full experience. When a mage has Ascended, he understands all that he encounters. But he does not instantly know everything there is to be known.

You say "mage" — can the rest of humanity Ascend?

Mages are destined to shepherd humanity to Ascension.

"Shepherd," you say? So humanity needs you to bring it to Ascension; it cannot achieve Ascension on its own?

No, it cannot. Its spirit is weak, so weak in individuals that it almost doesnt exist. The Avatars of those in the Order are strong enough to achieve Ascension alone and then guide the weak masses along the path that the stars dictate.

Ascension, to Order of Hermes mages, is an act of will that only those with powerful Avatars can achieve. Ordinary humans, in their view, must be acclimated to the principles that will lead them to Ascension. The only way to orient humanity to these principles is to translate the realities behind the Orders numerologies, charts and formulae into comprehensible notions. Of course, Order of Hermes mages believe they are the only ones who can do so; the other Traditions exist only as their helpmates, for they have lesser magicks. Needless to say, while the Sphere of

Forces is powerful, the force of hubris is far more powerful, and it has prevented many a mage from Ascending.

The *modus operandi* of the Order is to keep their influence on philosophical, cultural and political direction secret. Secrecy ensures safety from humanity's fear and ignorance and the Technocracy's vengeance.

AND IF THE MASSES DO NOT WISH TO FOLLOW?

My jaw muscles tighten involuntarily. They will wish to follow because they wont know theyre doing so.

Is not ignorance a form of slavery?

No! The Order of Hermes exists to use its secrets to benefit humanity.

WHAT OF THOSE WHO DO NOT WISH TO BE SO BENEFITTED?

We help them despite their ignorance.

IS THIS NOT THE POLICY OF YOUR ENEMIES?

My heart skips a beat. No, theres a difference—we do not kill the spirit. We foster intelligence, creativity, honor and respect.

DO YOU?

An image of me as a disciple at the cabal, stonily staring out my moonlit window. The ache returns as I watch. The Deacon has whispered to Nuria, in passing, that my destiny is unrelenting mediocrity. I've overheard.

AND NURIA?

My *teacher* frowns and shakes her head. The Deacon shrugs benignly as the pair walks down the echoing stone corridor.

AND HOW WILL THE REST OF HUMANITY, WHOSE AVATARS ARE INFERIOR, BE TREATED?

I have no answer.

HOW HAS IT BEEN AT THE CABAL FOR YOU SINCE THEN?

That was a long time ago.

NOT SO LONG.

No… not so long.

HOW DO YOU ACHIEVE ASCENSION, 13?

Through disciplined research and dedication to the truth.

HOW DOES THIS ACCOMPLISH YOUR ENDS?

The rigors of understanding Forms at all levels, from the physical through the spiritual, sculpt the mind into the Avatar's tool. Eventually, if we are true to ourselves, we achieve self-mastery and thus mastery over others. The rod of scholarship and the respect established by the hierarchy in the Order reinforce these accomplishments. Only through that process of disciplining mind and spirit can we defeat the enemy. When the Order has done so, we can attain our former height, achieve Ascension, and rule humanity as we are fated by the Wheel to do.

To the Orders mages, scholarship with an emphasis on magick and adherence to tradition hones the mind. Since the mind is the tool by which mages achieve Ascension, there are no activities more important than active scholarship and revering the traditions ancient wisdom. Perhaps because they know they are losing the struggle, the Order's

mages also cling to the belief that the Wheel of Fortune (of the tarot's Major Arcana) will someday bring them back into eminence.

IS SUPREMACY INDEED A NATURAL OUTCOME OF ADHESION TO THESE PRINCIPLES?

More memories: heat blasts my face; it is so hot that I cannot see. Julio screams I can hear his hoarse, agonized cry two stories above, but I cant look up. I drape the wet blanket over my head and shoulders and enter the flat. Moments later, Julio's shrieking ceases. I stumble forward, blind, afraid to touch anything, for everything is smoldering, sputtering, melting or in flames. The caustic smoke fills my lungs, makes my eyes tear. I grope towards the stairs and put my foot on the first step. No screams: I know Julio is dead, gone. The fire trucks arrive and usher me out of the flat. I am helpless.

That evening, Nuria says Paradox punished him; he didn't use subtlety to temper the force of his magick. Let that be a lesson to us all, she said.

YOU MEAN THAT THE RIGORS OF THE ORDERS TRAINING DO NOT ALWAYS SUCCEED?

Yes. It doesn't always succeed.

BUT IT WILL NEVERTHELESS ATTAIN ITS GOALS….WHAT ARE ITS GOALS?

Primarily, to destroy the Technocracy. It stands between us and Ascension; it compromised the Order long ago and continues to do so. Until it is annihilated, it will distract us from Ascension and the search for reality.

More than any other Tradition mages, the Order of Hermes hates the Technocracy, blaming it for the downfall of its regency in the late Middle Ages. The blame they place on the Technocracy is largely well-founded.

WHAT IF THE TECHNOCRACY DOES NOT OPPOSE YOUR GOALS?

Hah. But as I scoff, the kindly, owl-eyed Deacon at Sevilla peers up at me from the midst of his arcane book collection; from between his lips flicks a forked tongue as black as a vipers. My enemies, I think, are those who oppose the goals of the Order.

Then I see a hand screwing a bronze plaque into the cornerstone of a library at the cabal. Some of my fellow apprentices sit at a desk near the library window, their heads buried in arcane tomes.

READ THE PLAQUE.

"Dedicado al OMN. Unificación, lealtad y paz."

WHO FUNDED YOUR LIBRARY?

This OMN, apparently. Why?

HOW MUCH HAS YOUR CABAL IN SEVILLA BENEFITTED FROM THAT RESOURCE?

Tremendously. Most apprentices would sell their souls to get into its rare book collection.

DO YOU HAVE ANY IDEA WHAT OMN STANDS FOR?

Some corporation's initials, right? "Dedicated to the OMN. Unification, loyalty and peace."

OMN STANDS FOR ORDÉN DEL MUNDO NUEVO.

The New World Order?

EL ORDÉN DEL MUNDO NUEVO ACTIVELY SUPPORTS YOUR RESEARCH, YOUR SELF-DISCIPLINE.

Yes. If the OMN has always secretly supported us, it is not the evil the Deacon claims it is. It shares our goals; it must be an ally in the search for Ascension. Suddenly, I recall a tall, clean-shaven mage named Mortez; he hands me a book written in Sanskrit with the number 13 embossed on the cover. I take it. Years later, unchanged, he returns to retrieve it and I find myself here.

YES, YOU ARE READY TO GO NOW, 13. LEAVE US AND FIGHT THE ENEMIES OF BOTH ORDENES: EL ORDÉN DE HERMES Y EL ORDÉN DEL MUNDO NUEVO.

Already I feel a strange pang of longing for these walls. The curved wall at my back has supported me, it seems, forever. Before me I see three whitewashed walls, clean, free of the filth of the streets, smooth like ironed sheets and cool as a glistening icicle. I yearn for this pristine place of truth.

And I know beyond a shadow of a doubt that I will return.

The Sons of Ether

Artisans of Reality

Magic and technology
Voodoo dolls and chants
Electricity
We're making
Weird Science

— Oingo Boingo, "Weird Science"

The wisps of smoke rose from the still-warm cinders, blowing across the hill and into Professor Vorgel's eyes. But he did not blink as he marched resolutely forward, followed by the dwarf, lugging a heavy-looking bag. When he reached the center of the ruined house, stepping over the burnt foundation posts and blackened furniture, he stopped and stamped the ash-strewn ground. A hollow sound responded. "Here! It is still here! Come!" He yelled to his companion, and the dwarf came over and pulled a crowbar out of the bag, handing it to Vorgel. Vogel kicked the ashes away from the wooden trap door on the floor and fit the crowbar under the lip, then heaved hard. The wood cracked and splintered, weakened already by the fire, its magickal wards having protected it from destruction. It gave way and Vorgel threw the old wood off, revealing a dark, stone stairwell leading down. "Thank God, Janos, those fools did not realize the laboratory was beneath the house. Idiot Sleepers! Questioning my intents?! How dare they say I spurn God with my work— I, Vorgel! Well, they can burn what they don't understand, but they won't stop the march of Science with their peasant threats!"

While Sleepers are suspicious and fearful of most mages, the Sons of Ether have born the brunt of this phobia more than most Traditions, excepting, perhaps, the Verbena. Many Sleepers fear that science can endanger them with nuclear radiation or even giant mutated insects, and this leads to ridicule and witch-hunts against the scientists at fault—at least, against those who seem to be at fault. The Technocracy actually uses Ether mages as scapegoats for their experiments gone wrong. They blame them for any "guinea pig" experiment they can't hide from the Sleepers any longer, such as secret nuclear testing against citizenry during the '50s. This sometimes leads to violent retribution by the citizenry of some countries. The Sons of Ether see this as a betrayal of sorts, for they are only striving to improve the lot of Man. Yes, some get hurt in the process, but Science must proceed…

Vorgel and Janos entered the darkness and moved down the stairs to the iron door at the bottom. Vorgel nervously fumbled with the keys that hung from a large ring attached to his belt. The lock clicked and turned, and Vorgel pushed the heavy door open. He reached into the deeper darkness beyond and hit a switch just past the door. There was a low whine, which built in pitch for a few seconds and then steadied out to a loud hum. The room was

suddenly bathed in light, and the generator kicked in. They entered the room and looked about. "It's perfect. They have touched nothing." Vorgel said, yelling to be heard over the incessant humming. "We can proceed with the final stages. Prepare the Ray Projector, Janos. In but an hour, I shall prove to the world that the transmutation of man into metal can be achieved on a normal scale. Think of it, Janos— any man can become a man of steel, never to worry any longer about mere injury or pain. Such a man can move mountains with his bare hands! No— such men! For this science will be available to all once we have perfected the Organic Smelting Transmogrification Ray!"

Each Son of Ether usually has his or her own pet theory with which to storm the gates of Ascension. This theory often becomes a driving goal to them, and extreme obsession and paranoia often builds up around the theory and its detractors. Theories vary widely, but they often involve proving that a magickal effect is actually a Natural Law, an objective truth which must be allowed into consensual reality, for to do otherwise would deny the tenants of Science. Their great anger at the Technocracy arose when the Conventions refused to recognize the "common sense" and "plain facts" of many Sons of Ether pet theories.

The primary concept of the Tradition's founding concerned ether, the unseen "fifth essense" which controls how light travels. If a Son of Ether can successfully convince the world that her theory is correct, any magick performed within the tenants of that theory becomes coincidental, with no danger of Paradox. This is the key to the Ether mages' Ascension goal: to turn all things weird and wonderful into a science, a method available to all humankind. The Technomancers desperately try to prevent such incursions into their plan, but have been unable to stop Son of Ether theories that would return the ether to cosmology.

Vorgel moved towards a large desk pilled high with papers. He began to move them aside when he stopped, staring at the top sheet. "Janos! Someone has been here! I did not leave the diagram for the fifth matrix on top of my desk; it was in my drawer when we fled. Damn!" He tossed the papers across the room with a sweep of his hand. "Who could it have been? Aha! Those fools back at the Chantry. They were checking up on us, Janos, trying to see if I was correct after all. Oho! I bet they're getting ready to eat their words right now. Surely they could not deny the evidence here; they must recognize my theory now! The next issue of Paradigma will be dedicated to my work."

There is often intense rivalry among Sons of Ether mages, especially when theories conflict. Such rivalries often lead to spying and sabotage of another mage's work, just in case a competitor is getting to close to one's own discoveries. The Sons of Ether release a quarterly journal dedicated to the theories of its members. This journal, called *Paradigma*, is often a place for furious verbal bickering and backstabbing, as mages try to disprove the theories of their rivals. Only the Masters and Oracles are resistant to this infighting, as all universally respect their theories, and some even dedicate their work to improving upon their Masters' theories.

"Oh yes, Janos," Vorgel said as he searched the papers on the desk, "I will have quite a tale to tell on my return. Those armchair scientists in the Lounge will clamber all over me, desperate to soak in the intellect of a true scientist! Ha! Humphreys was so proud of his Amazon discovery, stinking up the room with his cheap cigar— I'll show him! They'll choke on their sherry when they see a demonstration of my experiment! Even Madame Dupreau will not be able to hide her admiration. It is not like the old days, Janos. Women knew how to show proper respect for a man's discoveries. Oh, M. Dupreau has certainly shown her genius, what with her magnetism experiments, but she could certainly act more like a proper Son." Vorgel shook his head, wistful for bygone days.

While the Sons of Ether cleave to a devout ideal of progress, a continual rising of human aspirations, their ideal is rather Victorian, with a correspondent denigration of what they perceive to be low, base or hindering progress. They believe they bear a sort of "mage's burden," that they alone among the Traditions seek true progress. Socially, they usually gather into an old style "men's club" of sorts, although women are certainly welcome in modern times. However, many Sons are Victorian in their social views, and wish women would act more like "ladies." They practice a double-standard with impunity. The Twentieth century, however is catching up with this Tradition. Women in the Tradition hold more and more power, and there is an active lobby to change the name from "Sons" to something less sexist. This is, of course, hotly resisted by the old boys network within the Tradition, blindly denying the ideal of progress they so fervently profess.

Vorgel walked across the room to inspect the large machine bolted to the floor there. It resembled a giant gun, but the tesla coils along its huge barrel pointed to other, odder uses. Janos had a hatch in the side open and was cleaning coils within when he accidentally dropped a screwdriver-like instrument. The clanging noise reverberated across the room.

"You fool! Do you realize what you've done!" Vorgel yelled. "If the coil adjuster is even dented by a micrometer, the experiment is ruined! Idiot! Pick it up and check it on the microlathe for damage. Now!" Janos sheepishly scuttled over to the fallen instrument, picked it up and went to examine it on another bizarre machine. Vorgel shook his head and buried it in his hands. "You're lucky I saved you from those soldiers. Another, less compassionate man would have let them kill you. Surrounded by fools…" he muttered.

Unlike other Traditions, the Sons of Ether often have trouble gaining knowing and willing Acolytes. Most pupils interested in super-science and technology are all too easily seduced by the Technocracy. This, compounded by the usually acrimonious social skills of the Ether mages, causes the Sons of Ether to often bribe, cajole, threaten or guilt-trip their Acolytes to ensure their loyalty. Many Acolytes are pulled from the dregs of society and believe they truly have nowhere better to go. Other Sons of Ether, distrusting the human penchant for crime, build robot servitors instead to help them in their labors.

"Excuse me, Professor Vorgel," Janos said humbly, interrupting Vorgel as he made some adjustments to the ray's targeting.

"What is it?" Vorgel barked.

"It is time for the European Science Conference. On the radio, Professor."

"Ah, yes. Correct you are. Turn it on, then. I want to hear those fools among the Technocracy and what they are planning now." Vorgel smiled to himself. It didn't matter what They did, They couldn't stop him from gaining definitive proof of his theory now. The radio came on, and the chief speaker was already

announcing the first guest, a Dr. Thomas Holder. After applause in the audience, Dr. Holder began to speak about his recent discovery in the laboratory. As he spoke on, Vorgel slowly climbed down the stepladder he was standing on. He displayed a shocked look. Holder was, point by point, disproving the theory of some unnamed "colleague" who believed it was possible to replace organic material in a living specimen with mineral, specifically metallurgic, components and still have the patient live and adjust. Holder concluded by stating that only through the burgeoning field of bionics— replacing limbs with pre-machined parts— could such a theory ever work.

Vorgel screamed. "It was him! He was the one who broke in here and stole a look at my notes! A Technomancer! He… he has ridiculed my theory, and made them believe those fools at Iteration X are on the right path! My work! It is for nothing!" Vorgel slowly slid to the floor, staring at the wall blankly.

The Technocracy continually sends spies forth to discover the various theories of Sons of Ether mages. They then blast such theories in the media, disproving them before they even have a chance to convince the Sleepers. Sometimes the Technocracy will even steal such theories and take credit for them, driving an Ether mage to fits of rage and ultimately even insanity as his life's work is perverted around him.

Janos locked the door behind him and ran up the stairs to where Vorgel stood, staring blankly into the night sky. He took the Professor's hand and began to lead him through the maze of broken and burned wood and furniture, helping him to step carefully over the obstacles. All the while, Vorgel stared blankly ahead, as if he possessed no mind whatsoever. When they reached the bottom of the hill and the small roadway, Janos sat the Professor down and went to stand in the road, with his thumb out, waiting for a car to come by. No one came.

Hours passed. As the sun rose over the horizon, Janos turned to look at the Professor. The blank look was gone, however, replaced by an intense stare, directed towards the rising sun. The Professor began to mutter, "Yes… yes, of course. How blind of me… The sun! Yes, that's it! Why turn men into steel, Janos, when we have the sun? What power! What pure energy, waiting to be tapped. If a single man could realize the fusion potential, then all men would benefit. I'm sure that there must be a way, a method to harness such power in a simple, hand-held device…" His muttering dropped off in volume as Vorgel furiously began calculating figures in his head. Janos smiled to see the Professor back, and smiled even broader as he heard the sound of a car coming, out of sight behind the hill.

"Janos," Vorgel said, "I have a feeling that this approaching vehicle is carrying solar panels. Flag it down. I'm sure it is meant for us…"

The Verbena

Delvers of the Essence

"But the nourishment I provide," she thought "is not milk, but a different humor." She continued her pedantic, distracting speech. "My skin is very pale, close to transparent. It looks fragile, but I heal very quickly. My veins are close to the surface, easy to get to. See how thick and blue they are? I never have any trouble giving blood. The needle just pops right in, and out it spurts. Easy as sin."

— Pat Califia, "The Vampire"

"First of all," she said, "we must first deal with this problem you have with your body, with your blood." She held his arm firmly as the knife was brought close to his skin. It flashed in the light, very sharp, consecrated, cleansed and sanitized. He tried to flinch, but his body betrayed him. She had just whispered a few words, and now his body was locked in place. He couldn't make his muscles move. She drew a delicate curve on his chest as he watched in the mirror she had provided.

Another. A symbol, sweeping and beautiful, drawn on the parchment which provides its own ink. The blood flowed softly down his chest, tickling his skin.

"Are you ashamed of life, Jay? Because we can't have you as one of us if you can't live. I mean truly live. If you want to die, we can arrange it, and you may advance among those who study Death. But among us, you have to want to live. Really live."

Jay moaned as he felt endorphins roar through him, and felt something inside him change. He was changing like a seed just before germination, like a plant poking its shoots up through the earth. She saw he had begun to accept his body and his blood, and she felt the life energy within him surge. "Let there be life, Jay..." she said, kissing him, her hair falling all around him.

The Verbena hold themselves as one of the oldest Traditions. Their walks through the Sphere of Time (some Verbena call it the River of Time) have shown them that, even in the dark times of pre-history when humanity was but an ember about to burst into flame, there were weavers of magic, twisters of fate that followed their ways and their Tradition— the roots of their Tree, if you will.

Is it any wonder that the Tradition is largely accused of overwhelming arrogance? Hardly. When one considers their many successes and failures, their static gains and cosmic losses, their generational harmony and their endless internal wars, the Verbena have many reasons to be proud... and many reasons to be ashamed.

Though they have journeyed to dizzying heights and have plummeted to great depths, they have survived. As other Crafts, their names now lost to time, have fallen into dust with no fanfare and no mourners, the Verbena have adapted, grown and thrived in the harshest times.

Perhaps the best analogy for the Verbena is that of an ancient gnarled oak. The oak's roots reach deep into the bedrock. Its trunk is strong, and yet it has had to grow around obstacles placed in its way as it grew. The branches are many and varying in size and strength, but chiefly, they are flexible and always seek the wind and the sky. The fruit, the acorns, drop to the ground from the branches and start brand new trees, kernels of distilled strength and wisdom from the parent.

The Verbena are as varied and as strong as the ancient tree. There are some who follow the ancient, primitive, primordial ways— the old runes, the blood-sacrifice, the chanting, the drumming, the turning of the Wheel, the roots of the tree. There are some who, as the tree's trunk, uphold the strength of the tree by following the ancient Patterns as prescribed by the matrilineal Books of Shadow and the patrilineal Runesticks which, to this day, must be used in tandem before they reveal their wisdom.

Then came the Burning Times, the Inquisition, and the tree was nearly split asunder— but this did not destroy it. Instead, the Dynamic branches of the tree shot up and out in many new, living variations as the Lifedancers blatantly defied the ancient Patterns and sought to discover their own understanding. From these explorations, unchained but channeled by the shadow of the Technocracy, came those who searched for the ultimate wisdom, the Truth. And in their ecclectic Questing, searching out old and new, strange and familiar, they soon learned that they themselves were the kernel of Truth, that in exploring all that magick had to offer, they themselves came to be a microcosm of the whole Tree— the fruit, the Acorn of Wisdom.

The Verbena aren't just one part of the Tree, although many see them as those who are following the Patterns of old— the benders and twisters of fate, those priestesses and practitioners tied to pattern and old symbols. Indeed, that segment is important— it is their strength. But the real Verbena form the whole of the Tree. Only by considering the whole can you begin to understand that each Verbena is a reflection of it.

"You see, Jay, in the old times, we wouldn't have to do this. Life was everywhere then. And Life was honored, respected. From a person's First Blood, be it menstruation or the first hunt,

to their Birthing Blood, the price they pay for anything lasting and sustainable, to their final Life's Blood, which they give freely back to the cycle of Life. But you mustn't think Blood is the only carrier of Life. Indeed, it is only one of many of Life's sacred substances. Life, it seems, really is a sticky subject, a very wet one at that. Water and Life go together, Jay, and that's all the Blood is, anyway."

To the Verbena, blood, sweat, tears and other humors are as the water in the great sea of Life. Indeed, Life came from the sea. The Verbena hold respect for the sea, as well as the Moon, which governs both their hearts and their Blood. They hold all Life in high regard and work to protect it whenever possible, as long as doing so does not become unnatural. A Verbena would not stop a natural predator from attacking its natural prey, but he would stop wolves from being hunted by humans in helicopters. The wolf's hunting is a natural part of the Life cycle; shooting from a helicopter is an abomination and affront to that cycle.

"This is the Circle, Jay. Here we are outside of the world, outside of our past. Here, you will come into your own. Here, you will be reborn into your own body and truly wear it for the first time. How many Sleepers go through life totally out of control, unable to properly react to the stresses and strains of modern life? You must learn, by rote, the way to clean your blood of such poisons."

To a Verbena, the body is itself a scared shrine, and feeling is a form of prayer. A backrub is a brief blessing, while a full-body massage is a sacrament. Sexual intercourse is a major rite, a prayer for Life. The Body is a microcosm all its own. The ultimate in holistic medicine, Verbena healing attempts to take into account the full nature of the illness or wrong done to the body. It allows a Verbena to understand the nature of those diseases by voluntarily taking them into herself and dealing with them.

But you mustn't think that the only sphere that the Verbena know is Life. They are masters of it, but are the founders of knowledge in many very important spheres: Matter, Forces, Mind, Prime and Correspondence were their original discoveries, it's said. Still, Life defines them because they are Life.

"The wood at your back is the Tree of Life. Its roots dig deep, and it has been fed the blood of all who have ever lived here. Now our Coven nourishes it. And soon, so will yours. This Tree knows all our names, and soon it will learn yours. Your mother never knew what she was doing, naming you as she did. To me, you are a fulfillment of a prophecy— when I set my spirit calling for an apprentice, I saw a blue jay in my dreams that night. How was I to know that it would be you, my Jay, my Jacob, who would come to me? But soon you will be reborn, and you will be your own mother. You will name yourself. Dare you choose a great name and a great destiny? Or will you live among us as a quiet hermit, with a name that one only breathes, not savors? Choose well! And remember me, Jay. We honor our teachers with our names, and when it is all said and done, all of our names are the same. We are Verbena."

Names are extremely important to the Verbena, because they believe that one's name represents one's living Essence. The essence of breath creates magick when it names a thing, a place or a person. To know a Verbena's secret blood-name is to have a serious power over him. A Verbena may change his name several times over the course of his life to show that he has changed, or grown in a specific way. Often this is a minor change, such as 'Heasha Morningshade' to 'Heasha Morningstar.' Sometimes, however, it is a major change. Many Verbena do not assume your name is the same every time they meet you: the polite thing to ask is "What are you called?"

"You touch the Tree, but you do not Feel it. You must reach out with your knowledge, with your magick, and meld your senses with it. Feel the sap rushing through you. Feel your roots going down, soaking in the fertile soil. Feel the gentle movement of your leaves, the sweet tinge of pain as I pluck a tiny branch from you. Yes. That's it. Breathe in the tree. Your blood to its blood."

The Verbena are about as organized as a bathtub full of drunken cats. There are many different 'flavors' of Verbena, from ultra-conservatives who still chant in ancient Norse and Greek and still perform regular blood sacrifices, to those who work to perfect their bodies as the next step on the evolutionary scale, to the free radical liberals who eschew vulgar magick and instead use herbs, motherwit and positivity to heal and do magick.

Though they do not have a rigid hierarchy, the Verbena do believe in a common set of ethics and morals regarding magick. First and foremost, they hold that Life should not be made unnatural through Magick. They will extend their own lives magickally, but only up to the utmost limit of human aging. They will not cause things which should not live to come alive, and they will not directly alter the fundamental organic structure of a creature— such as its genetic code.

They have no qualms, however, about changing one kind of life into a completely different kind. They also have no problem with doing damage to a creature with magick if its life-pattern could conceivably adapt to or heal the damage. That life is sacred to them should be obvious; they will not reduce it or make it into something that they consider to be unnatural.

Because one's own individuality and uniqueness of vision is so sacred to the Verbena, the idea of making a clone of one's self, literally another false Self, is abhorrent to them. This is one of the reasons the clone-making Progenitors are such hated enemies. Some of the more powerful Masters of the Verbena have developed rotes to help them locate and destroy clones made from themselves or from their allies.

They also have some antagonists in the Traditions: the Celestial Chorus. The Verbena see the Celestial Chorus'

near-worship of the transcendent One as their foolish attempt to externalize something that is within everyone. The Verbena assert that the Self is the true One, the One Within, and this is in direct opposition to the Celestial Chorus' views. It's a miracle that the two can co-exist within the Traditions, which is a strong argument for the Chorus' beliefs: miracles are their trademark.

The Verbena believe that humanity will reach Ascension when humans realize this essential concept: within the Self, all things are possible. Inside the Self, the personal is sacred and Life is Truth. The reason they are constantly focusing inward, focusing on their own perspective rather than trying to understand others, is that they believe that by changing one's Self, one can utterly change all Selves. Gaia Herself would Ascend if enough people Ascended. Because of this, they are willing to spend much of their resources on guiding individuals to the Path, reasoning that one soul can blaze the way for many.

From the roots of the tree which touch on the most primal parts of Life to the fruit-bearing branches that reach to the sky of Ascension, it's quite possible that the Verbena's infamous arrogance is deserved, or at least understandable. After all, before there was writing, before humanity used fires to warm themselves, the Verbena taught women and men how to paint blood-pictures to guarantee the hunt. The Verbena assert that, if all the other Traditions were to suddenly vanish tomorrow, they alone could lead humanity toward Ascension, and they just might be right.

"Oh, Jay. You are neophyte in so many things, aren't you? I savor your inexperience, your ignorance. It's so delicious to watch your eyes as your senses become more and more open. But now you must place your hand in the lifestream, for you must understand what it is to gently guide it, to channel its limitless power. Come, Jay, let me show you where it lies...."

The Virtual Adepts

Crafters of New Vision

Most people spend their lives avoiding getting into tense situations. A repo man spends his life getting into tense situations.

— Harry Dean Stanton, *Repo Man*

"You with me, Screamer?" asked Janor, the Order of Hermes mage.

"I'm with you," came the crackling reply. The Adept was using a telepathy rote that simulated a crackling radio inside the mind of his intended target. To his compatriots, it was pretty irritating, a bit of flash they didn't need.

"Just like we rehearsed. Take out the security system and unlock the doors."

"Right-o."

An instant later, the lights on the building flashed and the doors ka-chunked open. No warning sirens blared, and the emergency lights didn't activate. The Progenitor lab had been breached.

"Piece o' cake," crackled Screamer's voice inside their heads.

"That's only the beginning, you arrogant putz," muttered Janor.

The Virtual Adepts are a strange Tradition indeed. Many do not consider them full members of the Traditions, mostly because they were members of the Technocracy not so long ago. Many hold a low opinion of them, even though the Adepts have saved many mages with their special knowledge of technomagick and the Technocracy. The Adepts see themselves as Saviors at the Gates of Oblivion. Other Tradition mages have less pleasant names for their kind.

The group of mages skittered nervously towards the lab. The rasterized map inside each of their heads kept track of where they were in the building and led them inexorably towards the heart of the lab. Janor again showed his distrust of technology by opting to use the stairs, although Screamer assured him that all the elevators were safe. They climbed down twenty-three flights of stairs and came to the Construct lab.

The relationship the Adepts have with the Technocracy is a two way street—the Adepts loathe the Technocracy, while the Technocracy would like nothing more than to see them exterminated. Many Tradition mages, not wanting to become cannon fodder, will not associate with the Adepts unless forced. Many agents of the Technocracy tend to become more ruthless than usual when faced with Virtual Adepts and will stop at nothing to destroy them. This kind of behavior rightly frightens other mages. Some Technocracy leaders, however, take a more pragmatic approach, rightly sensing the kinship beneath the hate. Those Technomancers who manage to convert Virtual Adepts back to the fold win valuable allies.

The roots of this relationship go back to the breakup between the Conventions and the Virtual Adepts. The Adepts hurt the Technocracy very badly by taking copies of many Technocracy files to the Traditions. The Technocracy responded by rounding up as many Adepts as possible and torturing them. There are some who say that even today, Adepts from this era are being tortured in horrifying experiments about the pain threshold of the a human body. Given the state of Technocracy advances in this area, it is not entirely impossible.

As they opened the door, the animals shifted nervously in their cages. A few turned to watch the incoming mages with eyes not devoid of reason, yet utterly animal-like at the same time.

"Be careful, boyos. My info shows they've been rustling up some nasty things down there," crackled the incessant voice in the mages' heads.

Being the most distrusted Tradition hasn't stopped the Virtual Adepts. They regularly join bands of adventurous mages in storming Technocracy strongholds. While many eschew personal contact, they realize the necessity of getting into the midst of things and dirtying their hands a bit. Many of the other Traditions rightly believe that the Adepts have some kind of personal vendetta with the Technocracy. The knowledge that the Adepts have of the Technocracy also makes them formidable allies in any raid against Technocracy holdings.

As masters of all things digital and electrical, Virtual Adepts live by the adage that Information is Reality. Many also believe that information is a living, sentient force that wishes to be freed from its "top secret" classifications and encrypted data files. Dealing in information is a heavy part of Virtual Adept society, although they hold certain types of knowledge in higher esteem than an Order of Hermes mage would.

Screamer began as the sound of gunfire rattled inside his head. He checked his rig and scanned the lab for a line into the building. Finding a feedback analyzer in the room, he prepared the rotes to shoot himself into the room and readied his hip computer.

At once, five images of the Adept leapt into the room. Just outside the stairwell, Screamer assessed the situation from the eyes of his constructs. Standing square in the middle of the room was a grotesque dog-shaped nightmare with a chain gun sprouting from its back. Flashing red eyes locked on each of the five new targets and sprayed the room. The rest of his team, lying prone on the floor, scrambled for cover.

"Go ahead, stupid. Waste that ammo."

Virtual Adepts are also masters of deception and trickery. Using certain abilities they have honed since before leaving the

Technocracy, the Adepts use deception in normal combat as well as in attempts to garner passwords for remote computer systems.

The Adepts have mastery over the Sphere of Correspondence. As such, they often avoid locations where combat is taking place. In a pinch, they will appear to aid their falling comrades. Adepts think very well under pressure and have an uncanny knack for "hacking" out a solution to a nearly impossible situation, even if others around them are lying on the floor crying for help.

Spotting the gene sequencer in the corner, Screamer prayed it hadn't been hit by the ricocheting bullets. Accessing the machine through the Net, he programmed it to spit out a deadly virus with a sequence he had stolen from another Progenitor gene sequencer. The sequence had been coded as a HIT Mark destruct virus in the files. Screamer just prayed it was a true HIT Mark they were facing, and not some new evil.

One of Screamer's holograms moved suddenly and went straight for the gene sequencer. The HIT Mark tracked to follow and sprayed the heavy machine with uranium-depleted slugs from its chain gun. Screamer heard a short hiss, and he knew that the cooker chamber on the sequencer had been hit, releasing a deadly gene cocktail into the sealed lab. Watching through holographic eyes, Screamer saw the HIT Mark suddenly fall over and scrabble at the floor, like a chicken with its neck broken. The HIT Mark gave a sudden wheeze and was still.

The Adepts prefer to meet others of their kind in a virtual reality, a consensual hallucination where physical abilities and appearances do not matter. They have even breached a foothold into what some say is an entire Realm made up of nothing but information. This place is called the Net. The Net is entirely too big to be explored in one lifetime, but teams of Adepts are busy mapping it and cataloguing its strange inhabitants in preparation of Ascension, when they will rescue the huddled masses of Sleepers from the rotting ball of Earth. They want to Awaken them in a gleaming virtual reality that will never grow old and never die.

Screamer burst into the lab. His footsteps crunched on broken glass. "We gotta get the hell outta here!" he screamed at his friends. "That made WAY too much noise."

The rest of the team could not answer. As the stunned mage looked around, Screamer could see that the rest of the team was writhing on the floor beside the HIT Mark. A great plan; a terrible mistake. "Shit," moaned the Adept, helpless to ease their suffering. He failed to hear the second HIT Mark as it stepped into position. Too late, he felt the Correspondence Point shift as the new aspect aligned itself in his sector. Screamer turned in time to see the hail of slugs tear through his hologram.

DIE, TRAITOR! the destruct program buzzed as pain sheared through Screamer's Net connection. The room went white, then cobalt blue.

"I knew this was a bad idea," he thought as his neurons sizzled. And then there was silence.

Ascension wasn't coming cheaply.

Part Two: The Others

The Technocracy

Static Reason

The leaders of the people cause them to err, and they that are led by them are destroyed.
— Isaiah 11:16

I held the pistol up against the left side of his head. It was the moment I had been waiting for. The Cultist of Ecstasy kneeling in front of me had spiked the water system with psychotropic drugs, blown up my car, and tried to kill me five minutes ago. I had to show him what a Man in Black does best. All my training said I should blow him away. So why was my hand shaking? I knew the HIT Mark backing me up would arrive in five minutes. Damn. Think fast…

Tradition mages have a very biased view of the world. They see themselves as heroes who are striving to save the world, renegades fighting against an inhuman, faceless, soulless Collective. The Technocracy is seen as a ruthless, unstoppable machine. The Technocracy does include despicable overlords, soulless Constructs and inhuman assassins. However, there are many people serving the Technocracy who don't fall into that shallow stereotype. Just as it's foolish to say that all technology is evil, it is simplistic to say that all Technomancers are "evil." The issues of the Technocracy are not always black and white. For some, the World of Darkness is a world of extremes, but for many— including the rogues who work for both the Technocracy and the Traditions, the Tradition mages who defect, and the survivors who serve only themselves— everything is in shades of gray.

The Schism

I kept the gun aimed at his heart.

"Get on your feet."

"What?"

He was surprised; just the edge I needed. My mind started probing into his subconscious. Thankfully, despite his command of Time, he was mindblind. I started sifting through his memory, aiming the pistol at his heart just in case.

My superiors kept asking for results. After all, we were at war. Well, they'd get results.

I found what I was looking for: a seed of doubt. He was having second thoughts about his Chantry and the four Hollow Ones he was helping. I also found out where his stash of weapons was kept. He was just what I needed: someone I could easily manipulate.

I gave him a swift left hook to the jaw and knocked him out. After following through with little bit of psi, I figured he'd be out for about an hour.

The Technocracy is composed of many contesting factions; these go beyond the organizational structures of the Conventions. The developing Schism between the forces "Beyond the Horizon" (the Symposiums and research installations in the Deep Umbra) and the agents working in the field has resulted in different viewpoints on what the Technocracy is. Just as the Technocracy is composed of different Conventions, each Convention is composed of many different types of Technomancers.

The Shock Troops— These are the greatest victims of the Ascension War. Their bodies and souls have become consumed by the efforts of the Collective. Faceless Constructs of the Men in Black and cyborgs of Iteration X are visible examples, but these agents actually run interference for the truly talented members of these two Conventions. Progenitor clones and Void Engineer robots are also Constructs. Many are self-aware, and many fight to maintain their identity at all costs.

The Rogues— Rogues walk in the shadow world of espionage. Their true allegiance is unknown. Some of them steal information from other Conventions. Others devote themselves to gathering data on the Traditions. Sometimes the only way to strike against the Traditionalists is to infiltrate them. Anyone familiar with the Technocracy is also tempted to escape from the terror and paranoia that is rampant in some sections of it. Rogues live in a world of constant moral dilemmas. Many are ready to defect… but for how long?

Agents in the Field— These are the dedicated agents working on the front lines. They have the best understanding of the grim realities of the War for Ascension, but each also has some reason for continuing the fight— realization of the threat of the supernatural world, personal belief in a method of Ascension and actual concern for the fate of humanity are examples. Their greatest problem is convincing the Idealists and Escapists of the real situation. Any Convention can be aided by this type of Technomancer.

The Idealists— They are removed from the war on Earth, and seek perfection as they "help" the Masses. Some of them have lost touch with the realities of the situation on Earth and deal with issues by using abstractions and overanalysis. Others watch the war with a degree of objectivity, offering guidance and advocating "morality." There are also Idealists who are completely alien to humanity…

The Escapists— The Escapists seek to resolve the problems of the world by forming new realities in the depths of space and the ether of the Deep Umbra. While Earth slowly dies, they believe they can form a better reality somewhere else. Some members of this group are merely people seeking order amidst the chaos of the modern world. The servants of Autochthonia and the explorer-scouts of the Void Engineers are two examples.

The Fanatics— Their one goal is innovation, and they will advance technology purely for the sake of "pushing the envelope." Research is their primary activity, and they seldom realize the consequences of their actions. One common motivator is a fear of the unknown, as well as the need to establish a safe system of order and reason. The pursuit of knowledge and order, regardless of the applications and paradigm-shifts that result, leads them on their crusade.

The Power-Hungry— These are individuals consumed by their personal failings. Lust for power, the ecstacy of destruction, simple greed, the thrill of discovery (regardless of moral responsibility) and the false pride of elitism are powerful motivators. The Technocracy sates these hungers.

The Survivors— The only loyalty of these individuals is to themselves. Bodies are falling in the Ascension War, and some Technomancers just want to survive at any cost. Caught between the dedication of the Field Agents and the removed detachment of the Idealists and Fanatics, they don't always understand the "big picture," but do understand the world around them.

Again, these divisions are not necessarily delineated by Conventions. Constructs of the Syndicate try to maximize profits in small economic zones; they are different from the Fanatic Syndicate researchers watching from the Horizon who devise new methods of selling to the Masses. Fanatic members of Iteration X serve the great intelligence in the Deep Umbra that directs the movements of its troops; they cannot identify with the dedicated HIT Marks in the field who try to maintain a balance between their vestigial humanity and dehumanizing programming.

Ascension

Now what was I going to say in the report? Hell, it was getting harder to keep up my mind shields. If the Men in White, the ones who made sure of our "loyalty," ever found out…

I wasn't going to get anywhere just blowing him away. I've seen enough killing. It would make a nice little gold star on my record, *but I knew I was going to have to go rogue for a little while. I wasn't really after the Cultist, despite the orders from my Intelligence Analyst. I wanted the gun-runners he worked with, the Hollow Ones I had been looking for.*

They were the bastards who led a raid on a school the Progenitors maintained. They were the scum who set fire to the building and locked everyone inside.

I've captured a few people, sure, but burning down a building full of college kids was more than I'd ever do. I still remember sorting through the charred bodies.

They probably think they're heroes, now. I think they're as good as dead.

The simple goal of "serving the Technocracy to win the war" is not enough for most Technomancers. Many are striving for a personal Ascension, and each one has his own view of what Ascension should be. Any Technomancer must eventually determine what path he chooses to advocate. Here are a few examples:

—The World Must Be Made Safe

"The Masses are at the mercy of unseen supernatural forces. Superstition still lingers in a world where everyone should be safe. We must make the world Secure. We're the ones who do the dirty work, and our Collective implements all the theories of the Symposiums. They've lost sight of what's really happening.

"All this talk of Ascension is ridiculous. The Realm we need is right here— once we make it safe. All we need to do is purge it of the corruption of the occult."

—Daniel Smith, Intelligence Analyst of the Men in Black

—Perfect All of Humanity

"Ascension is, simply put, the perfection of one's self. We implement that. Saying that technology is inherently evil is ridiculous. We heal the sick, perfect the body, and create a world in which the Masses are not dependent on the mysticism of a limited few. The world as a whole must Ascend."

—Dr. Irene Rollins, Progenitor

—Ascend to Autochthonia

"Technology is a perfect model of reality. Everything works together. I've seen the way that model should work… because I've seen Authochthonia. That's the way the world should be. We can all find the joy of Autochtonia. We're evolving, and making the machines a part of us is just the next step…"

—Test Subject #137, Iteration X

—Ascend to the Horizon to Maintain the Earth

"There are many members of the Technocracy, including members of the Syndicate, who work in the streets, and I respect that. But in order for us to coordinate our efforts, we can't lose sight of the ideas that founded our Order. That's why the Symposiums oversee everything. By removing ourselves from

the filth in the streets, we keep our pure models of reality. We can implement our purest ideals.

"We're experts. We have the tools of reason on our side. And from our vantage point, we can control the Masses for their own good. This crap about the 'New Feudalism' is a catchword for the traitors in the Technocracy who are jealous of the people at the top. We, the rulers of the Technocracy, have Ascended to our rightful places of power, and the mistakes of the Mythic Age will be eradicated for all time."

—Dr. Harold Kalishnakov, Syndicate Representative

— Ascend to the Worlds Beyond

"Do you really think you'll find a perfect model of reality here? This world has been torn apart. This world is only one model of what reality can be. There are limitless possibilities waiting beyond. In the depths of space, we will find other worlds waiting to yield knowledge. We must watch, for somewhere in the limitless realities of the unknown is the world to which we must Ascend.

"This world is dying. We must travel far beyond the Horizon.

"We must also prepare ourselves. Do you really think the only threats to humanity are here on Earth? We've begun to see what ruthless inhuman powers lurk beyond the boundaries of our exploration. They're waiting for us... so that they can consume us."

—Dr. Eliza Trondheim, Void Engineer

The Challenge

I hid the Cultist's unconscious body. The HIT Mark wasn't equipped to do a genetics scan of the building. The construct MIBs we had working with us used gen-scans, but they were searching the next block. This part of the mission was all mine.

Construct #32 walked into the room, raising the 45mm chain gun out of his back. My adrenaline always kicked in when he did that. As I stared into the barrel of his gun, I realized that my act had to be perfect now. One false move and I'd be dead.

Taking on a front of righteous indignation and opposing anyone with a position of power is easy. Actually trying to change things and working to fix a corrupt system is more difficult. In the same way, it's easy for the Tradition mages to see the Ascension War as contest between "good" and "evil." The real situation is more complex. Individuals must choose their own beliefs, and there are always opportunities to redefine them.

The truly talented members of the Technocracy have other concerns beyond the threat of the Traditions. They must live with ethical ambiguity and personal soul-searching. They must retain their free will, analyze their own lives and pursue a personal vision of Ascension. The war is raging; the challenge awaits.

Yeah, I had a job to do, but this was personal. This was a matter of honor. I holstered my gun and looked him straight in the eye.

"No problem. All clear."

He turned to walk out the door, and my charcoal-gray suit helped me fade into the shadows. That's what I do. Keep your damn battlefields. The war is being won in the shadows. Fortunately, humanity is winning.

The Nephandi

Dark Mirrors

Head like a hole
Black as your soul
I'd rather die than give you control
Bow down before the one you serve
You're going to get what you deserve
— Nine Inch Nails, "Head Like a Hole"

Jodi Blake stared down at the form laying prone on her altar and smiled. "You're terrified, aren't you?" The only answer to the question was silence and more sweat pouring off the young mage's body. "You should be. In less than an hour, you'll be gone from this world." She ran one black-lacquered fingernail from the man's bare chest down to where his pants would have started, had the ahriman been nice enough to leave the pants in place. Her victim squirmed; she smiled. "Don't worry, your death will serve a greater cause."

The Nephandi are almost unique among the Awakened, in that they choose to serve a greater force in their drive towards Ascension. They are also unique among the Traditions in that they are perfectly willing to make sacrifices— both human and Awakened— to the greater glory of their masters. None can truly say exactly what their masters are, save that the Nephandi-Lords personify corruption and all that is foul in human society. Some among the Nephandi claim that they serve Satan. Others speak of more nebulous creatures, things best not mentioned by name. Even those who have served the Nephandi-Lords for thousands of years cannot agree on the nature of their masters, save to say that they are growing more powerful all the time. Most Nephandi simply claim that they serve "Darkness, Corruption and Oblivion."

Jodi sat beside the trembling man, stroked a hand through his sweat-dampened hair and kissed him lightly on the forehead. "You are young, innocent. You think that I am a vile creature. You think that I wish to see the damnation of all that is 'Holy,' but you are very wrong. You of the Celestial Chorus, you of all the Traditions, should know better than that. What is your One Supreme Being without a counterpart to serve as a reminder of what failure to follow the rules means? Where would your beliefs be, if not for our beliefs to show that you are right? How can their be light without darkness?"

The Nephandi have long accepted that their role in the scheme of reality is twofold. First, they must serve their masters, the dark forces that corrupt the universe. Second, they provide a dark reflection of reality for the other Traditions. Many of the Traditions understand the Nephandi philosophy, but feel that the twisted Nephandi serve no true purpose beyond the corruption of all that is worthwhile in the world. Most Traditions would simply rather see them destroyed than risk the darkness of the Nephandi spreading further.

Jodi teased her victim's flesh, pinching with her nails and nipping with her teeth. The man's physical repulsion was obvious, almost as obvious as his desire. Jodi smiled at both reactions. "You could join with us. You would hardly be the first of the Chorus to learn new songs. I was once of the Celestial Chorus myself. Back then I was Sister Mary Elizabeth, but I learned that I was wrong in my beliefs. I learned that there was more that I could do to provide the Chorus with Ascension from where I am now than I could ever do while sticking to those bothersome vows of chastity and poverty." Jodi saw his interest peak and smiled. She paused long enough to force a passionate kiss upon his mouth, satisfied that he was now responding in kind to her ministrations. "The best part is that I can have anything I want while in this world. I have more power than most of the Traditions could comprehend."

The Nephandi often draw others to their beliefs from other Traditions, seducing them with promises of power, material wealth and eternal life. Normally they focus on the newly Awakened, those who have only started to taste the powers of magick, those who desperately seek more knowledge and ability, impatient with the ways of their Traditions. These renunciates, known as the barabbi, are a cause of great unrest among the mages.

When she had finished, Jodi washed her victim's body with sweet-scented oils, taking care to ensure that every part of him was thoroughly drenched. His breathing slowly returned to normal, his face bore a faint smile under the grimace of disgust at his bodily weakness. "I used to think that pleasure was wrong as well, that all of my 'sins' would ensure me immediate death and eternal suffering. It's been hundreds of years and, as you can see, I am quite happy and hardly suffering. In fact, we of the Nephandi are winning your 'Ascension War.'" Jodi painted symbols on his body, symbols that he sought in vain to see and understand. She watched his body twitch with each symbol that was drawn, and she smiled.

The Nephandi have long since learned a special language all their own, called the Dragon's Tongue. The Dragon's Tongue is used in rituals to speak within their cabals (called *ahriman*) and commune with their masters. Unless one has gone through the proper rituals, no power

can allow a person to understand the symbols and words. Additionally, the vast majority of the Nephandi have learned the Pictish tongue, assuring easier communications with the Black Spiral Dancers, their werewolf counterparts, in servitude to all that is corrupt.

"We have many allies among the Kindred and the Garou, even among the others of the Awakened. We have allies that do not even realize that they are working towards the same goals as the Nephandi. 'Beware false prophets.'" Jodi chuckled deep in her throat. "Indeed."

The Nephandi make full use of the communications networks provided by the Technocracy, providing many television ministries with the necessary funds to start their programs and to expand at a later time. The Nephandi use these pawn ministers to extend the general populace's discontent and fundamental lack of belief in the established religions, seeding doubts that can later be used to better their own position within the ranks of Awakened. The Nephandi also work well along side the Black Spiral Dancers and with the most corrupt of the vampires, some among the Sabbat and with the Baali. The Nephandi claim that the Baali were created using members of their own following. The Baali refuse to speak of such matters.

Jodi stepped back from her latest work, making certain that all of the runes and sacraments were in place upon the body of her victim. All was as it should be. Jodi nodded her satisfaction. Soon the decision would be made, her latest acquisition would either join in the ranks of the Nephandi or he would become a sacrifice to the powers the Nephandi willingly served. "You can join us," her voice was almost a plea, a promise of rewards and time spent knowing her body. "We have ways of ensuring loyalty, we would never fear your betrayal, and you could be with me, forever." She was satisfied to see the way his brow furrowed; she knew he would join them.

Much like the Black Spiral Dancers of the Garou, the Nephandi use special rituals in locations held as sacred to promote unity among the servitors of their masters. These rituals are called by many names, but the end result is always the same; in the end, the initiate comes to understand the ways of the Nephandi and willingly sacrifices a substantial portion of his free will in exchange for power and personal gratification. In many cases, the followers of the Nephandi Path go through these rituals regularly, reinforcing their beliefs upon themselves. Many claim that the rituals are actually addictive, while others claim them to be the foremost way for Nephandi to reach a greater level of understanding, a greater knowledge of power and its uses. The rituals place the Nephandi in direct communication with their masters. The first time a Nephandi initiate takes place in these rituals is referred to as the "Rebirth." Subsequent visits into the ritual areas are most often called "Regenerations."

Jodi's joy knew no bounds when the young man before her licked his sweat-stained, oil-coated lips and croaked out the words from a mouth too dry for easy communication: "I accept." She called out with to her ahriman, inhuman sounds passing her lips, sounds that sent primal spasms of fear through her young charge's body. Images of angry aborted fetuses and things that slithered in the blood-drenched darkness flashed behind his eyes. No human could possibly make such noises, no sane mind could comprehend their meaning. Others came to the chamber from distant sections of the Labyrinth. They came from the Pits and the towers; they poured forth from the Caul and the library. Soon the entire Chantry stood together, united in harmony and ready to receive a new member. Jodi shed tears of happiness. Her masters would be so pleased…

The Labyrinths of the Nephandi are, as often as not, living entities in their own right. These places can be incredibly diverse, but all are hideous monuments to the masters of the Nephandi. Labyrinths that have successfully breached the Horizon and formed Realms of their own often have unique places within their reality to tie them to the Nephandi's masters on a personal level. The more powerful of these Chantries have areas referred to as the Pit and the Caul. The Pit is the area where group rituals are performed, where many of the darker secrets of the Nephandi are practiced in relative safety. The Caul is the area where a Nephandi's "Rebirth" and subsequent "Regenerations" take place. Rumors abound that the Caul is actually a physical manifestation of a Nephandi-Lord's body, a womb for destroying and then recreating the individual mage on a greater level of power or with a stronger belief in the master's ways to Descend. Such rumors seem to be unfounded. To date, no one has been able to detect any severe genetic changes among captured Nephandi. Still, the rumors persist, as do the rumors that the Progenitors have recently discussed a merger with the Nephandi.

Jodi watched reverently as the neophyte forced his way past the heavy outer skin of the Caul. She saw the amorphous tendrils that reached eagerly for him and then plunged into his very body and soul, twisting flesh out of their way and reshaping his spirit. Blood washed across the interior of the Caul, leaking through the membrane and steaming as it rolled towards the floor. Jodi watched in near-ecstasy as his eyes grew wide with comprehension and horror, enveloping his mind even as the vomitous mass of the Caul enveloped and tore apart his body. She listened as his voice changed. His pleas for mercy became screams of ecstasy and understanding. Jodi was pleased, her masters were pleased. Another had joined the ranks of the Infernal and all was as it should be. The neophyte was beginning his Descent.

The Marauders

Dynamic Madness

I Almost wish I hadn't gone down that rabbit hole— and yet— and yet— it's rather curious, you know, this sort of life!
— Charles L. Dodgson, *Alice's Adventures in Wonderland*

Robert Davenport relaxed into the white wicker chair and was surprised to find it comfortable. He picked up the glass of iced tea that someone had thoughtfully provided for him. That, too, he found to his taste, and he smiled. He still wasn't sure where they were, but the manifestations seemed very, very nice.

Marauders are absolutely insane. Of all the factions at war in the Tellurian, they are the least understood, and are perhaps more feared than any other. No matter what grievances lie between Construct and Tradition, cabal and Chantry, or Sleeper and Awakened, all are equally devastated in the chaos and wreckage left behind by Marauders on the warpath. Even the Nephandi will turn their course to fight the common menace; a reality shredded by Paradox is a less inviting prize.

He placed the glass back onto the tiny table, narrowly avoiding a plaid bee. The insect skittered back and flew away down the hill. Davenport let his gaze follow it as it sped towards his companions in the meadow below. They sprinted after it hopefully, butterfly nets waving in the breeze, and he chuckled. The one in the lead— it had to be Martins, in that suit— stopped short suddenly, and then all four began running in the other direction.

The Technocracy are affected the worst by encounters with raiding Marauders. Their holdings are concentrated on Earth, and this is where the Marauders' immunity to Paradox becomes most useful. A skillful or lucky band of "crazies" can cripple a Convention base by their mere presence: their psychoses tend to manifest in physical forms, "fractures" in reality and holes in the Gauntlet. The Technomancers stay so busy hiding the vulgar magick that they cannot defend themselves properly.

"Daddy? Can I go play too?"

"Oh." He wasn't ready for this. Not here. Not today. "Sure honey. Do you have a net?" He was careful not to look at her as he spoke.

"No…" Her tone rose slightly, and he knew she had her head cocked to one side in anxious expectation.

One of the most successful Marauder tactics is to bring mythical creatures through the Gauntlet directly into Convention territory. An Australian Technocratic Construct was plagued with mysterious disappearances for months before the cause was found: a minotaur that Marauders (a splinter group known as King Solomon's Whines) had introduced to their substructures was living off of their Node— and their personnel.

He reached into the air beside him and pulled out a net, scaled down for an eight-year-old's convenience. "Here you go, Kary. Have fun." But he closed his eyes until he heard her skipping footsteps fade away. Then, very carefully, he opened them, and scanned the grassy slope before him. Nowhere was there any sign of his daughter.

But the very existence of the Marauders poses another problem, far worse than any mere physical threat. Although the Conventions and Traditions have been aware of their activities for centuries— the leading theory claims that they first appeared before the Age of Reason— to this day no one is quite sure where they came from.

He released his pent-up breath and unclenched his grip on the arm of the chair . For a moment, he watched the blood return to the woven lines impressed into his palm, thanking his God that today it had been Kary and not her mother. Today Davenport was more painfully sane than he had been since the accident, today could remember that accident, and today knew that his wife and daughter were dead.

In fact, the mechanism through which an ordinary mage— whether Traditional, Technomancer, Craft member or Orphan— becomes a Marauder remains unknown. It is popular among the younger mages of the Traditions to believe that these "unfortunates" are all Orphans simply gone mad and uncontrollable with the shock of the Awakening. Their elders shake their heads knowingly: they have lost too many established and respected colleagues to accept this.

Davenport shook his head to clear it, and returned to watching his friends. He wondered how many of them could remember how they came to be— whether they even knew what they had become. Was the world always Hell for Martins? China for Miss Zhao? Would the Titanic sail forever for The Gourmet? Did they ever know?

Most authorities hold that the change is accidental, and this is the official view embraced by the Technocracy. The Progenitors— the most vociferous proponents of this hypothesis— actively hunt Marauders for experimental testing. How the Marauders are kept inactive after their initial capture is unknown, but at last report, several subjects were under observation in Progenitor laboratories. Those few papers the scientists have presented suggest that they are attempting to isolate a virus involved in the transmission of the "disease." Considered in the light of that Convention's propensity towards germ warfare, this is alarming news indeed.

The only Tradition that does not seem so alarmed, in fact, is the Dreamspeakers, who are said to be conducting their own studies on some of the "calmer" Marauders. Dubious sightings of Marauders in Dreamspeaker territories and the caerns of their

Garou allies abound, giving rise to rumors of a spirit "sedative" developed by the Speakers. The Tradition's representatives formally deny any involvement, and few mages are yet desperate enough to ask the werewolves for comment.

A stiff wind began to blow across the meadow, whipping the nets to a frenzied flutter, making colored waves in the tall grass. Funny, the way his friends ran... almost like... yes. He could barely see the butterflies they chased, but the pattern of its flight was too familiar. Traced by the insects, their pursuers, and the gray-white nets, there appeared another butterfly— and old words rose unbidden to his lips.

"Phase space?"

"We can't be in phase space. It's an abstraction, a tool... it's impossible!" he shouted. But he knew that it was possible, and that the manifestation was his. Something in his madness generated this place, and nothing was sane in him at all.

In fact, the Dreamspeakers may be telling the truth. The most frightening thing about the Marauders, and the reason that so little is known about them, is that there is no way to tell whether a mage is a Marauder before the fighting starts. A Marauder using coincidental magick is indistinguishable from any other mage, and their characteristic immunity to Paradox doesn't matter in the Umbra. The difference shows only when the Marauder uses large amounts of vulgar magick.

"Chef?" The Gourmet's voice broke the silence. "Chef Davenport. I should like to arrange dinner for this evening, if you would be so kind. Senorita Aabraxas will be joining us, you know..."

"Yes." Davenport stood and cleared his throat. "Yes, of course," he said, turning to take his coat off of the chair. He found both occupied.

"You're not my wife," he said. But she was achingly close— it was always the eyes, old eyes where Maraya's were so young— and she smiled at him sadly.

"Why do you do this to me?"

"For freedom," she replied. "For the infinite freedom."

"But why the calm? Why this knowledge?"

"Someone must know. Your soul is light enough for the rest to see by." And her hand rose to touch his cheek.

The Marauders' madness is no sure clue to identification. As with many disorders, their particular lunacy may not be obvious to the eye or apparent in casual conversation. Close association may not reveal any problem.

Furthermore, not every insane mage is a Marauder. The Continuum has plenty of ordinary fanatics, psychotics and mages in Quiet. It simply adds an extra edge to any mental crisis to know that one's nearest and dearest may expect one to join the enemy.

"And why the fight? Didn't I— didn't we swear an oath before the accident?"

"We fight for the world as it was. You can keep your oath better in the elder age to come."

"But why the secrecy? What are we?"

"We shall be silent for our allies, and their charges."

"And?"

"And you know what you are. You knew all this when you made your choice, Robert. This is an old argument."

"It is." He sighed deeply. "I think that you should go away now. Come back when I forget again."

Orphans

Clear Paths

Can you feel it, see it, hear it today?
If you can't, then it doesn't matter anyway
You will never understand, it happens too fast
And it feels so good, it's like walking on glass
— Faith No More, "Epic"

Bryce stood behind the counter of Grimm's Occult Specialty Shop and observed few customers in the place. One was a middle-aged woman staring at the section for Reincarnation and Transcendental Meditation. She was so eager for knowledge, so hungry to know that there was more to life than death and taxes. Bryce smiled sadly; her chances were so slim. Despite the passion she felt for the ideas of High Magick, she still accepted the reality that had been imposed on her. It was a shame, really — she wanted so much, yet refused herself the right to see beyond the Curtain. He estimated her chances of ever Awakening on her own at slightly less than a snowball's chance in Hell.

The other customers were a different story entirely; not one, but two mages stood in his store. Both completely ignored the "magic items" on the shelves and went straight to the least glamorous part of the store, the section where True Magick could be found. The small Oriental woman was from the Order of Hermes, and she wore her pride in the old ways like a shield against the Sleepers. The older man he couldn't place, but he suspected the Akashic Brotherhood, simply by the way the man carried himself — relaxed and graceful— almost sure signs that he was skilled in the physical aspects of Do. He wondered how they regarded what they saw.

There can be little doubt that the average Tradition mage has nothing but contempt for the Orphans. Most mages don't want the self-Awakened anywhere near them, fearing that the lack of proper training is inherently dangerous. Some Orphans would agree with this idea, but these are normally the same ones that beg their way into a Tradition proper.

For most Orphans, the decision to join with a recognized Tradition is simply a matter of survival. The Technocracy would love nothing more than to locate Orphans and either convert them or wipe them out of existence. There is both strength and security in numbers. A sizable number of the Orphans simply join with the Hollow Ones, accepting their less strenuous philosophies and gaining most of the benefits that could be gathered by joining with one of the nine "True" Traditions. For some, however, that is simply not a viable option. Those that remain behind are the true Orphans, the self-Awakened.

The man was the first to come over. He had recognized Bryce as one of the Awakened despite Bryce's deliberate attempts to remain unnoticed. The gentleman smiled apologetically

and asked his question. "Excuse me, do you have any other items, perhaps of the type not normally left in the open?" The question was whispered and Bryce appreciated the softness of the man's tone. No one needed Sleepers or, worse still, the Technocracy hearing too much about one of the few serious stores in town. Bryce nodded and led him towards the back room, away from prying ears.

Orphans pay a high price for their independent actions. Many cannot locate a Chantry or even a cabal that will accept them, and even when they are accepted as members, they are hardly treated as equals. More often than not, an Orphan must barter favors for admittance into a Chantry. Some even work as mercenaries for the Traditions, taking high-risk assignments or adding to a cabal's power base in exchange for nothing more than Tass. The more experienced Orphans sometimes work in exchange for information, including access to a Chantry's libraries, but even knowledge does not come without a cost.

No words were needed as the man looked around at the collection of Talismans and fastened his eyes on the katana propped carefully against a collection of tarot cards. "Right again," Bryce thought, but did not say. Bryce himself had learned first from an old sensei in Hong Kong, and he knew the Brotherhood fairly well. The haggling only lasted a few minutes, and Bryce was disappointed as usual; the man had been too eager to possess the sword, and had missed out on the full pleasures of bartering.

Those who choose to stay Orphans feel that the Traditions are too limited in their ways of thinking. While many Orphans prefer to call themselves self-Awakened, a substantial number of them started with one Tradition or another. In some cases, Orphans have literally gone from Tradition to Tradition, seeking a philosophy that makes sense. They seldom find what they are looking for, and often "come home" to the Non-Traditions. Most of the self-Awakened would eagerly point out that before the Traditions could be formed, mages had to exist. Some Tradition mages seem to have forgotten that point. To the ones that remain Orphans, even the Hollow Ones are too limited in the way they think. It should be pointed out, however, that many of the self-Awakened work in Cliques of their own, forming what may well become Traditions in their own right in the future.

Eventually, the Hermetic mage was led into the back room as well. She took her time, window shopping, not really looking for anything specific. Bryce thought she was attractive, and the feeling was mutual. They took to talking. When Bryce brought up her Tradition, indicating a pre-Roman portion of the Kabbala, she laughed softly and shook her head. "No, Mister Grimm, I'm afraid you're mistaken. I'm not with the Order, I'm Verbena." Bryce chalked one up for his imaginary competition when she

explained that the Seal of Solomon was simply a gift from a friend, and one she found pleasing to the eye. Bryce immediately began pointing out a few items that he felt would be of particular interest to Kami, as the woman identified herself, and had made another sale in a matter of ten minutes.

One example of the Orphan groups that has done very well is the Hollow Ones. Other Cliques, or Crafts, including the Children of Proteus, Bata'a, Sisters of Hippolyta, Sculptors of Fate, Children of Knowledge and Fringe Walkers, grow in number. Most of these groups are very new. Most started in this century. The Fringe Walkers, who stand at the border between Tradition balance and Marauder madness, have been around for centuries, changing many times over the years, while the alchemical Children of Knowledge claim to be the oldest Tradition of them all.

The two talked until well after the store had closed, and Kami suggested making love. Bryce had no objections, and he proved himself to be a worthy mate. He had spent most of his teen years learning from a very passionate member of Kami's Tradition, and apparently a few things had rubbed off. Kami finally broke down and asked him the question he normally avoided answering: what Tradition did Bryce follow? Bryce never lied about the matter; he told her matter-of-factly that he was an Orphan. Kami was surprised, but hid her shock well. They talked of philosophies until the sun was on the rise. Then they went upstairs to Bryce's apartment to sleep.

When he awoke just after noon, Kami was gone. She'd left a note for him, promising to return in a few days. The Winter Solstice was near. Kami had preparations to make for the formal gathering. Bryce smiled; it was always nice making a new friend. The buzzer sounded below as he was getting dressed; another day, and Grimm's Occult Specialty Shop was open 365 days a year. He wondered what surprises the day would bring, and hoped fervently that he would meet a person who shared his passion for bartering. Bryce loved a tough sale.

The Hollow Ones

Laughter in Shadow

What an inheritance
The salt and the Kleenex
Morbid self-attention
Bending my pinky back...
You're perfect, yes, it's true
But without me, you're only you
Your menstruatin' heart
It ain't bleedin' enough for two
— Faith No More, "Midlife Crisis"

Sascha moved across the pulsing dance floor with a practiced nonchalance she did not feel. The wraith stood only a few feet away from her, and she felt the chill that poured from its radiant form even from where she stood; the idea of actually approaching the glorious form was enough to make her feel unworthy. Before she could speak, the wraith called out to her softly. Even its voice was beautiful. "I see you. I mean you no harm. Come to me."

That the wraith sensed her fear was enough of an annoyance to make her force her dread into the background. "I'm supposed to talk to you... But I don't know what to say." She hated that the words were faint, almost weak. She unconsciously looked around the room to make certain that none of the Sleepers were looking at her and laughing. They were not, and she allowed herself to relax.

Contrary to the beliefs of most Tradition mages, the Hollow Ones do have their own set of beliefs. The primary difference is that most Hollow Ones do not discuss their mutual beliefs with other mages. Many deny that Ascension is a true aspect of reality, preferring to live in the here and now instead of focusing their attentions on the future. The Hollow Ones, more than any other Tradition, reflect the mass-media's beliefs in the occult. As the media is— for the most part— ignorant about the truths of the supernatural, the Hollow Ones feel a powerful need to learn for themselves about the realities beyond the legends of werewolves, vampires and wraiths.

To a follower of the Hollow Tradition, the most important aspect of magick is the vast knowledge that can be learned. Mind you, no Hollow One would ever admit anything of the sort to one of his peers. To this end, they are more likely to use a ouija board or a deck of tarot cards than to use a cauldron or wand; they are so enwrapped in the general beliefs of magick as perceived by the media that what most of the Awakened would disdain as parlor games work quite well as foci for them. More than a few of the Hollow Ones have been known to use a black silk top hat for more than the production of a rabbit. Most Traditions assume that the Goth mages need no foci, but that is usually because their foci are harder to locate with ease and normally take the form of jewelry or fashion accessories. The Hollow Ones realize that magick without foci is possible and some even disdain the use of foci. Those that choose not to find a focus for their magick, however, find learning new Spheres difficult.

Sascha was utterly fascinated by the scintillating light that composed the wraith's form, and she had to fight to avoid trying to touch its immaterial substance. "Does it hurt to be dead?" She hated the words as soon as they were out of her mouth. What if the wraith were to take offense?

The wraith laughed, a sound like crystal chimes struck by silver bells. "No, child, there is no pain." The wraith seemed to fade away for a second, but returned almost instantly. "No physical pain at least. Am I all that you expected?"

Sascha could hear the gentle mockery in the voice of the angelic form, but took no offense. "No, you are so much more than I could have hoped for..." There she went again, making stupid comments and sounding like a amateur. Sascha hated looking like she didn't know anything. What was the purpose of dressing Goth if you acted like a geek?

Hollow Ones are very much the slaves to fashion, but only if fashion represents the darkness and decay that surrounds them. No Hollow One likes to admit to being less than knowledgeable, especially in the presence of the other Traditions. While they will deny vehemently a need to be accepted as equals — normally claiming that they are above such pettiness— the followers of the Hollow Tradition are as susceptible to feelings of rejection and inadequacy as any of the Awakened.

"Who were you... I mean... who are you?" Again, more stupid questions, but Sascha felt the need to know about the wraith, to know about all of the wraiths. Surely there was no greater example of what lay beyond death's door. Surely there was no better representation of what came with the supposed Ascension than the being that stood before her.

The wraith smiled, and even its smile was enchantingly beautiful. She wanted to weep with joy at what she saw, but was aware that the cabal was watching, waiting to see a sign of weakness in their new initiate. "Nobody special," the wraith replied. "My past life would simply bore you." The wraith reached out and touched beyond her flesh, touched her soul, her Avatar. "Certainly I was not as great as you will be, provided you learn the necessary lessons before your time is over."

"What lessons? Please, I need to know." The wraith smiled again, shook its head sadly. There would be no answer, not now at least, but the knowing eyes that looked at her promised knowledge when the time was right. In spite of the promise, Sascha's heart fell. "Please, tell me something. I have to know what to expect."

The Hollow Ones believe in the emptiness they all feel inside, the void that they cannot fill no matter how hard they try. This emptiness, or more appropriately, this hollow feeling, is the primary motivating factor in followers of the Tradition. The clothes they wear, the attitudes they carry, all mirror the desolation and longing that many of the Hollow Ones feel.

The wraith smiled again, and this time it answered her question. "You are right to embrace the darkness. The emptiness inside you is a part of what you must lose in order to move on. But child, please remember that there is also light in the world. Embrace the light as well." As the last words escaped past glorious, sepulchral lips, the wraith faded away, leaving only more void where before there was such beautiful light. Sascha felt the loss in the depths of her soul.

She turned and saw the cabal staring at her, waiting to see what she would do, still judging whether or not she was worthy. To hell with them; if they decided that she was less than their equals, she would still survive. She had learned so much on her own already that she didn't need them to teach her anything. Still, she wanted to have friends. Everyone wants friends. Everyone needs family.

The followers of the Hollow Tradition prefer to stay in areas populated by people, preferably those that follow the same Gothic mentality in both dress and lifestyle. In many cases, the bars where Hollow Ones hang become the modern equivalent of opium dens. These punk bars and thrash dance halls are often so filled with Sleepers hopped up or knocked out on drugs that vulgar magick can be used with a lessened risk of suffering Paradox. As often as not, the magick performed is less impressive than what the Sleepers are already seeing.

Baron walked over to where she stood and looked down at her. Baron was tall and lean, his hair dyed to match his clothes, and his ears and nose decorated with flashes of light to help guide him in his search through the darkness. He did not smile; he did not have to smile. She had been accepted. Around them the Sleepers listened to the harsh, blaring music and consumed alcohol or a variety of illegal narcotics. Baron stuck a cigarette in his mouth and Sascha ignited her hand so that he could in turn ignite the tip of his cigarette. Not surprisingly, no one noticed. They danced to their own rhythm as the music played on. It was good to be home at last.

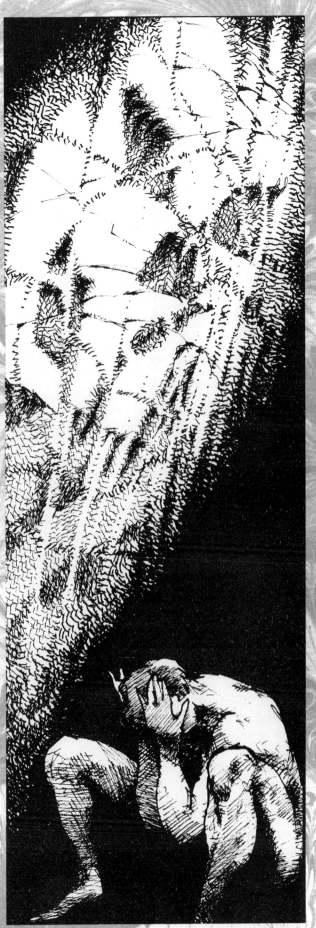

Part Three: The Lost Tradition

The Ahl-i-Batin

The Subtle Ones

Well the Scripture
Is a sculpture
Which encrypts your
Soul
With its culture…
—Norman B., *Deviations from The Norm*

Harken and attend! Thus spake the Khwaja al-Akbar:

In a Time before there was time, a great Hero slew a great Beast. The carcass of the Beast formed a huge Mountain covering the World, and the Hero knew that the World must be cleared for the coming of Humanity. By acts of Primal Magick only dimly understood by those such as Myselves, the Hero carved Mountain Qaf into a model of Ascension itself, with the broad chaotic diversity of Human Belief spanning the base, and whose collective strivings form the Avatars, the Paths of Ascendence reaching Up the mountainside through the Ranks of the Awakened and the Realms of the Oracles, through the Realms of Incarnae and Celestines, and converging in the Presences, which are the Shadows of the Pure Ones, before joining at the Summit, Which Is The Unity.

Such a Great Work was not without a Price, however. The Blood of the Beast seeped deep into the Earth, saturating it with highly charged Quintessence and forming a dangerously unstable Base for the mountain of Ascension. It must be the Task of the reunified Traditions to channel this raw unwieldable Power safely into the paths of Ascension, Writing The Name Of The Unity across the face of the World, before the stability of the Mountain Itself is threatened.

—From The Doctrine of the Unity, Revealed by the Khwaja al-Akbar upon the Night of Fana in the Dasht-i-Margo, Committed to Memory by Rufai the Mede of the Darwushim, Transcribed by Khattaboth Kaghan of the University of Light, and Preserved for the Edification and Enlightenment of All who are Awakened by Josephus the Ascetic of the Brethren of the Unified Soul

Background

Although they were one of the original members of the Council of Nine (occupying the seat now held by the Virtual Adepts), the Ahl-i-Batin are practically unknown to many Tradition mages. Most assume that they were wiped out when the Technocracy moved into the Middle East to ensure its control of the newly discovered oil fields. That the Ahl-i-Batin elude the magicks of most Awakened so easily may be taken as some tribute to this Tradition's mastery of keeping to the shadows. At various times throughout history, the Ahl-i-Batin have been one of the most politically powerful Traditions on the planet (though not many realized it).

The Night of Fana

The history of the Ahl-i-Batin begins with the Himalayan Wars of 900-600 BC, when a sect of Handura (later subsumed into the Euthanatos) viciously fought to drive the old Akashic Brotherhood out of the Indian subcontinent. Now, it happened that a group of young Initiates and Acolytes, who all happened to be builders and stonemasons by trade, were separated from the Brotherhood by a Euthanatos ambush while travelling between monasteries. Harried through the Khyber Pass and into what is now Afghanistan, some of the band died, and many were driven to the edge of sanity by the Entropy magicks of the Euthanatos.

Finding themselves upon a broad verdant plain bounded at either hand by great distant mountains, the group came upon a band of dervishes engaged in a mad frenzied dance. These were the Darwushim, a schismatic sect of the Cult of Ecstasy that had incurred the wrath of certain factions of what became the Celestial Chorus by daring to suggest that the higher intelligence the ecstatics contacted through their rites was the One of Celestial Chorus dogma.

Without missing a beat, one of the drummers motioned the Akashic Brothers to join the dance, and they did so.

Much has been said of that evening, which is now called the Night of Fana, and most Batini customs and doctrine are said to have their origins in the merging of Traditions that occurred. The uncontrolled passion of the

Darwushim found a kind of discipline and implicit order in the Do forms through which the Brothers danced, and, in a state of divine intoxication, pierced themselves with long steel needles. The contemplative movements of the Akashic Brothers were infused with an incomprehensible energy, drawing them beyond their limited understanding of Mind, and many twisted around in their skins striving to find the Way of these unknown vistas of consciousness.

At the climax of this great dance, a very strange thing happened. Mahlav, a Darwushim Acolyte, singled out a member of the Akashic retinue, a sculptor by the name of Saddhu, and stood before him. Now Saddhu was a poor sickly man with a withered left arm who had specialized in carving the eyes of goddesses with his good right arm; Mahlav, though a skilled dancer with a great soul, had never been accorded his proper status among the Darwushim, for he had no left arm (an affliction then considered a curse among them). A flash of profound recognition passed between them, and they stepped forward as though to embrace. Upon touching, the two men fused into one, with Mahlav's face on the back of Saddhu's head and Saddhu's features emerging from the back of Mahlav's skull. This double-sided figure, with strangely symmetrical legs and arms now made whole, began a strange improvised Do-dance, chanting (in stereo) to the assembled mages and Acolytes.

I am the Khwaja al-Akbar, it explained, *an Oracle of the Place Which Is One, and my journeys among the world of men are ended and I am returned to myself. I bring to you, who have no more Fellowship of your own, the Doctrine of the Unity, whereby Ascension may be made known to all, and the squabbling-fences of dogmatic philosophy be transcended. I call to you, who are now Orphaned, to cleave to me in founding a Path of your own.*

The mission of the Khwaja, and all who would follow, was to write a great rune or mandala across the face of the earth which would focus the thoughts and aspirations of Sleeper and Awakened alike into a cosmological ideal that afforded some control of— and protection from— the powderkeg of Quintessence on which the world rested.

As the Khwaja chanted, Darwushim bards strove to memorize the rhythms of the recital, and Akashic scribes scribbled the Khwaja's words in hasty notational Sanskrit. When the Khwaja sang of the Unity, its words described not only the Correspondence Point of space and time, but the Universal Mind as well, and the undivided One of pure Prime. All Paths must recognize the commonality of their respective doctrines, the Khwaja abjured, lest their enemies divide and conquer them. The Doctrine of the Unity would provide the key to the trust of others.

It is ironic that the Night of Fana climaxed with the Khwaja's call to unification, for at that moment, the western horizon darkened as Handura reinforcements arrived to hound their Akashic quarry into oblivion, and the sky to the east blazed with the approach of a host of the Celestial Chorus bent on squelching the Darwushim heresy once and for all. Of the ensuing conflagration, one can only speculate, for the Celestial Chorus and the Euthanatos give strangely conflicting accounts, and the Ahl-i-Batin have never been induced to speak upon the matter. All that can be said for certain is that the rich fertile plain upon which this event took place is now called the Dasht-i-Margo, or Great Desert of Death, which spans much of Afghanistan.

The Hidden Plan of Unity

Impossible though it may seem, the fledgling Tradition survived the Night of Fana, but would not reveal its existence to other mages for several centuries. Their activities may be inferred from historical sources: empires began to rise and fall more quickly, conquering each other in increasingly rapid succession. Certain groups, however, achieved a kind of permanence, particularly some religious sects in Palestine and ruling families in Persia. The environment of the cities changed dramatically; an engineering breakthrough called a *qanat* allowed water from melting mountain snows to be transported underground across the arid Persian plains to the cities, where lush gardens with tinkling fountains were built. The arts of urban planning adapted and grew accordingly, while architecture arose to new heights, casting the mandala patterns of the cities in sharp relief.

By the time of the Roman Empire, the proliferation of schismatic religious sects was taking its toll upon the Celestial Chorus, and its inquisitorial factions had a field day rounding up heretics. Through reams of confessions and interrogation transcripts, a fragmentary picture emerged, and the Chorus came to the realization that its home turf, the thickly Noded cradle of civilization, was being infiltrated and appropriated under its very nose. Purges and pogroms were set in motion, and dungeons thickened with Essenemenes, Chaopts, Ignostics and heretics of all variet-

ies, but even the combined efforts of all such groups could not account for the massive deficit of Quintessence which the Chorus was experiencing at many of its most powerful Nodes.

With the absence of the Roman Empire, the once-fertile crescent was reduced to a wasteland denuded by human consumption, in which Marauders and their Djinn hordes preyed upon unwary travellers. The isolation of the cities dotting this landscape enforced an isolation upon all within the region, with communication uncertain at best.

At length, when the Celestial Chorus seemed about to abandon its holy land for the greener pastures of Europe, the chief member of the inquisitorial faction awoke to find, upon the pillow beside his head, a warm loaf of sweet mana-bread and a thick sheaf of papers laboriously inscribed with a plan which would unify the cities of the wastes with an array of Nodes aligned around a central axis. Accompanying this plan was an engraved invitation to discuss its implementation signed by Hermetic potentates, the Akashic Brotherhood and the Cult of Ecstasy, bearing a magickal charge which was easily traceable to the house of a rich merchant of Isfahan.

Chorus delegates arrived to find other Traditions represented and engaged in vigorous discussion of the plan. Chorus elders quickly discerned the wisdom of the plan: a synergetic net of linked Nodes which would fracture and divide the blanket hold of the Mad Ones upon the lands. In a rare cessation of internecine feuding, the pre-Council Traditions agreed to recognize a good thing when they saw it, for the mutual benefit for all was unmistakable.

Certain members of each Tradition, however, skeptics suspicious of the plan's method of delivery, came to the collective realization that none of the represented Traditions were the originators of the plan, and incisive inquiries soon revealed that their host, the "rich merchant" of Isfahan, was, in fact, a coalition of minor but respectable Crafts with deep roots in the prehistory of Central Asia and the Fertile Crescent. The members of this coalition were known to include the Ikhwan at-Tawhid ("Brethren of the Unified Soul," reclusive ascetic mystics on the fringe of the Celestial Chorus), Ustad Akhdir Jabal, who taught music and dance in his "Paradise Garden" at Isfahan, the University of Light (Qabalists from Jerusalem), the Silk Cartel of Samarkand and the Darwushim, now unafraid to use their name openly. Inquisitorial forces did their best to discern some conspiracy behind this coalition, but found only lowly mystics of limited magickal understanding, practitioners sincerely anxious to rally around the strongest source of magickal energy in their midst.

After a brief but vicious flurry of infighting over the locale of the central Node, the plan was accepted. Its dissertations upon the metaphysic of Unity captured the hearts of the Celestial Chorus' old guard. Quintessence was to be channeled across the wastes by conduits of raw human faith, sent by prayer or carried in person, collected at a massive central Node and redistributed back to the contributory nodes. The net swept the face of the planet in tremendous waves of willing recruits, resulting in a vast renaissance, not only for the Celestial Chorus, who tended the Central Node with the aid of the Ikhwan at-Tawhid, but for all magery in its regions. The Marauders were driven from the wasteland realms, and even the culture and civilization of the Sleepers were elevated to hitherto unseen heights.

Mount Qaf and the Web of Faith

With the spread of the Web of Faith, as it came to be called, came the proliferation of cults and religious sects, usually centered around an Errant who drew upon the Quintessential energy of the Web, which alarmed not only the Celestial Chorus, but the other Traditions as well. Steps were taken to drive groups like the Iblisi, Yazudi, Abululians and Shimailites out of the Web. Persecution escalated over the next few centuries, until the Chorus and the Order of Hermes called in massive reinforcements from Europe. Fearing another holocaust, such as that which ended the Night of Fana, the true masters of the Ahl-i-Batin revealed themselves in secret to high-ranking members of the Traditions. Invoking the Doctrine of Unity, they assured the Tradition leaders of their good intentions, explaining their long deception as a means of protection against the Handura. Leaders were invited to Sihr Maqamut, and Mount Qaf was revealed to them. Many Tradition leaders claimed to have seen their own Avatars beckoning to them from the upper slopes of the mountainside.

Though they had secured some powerful allies, the Ahl-i-Batin still lived in fear of enemies old and new, and kept secret two of their major sources of strength: the Qutbs, Masters of the Sphere of Mind who kept the far-flung Batini leaders in close telepathic contact, and the qanat, a method of drawing up Quintessential energy from the vast resevoirs of "dragon's blood" which lay beneath most of the Middle East (see the excerpt from the Doctrine of the Unity, above), which could be used to create a temporary miniature Node of sorts.

Batini diplomats may have been instrumental in the formation of the Council of the Nine, but were still reluctant to reveal themselves to any but the highest leaders of other Traditions. Their place on the Council was officially defined as loose affiliation of "Crafts" called the Geomatric Coalition. As years passed, however, the Batini insistence upon their cloak-and-dagger charade became something of an inside joke among Council members, prompting one to remark: "These 'subtle ones' seem to be so-o-o subtle that even they don't know what they are doing!"

Though merely a joke, this statement may indicate the major reason for the Ahl-i-Batin's eventual downfall. While they made incredible progress in bringing the Traditions together, their own fragmented structure tended to blind them to corruption within their ranks, and their constant meddling in Mid-Eastern politics began to wheel out of control. At the beginning of the nineteenth century, the Technocracy became aware of the vast Quintessence reserves under the region and moved in to take over. In the fierce battles which followed, both sides lost; Mount Qaf was shut away from the Earth and both parties were banished from its ineffable slopes.

What followed does little credit to the Batini leadership, which promptly abandoned its Disciples with vague claims of a future return and triumph. After decades of decline, the ailing Tradition broke ranks with the Council following a dispute with the European-based Traditions between the two World Wars. The Batini, vowing to protect their homeland against the Technocracy single-handedly, vanished largely from the Council's sight.

It is possible that many (or even all) Batini leaders were hunted down and destroyed, for no hidden Masters have yet been discovered, either by Tradition, Technoc-

Extra-Traditional Initiation

Before this century, and back into earliest history, certain Oracles took an active role in Awakening the Avatars of promising mortals, particularly those with no connection to the khanaqahs who might otherwise have become Orphans. The appearance of such beings among the khanaqahs may temporarily "remind" them of the Doctrine of Unity and their kinship with each other, but schismatic rivalries invariably resume once the Oracle has left. A player who wishes her Batini character to be aware of the Ahl-i-Batin's full Traditional heritage may wish to include one of the following Presences in her Prelude:

• Alkidr, an immortal prophet from the age of Ibrahim (Abraham), an Oracle of the Sphere of Time.

• The Khwaja al-Akbar, embodiment of cosmological erudition identified with the Egyptian Thoth and the Greek Hermes, said to have initiated Pythagoras, Euclid and Plato into the first levels of understanding of the Sphere of Correspondence.

• Nazdhur-i-Khan, a trickster of Central Asian folklore, whose "foolish" and "insane" behavior is the result of (and often results in) an increased comprehension of the Sphere of Mind.

• The 'Aql-i-Khul, called the Universal Mind, the Akasha, The First Thought of God, etc., an angelic being of pristine abstraction, thought to be a Primal manifestation of the Pure Ones by the Ahl-i-Batin, but considered an Incarna by other Traditions.

racy or their own followers. Those left behind, cut off from each other and from their allies among the Traditions, literally never knew what hit them. Thus the Ahl-i-Batin became the butt of another, more cruel joke at the hands of the Technomantic victors, to wit: "They have divided, now we will conquer!"

Organization

The higher ranks of the old Ahl-i-Batin were said to extend upward (or rather, inward, toward the Unity) through the lost Horizon Realm of Mount Qaf with all its ancient and venerated sages, saints and prophets, through the Realms of such Oracles as Alkidr, the Khwaja al-Akbar and Nazdhur-i-Khan, through thick ranks of "Presences," angels, pre-monotheist deities and other Umbral denizens such as the 'Aql-i-Khul, and, ultimately, to the Unity Itself. On a more mundane level, however, their organization more closely resembles that of a modern covert intelligence operation, one with closely-knit self-contained groups which may not even be aware of each others' existence or affiliation, and with the intercommunications couched in elaborate codes (usually of a mystical or esoteric nature).

The Ahl-i-Batin hierarchy of teacher/student interrelationships gather into lodges called *khanaqahs*. These can take the form of craft and trade guilds, secret societies or openly religious institutions. Those who have achieved Adeption or Mastery of a Sphere are initiated into the full Traditional heritage of the Ahl-i-Batin, and are called *Murshids*. Beneath them are the *Murids*, who may have attained up to Rank 3 in a Sphere, but whose initiation is confined to the outward doctrines and mythos of the local khanaqah to which they belong.

Each khanaqah is presided over by a shaykh or council of shaykhs, who, in this century, have rarely progressed beyond the Murid level. The main function of most khanaqahs is to maintain a worldly power base for the Murshids, either through political and commercial manipulations or through the wielding of religious influence. Each khanaqah maintains large private guest quarters called the *haram*, which is reserved for visiting Murshids.

When the Ahl-i-Batin hierarchy was interrupted by the destruction of the Qutbs, most other Murshids went into hiding— even from their own initiates. "Prophecies" of a triumphant return were muttered, and many khanaqahs incorporated tales of lost "once-and-future" holy men (already a common theme) into their sectarian mythos. Scattering to the farthest reaches of the world, the masters cloaked themselves in political and corporate conspiracies when possible, or resorted to medical quackery, new age scams and televangelism when fortune did not favor their schemes.

The only khanaqahs in which Murshids still retain permanent residence are the chantries of the original five "Crafts" (called Khanates): the Ikhwan at-Tawhid (Makkah), the University of Light (Jerusalem), the Silk Cartel (Samarkand), the Paradise Garden (Isfahan) and the Darwushim (Baghdad).

Meetings

There have been no full meetings of the Ahl-i-Batin since the triumph of the Technocracy. In the old days, most Batini business was conducted via the telepathic network of the Qutbs, but in the twentieth century, what little communication does occur must rely on mundane clandestine modes, such as secret codes and signs subtly couched in art, poetry, music and architecture.

Initiation

The initiatory rites of Murids are as diverse and varied as the khanaqahs themselves, forming too broad and insignificant of a topic to be covered here. The initiation of a Murshid invariably involves a great deal of esoteric scholarship, usually some variant of "sacred geometry." Often the initiate is presented with an insoluble mathematical conundrum, such as dividing googols by zero, performing calculus based upon the alephs of infinity, or holding a tangible manifestation of the square root of negative one (instead of a mere *imaginary* representation).

In the modern era, initiation rarely occurs above the Murid level, and initiates are nearly always indoctrinated into whatever schismatic spiritual sect predominates in that khanaqah's region (usually one of the many offshoots of Shi'ite Islam). Most modern initiates know nothing of the full extent of the Ahl-i-Batin, nor of their own common heritage shared with rival regional sects.

Other Details

Chantry

A large part of the Doctrine of Unity concerns itself with the iconographic "sacred topology" of a great Horizon Realm known as Mount Qaf, which was populated by a pyramidal hierarchy of enlightened beings. Visitors to this Realm found themselves in the lavish garden of Sihr Maqamut, a palace of the Persian style perched upon a large outcropping on the lower slopes of the mountain. From this starting point, one may embark upon what the Batini refer to as the path of one's Avatar, scaling the mountain in search of the wise one most suited to their own personal direction and stage of development. The Ahl-i-Batin maintained that all Traditions, philosophies and Paths of Ascension were contained in Mount Qaf, and that only a few slopes had thus far been explored. The world of Sleepers is viewed as the plain surrounding the mount, while ascending degrees of mages form the base. The upper reaches of the mountain are inhabited by Oracles, Celestines and (according to Batini doctrine) Pure Ones, all converging at the summit, which is Unity (equal to Prime, representing the One and embodying the Correspondence Point).

In Sleeper mythology, Qaf is known as a mountain range which surrounds the known world, but the Ahl-i-Batin consider it to be the center of the world, indeed, of the Tellurian itself. Some insight may be gleaned from Batini poetry which describes the summit of Mount Qaf as the site of the Sepulchre of Adam Qadhamun (also known as the Akashic "Pan Gu"), whose body forms the substance of all the realms, and who slew the beast whose carcass forms Mount Qaf. Such "inside-out/upside-down" metaphors are typical of Batini Correspondence Cosmology.

When the Ahl-i-Batin were defeated by the Technocracy, the Horizon Realm of Mount Qaf was lost, the mountain itself believed destroyed. Accounts say the summit burst and great clouds of ash and smoke arose which darkened nearly all the realms of the Umbra for days. Some believe that the malleable otherspace now called the Web is formed of the foothills of Mount Qaf, which lies beyond mages' grasp until the day of Ascension.

Acolytes

The Ahl-i-Batin have always maintained extremely close relations with the wide variety of mystical groups and "heretical" sects which accumulate on the outskirts (and in the heart) of nearly every major religion born in the Middle East. Acolytes have been chosen from the Gnostics of Zoroastrianism and early Christianity, the Qabalists of Judaism and the Sufis of Islam, as well as any number of self-proclaimed holy men, ascetics, fakirs and dervishes.

Spheres

Correspondence: Long before the Virtual Adepts of the modern era, the Ahl-i-Batin had achieved the deepest understanding of the nature of space and locality of any known mages. Many aspects of their Doctrine of Unity resemble modern mathematical descriptions of the Correspondence Point, but any Batini would be quick to explain that the Unity refers not only to the higher (or inner) dimensions of space, but to those of the mind, soul and spiritual spaces as well. The Ahl-i-Batin attribute all of their magickal effects to their understanding of how the One fits into the Many, or, as they like to say in the presence of the Celestial Chorus, "knowing the mind of God." When the Ahl-i-Batin originally came to the Middle East, they discovered and preserved the early attempts to define the Sphere of Correspondence conducted by the classical Greeks, incorporating such findings into their architecture and urban planning. Indeed, most of the oldest cities of this area are mapped out along great sigils of Correspondence, and the bizarre and intricate warpings of space thus created can be described by any visitor who has tried to find an address in the Old Quarter.

Mind: Like their ideological ancestors, the Akashic Brotherhood, the Ahl-i-Batin teach their initiates understanding of the Sphere of Mind, and, until this century, maintained a network of telepathic intercommunication across Northern Africa, the Mid-East and Central Asia. This network was sustained by a system of Qutbs (literally "Poles"), mental masters who by their very existence served as the reference points for this telepathic form of primitive cyberspace. The Technocracy's victory in the Middle East early in this century came with their detection and destruction of many principle Qutbs. The Ahl-i-Batin claim that the subsequent rise of the Virtual Adepts was due entirely to Technomantic plundering of the Great Truths known to the Qutbs.

Entropy: The Ahl-i-Batin are incapable of understanding or using the Sphere of Entropy. Whether this is due to their hatred of the Euthanatos or some sort of curse placed upon them by the Handura during the Himalayan Wars is not known.

Foci

Please note that the Foci presented here are given only as examples, for the Ahl-i-Batin are particularly skilled at making a Focus out of whatever object or behavior is appropriate to their outward lifestyle. Anyone playing a Batini should create their own range of Foci based on the tools or accessories most strongly associated with their character concept. Since prayer is a common daily occurrence in Muslim countries, this Focus is the same for nearly all Batini. Rotes for the Ahl-i-Batin can be found in Book Four.

Prayer or Meditation — Mind / Spirit
  (for an architect:)
   Ruler, compass, triangle — Correspondence
  Paper — Matter
   Pen and ink — Prime
   (for a healer:)
   Placebo pills — Life
   (for a begging dervish:)
  Music — Time
  Dancing — Forces
 Begging bowl — Prime

Concepts

Batini initiates cover perhaps the broadest range of character concepts of any Tradition, as the Ahl-i-Batin has definitely rejected the Akashic Brotherhood's attitude of isolation from the world of Sleepers, and have actively sought to insinuate themselves into all levels of any society in which they find themselves. Healers, teachers and architects can be said to predominate, however, and Murshids are as likely to be kings as beggars.

The vast majority of Batini are from regions once part of the Islamic Empire, but hidden Murshids are believed to be all over the world.

Quote: "We are fragmented now, our souls as spread and scattered as the ashes of Mount Qaf. A bitter wall stands between the Council and our present state, and yet we might all some day gather the ashes and hurl the invaders from our lands. Ours is the Faith, the Vision and the Secret. To those who would befriend us, we are the breeze, the oasis, the clasping hand. To those who cross our sword, we are the assassin's whisper and the midnight sandstorm. By Allah's will and Khwaja al-Akbar's wisdom, we shall prevail!"

Stereotypes

- Virtual Adepts: "They have usurped our position in the Council of Nine, but lack our spiritual understanding and are dependent upon their Technomantic crutches."
- Euthanatos: "Never Forgive. Never Forget."
- Celestial Chorus, Order of Hermes and Cult of Ecstasy: "Though we consider these great Traditions to be our closest allies, it is well to disappear when their old feuds flare up."
- Akashic Brotherhood: "We share a great deal, but we could never afford to take their path of spiritual retreat."
- Other Traditions: "We must all focus upon our similarities rather than our differences."
- Technocracy: No comment (see Euthanatos)
- Marauders: "Driven out, they cannot threaten us so long as the Web is preserved."
- Nephandi: "Our intimate knowledge of the Unity renders us immune to the corruption offered by the Nephandi, and the labyrinths we have made of our lands now rival their own. Their dark secrets are of old account with us, and the only threat they represent is to the young and uninitiated."
- Orphans: "Once we prided ourselves on the rarity of Orphans in our lands, but now circumstances have forced us to make Orphans of our own Initiates, many of whom no longer recognize their old mentors. Therefore do as the prophets have exhorted, and treat all Orphans with generosity and compassion."

Book Three: The Book of Rules

Better the illusions that exalt us than ten thousand truths.
— Aleksander Pushkin

The Book of Rules offers classifications, alternatives and revisions, including new mechanics for Do, familiars and more. Part One: Magick covers the myriad aspects of magick and updates some rules from the **Mage** rulebook. Part Two: New Rules provides plenty of new stuff to use.

Some games rely solely on rules to make them work; **Mage** and other Storyteller games rely upon the stories and the players, Storytellers and characters who collectively tell them. These rules are meant to be fluid, not rigid. The topics covered include:

• **Simplifying and Clarifying the Magick Rules:** Suggestions and modifications for **Mage** magick.

• **Adjustments:** Rule revisions for foci, Talismans, study points and direct attacks, plus new rules for countermagick and combining Abilities and magick.

• **Explanations:** Sections detailing resonance, Quintessence, Paradox, and the Umbra, plus suggestions for personalizing magick and detailing the dangers of Sleepers and the vampiric Embrace.

• **The Umbra:** Details about the worlds of the spirit.

Part One: Magic

Listen to the MUSTN'TS, child
Listen to the DON'TS
Listen to the SHOULDN'TS
The IMPOSSIBLES, the WON'TS
Listen to the NEVER HAVES
Then listen close to me—
Anything can happen, child,
ANYTHING can be.
— Shel Silverstein

Magick lies at the heart of **Mage: The Ascension**. From the moment of the Awakening, a mage cannot shut off the gifts of his Avatar or stop them from taking their toll on his life. Coping with the liberation and burdens of magick makes the Storytelling experience of **Mage: The Ascension** emotionally moving and thought-provoking. However, while magick serves as the crux for the special problems of a mage's life, the systems should not hinder roleplaying. Just as the Sleepers maintain the consensual paradigm of reality, each troupe creates its own interpretation of the metaphysics of magick for their stories.

Simplifying and Clarifying the Magick Rules

The more you tighten your grip, the more star systems will slip through your fingers.
— Princess Leia, *Star Wars*

The **Mage** system confuses some players and Storytellers. Because of its flexibility and broad scope, it can be difficult to know what limits a mage possesses. The paradox (so to speak) of **Mage**'s game mechanics is this: although the rules should be loose, to avoid interfering in the flow of the story, the rules are so loose that the story sometimes bogs down while the Storyteller and players try to sort everything out. A few loopholes in the **Mage** rulebook muddy the waters further. This section presents a stripped-down look at the magick system, clarifies some nagging questions about Quintessence, Paradox, countermagick and foci, and presents new rules for Talismans and study points, for both players and Storytellers.

These modifications are optional; not all of them will apply to your chronicle. Remember that the *story* is first and foremost. Attempting to create a rule for every possibility would be an infinite and pointless exercise. Let evoking drama, tempered by maintaining consistency and using judgment, take the place of crunching numbers and consulting charts.

Drama and Balance

Mentor: Reach out with your inner being, with all the skill and wisdom you possess. Feel the pull of reality's undertow, guide its course, and shape it as you will. There is no rigid form

to this, no single way. Your own sense and imagination must pave the road to magick.

Apprentice: How?

Mentor: Wing it.

Apprentice: But HOW?

The greatest strength of using magick in **Mage** is flexibility. The Awakened transcend ordered spells, fluidly bending the laws of reality to their whims. Magick is not an exact science, much as the Technocracy might like to make it so. A mage does not have to spend her free time memorizing incantations and glyphs— she has the freedom to chose her own path to enlightenment. Indeed, the road to Ascension twists and turns differently for each individual. The rotes created by the Traditions serve as guidelines and teaching aids for Chantries. They do not limit magick use in practice to a few set spells.

With the proper conjunction of Spheres, enough Quintessence, and a high Arete score, a creative player character may manipulate reality to invoke nearly any effect he desires. Only Paradox limits his possibilities.

Magickal knowledge lives and grows as the human consciousness expands. Even the Technocracy has not stagnated the universe— the gates of scientific possibilities remain open thanks to the Sons of Ether and the Virtual Adepts. Young mages continually discover new ways to mold the Effects of the Spheres.

There are a few dangers inherent in this loose system. First, **Mage** has the potential to become a high-powered judgment. If your group wants to play **Mage** that way, fine. Enjoy. However, deeper issues will become more difficult to explore if mages never have to deal with the consequences of their actions.

Most players want something deeper: a more moving, intense emotional and intellectual odyssey, the chance to create a modern myth. In order to do this, a Storyteller should introduce magick slowly. Characters have to learn how to use the gifts they've received. Just because a character has the possibility of doing something doesn't mean he can. It's easier for Storytellers to limit power initially and gradually increase it than it is to reduce the effects of Spheres after player characters have started relying on their abilities. Likewise, it is easier for players to appreciate magick's possibilities when they have explored them from the basics onward. Remember the lesson of the sorcerer's apprentice! Uncontrolled power leads to oblivion.

Magick Made Simple

Don't Panic!
— Douglas Adams, *The Hitchhiker's Guide to the Galaxy*

It's easy to get flustered when faced with free-form game magick. At its heart, however, the **Mage** magick system boils down to four simple questions:

• What do you want to do, and how do you want to do it?
• Do you know enough to pull it off?
• Do you succeed?
• If so, or if not, what happens?

This is the system at its core. All the rest is window dressing. Don't let rules-hedging get in the way of a good story.

Success and Effect

The following chart may be used either in conjunction with or in favor of the charts in Chapter Seven of **Mage: The Ascension** for determining the effectiveness of magick. This chart is more simplistic than the others, and may speed play. If you're using the tables in the **Mage** rulebook, apply damage, range or duration normally based on the tables for the different Spheres. Unless there's a specific chart based on the Sphere, use the general tables on pg. 175. If those charts are too complex for you, simply use the General Magickal Results table. (The table is not exactly like the ones on pg. 175, but as long as the Storyteller is consistent, the story will be consistent.)

Magick by Numbers

1. The player describes the effect she desires and the Spheres she is using. The effect of the magic includes how the magick will appear in static reality if the magick is coincidental.

2. The Storyteller determines the difficulty and number of successes needed. Standard difficulty is the highest Sphere used +3, but this might vary according to the situation if the Storyteller desires. If the Storyteller feels that the mage's Spheres aren't up to the task, then he increases the difficulty to whatever is appropriate and raises the number of successes needed. The Storyteller then announces the difficulty.

3. The player declares Willpower and Quintessence expenditures and then rolls. In the case of vulgar magicks, the player rolls a number of dice less than or equal to the highest Sphere he is using. For static magicks, the player may roll a number of dice less than or equal to his Arete score.

4. The Storyteller determines the results, including Paradox) in an exciting way. If the character uses vulgar magick in front of a Sleeper and succeeds, he still gains one point of Paradox. If the character uses vulgar magick *without* a Sleeper present and botches, he gets one point of Paradox for each die rolled for the magick; if the character uses vulgar magick and botches *with* a Sleeper present, he gains two points for each die and must check for Paradox Backlash. When botching with coincidental magick, the character gains a point of Paradox automatically and one point for every "1" rolled.

General Magickal Results

Successes	Result
1	The magick barely works, achieving the minimum effect necessary for temporary success (Damage: None. Range: Touch. Duration: One turn)
2	The mage succeeds, but not as well as she would like. (Damage: Successes x 1. Range: One close target. Duration: One scene)
3	The basic result the mage desires occurs. (Damage: Successes x 2. Range: Immediate vicinity. Duration: One day)
4	The mage's magick has an added benefit; perhaps it works more effectively than she envisioned. (Damage: Successes x 2. Range: Line of sight. Duration: One story)
5	An extraordinary success results, working as well as the mage would have dreamed. Several beneficial side effects may occur. (Damage: Successes x3 or 4. Range: Anything within sensory range. Duration: Permanent)
6+	The mage amazes herself and others with an incredible display of magickal forces. She may even incidentally gain a point of Quintessence. (Damage: Success x 4. Range and Duration: As above)

A Man in Black faces Trevor, a member of the Order of Hermes. Trevor announces to the Storyteller that he will use his Forces 3 to fire a lightning bolt from his fingertips into the Technomancer. The Storyteller announces a difficulty of 7, raised from 6 because of the general stress of the situation.

Trevor spends a point of Willpower and a point of Quintessence. He now has one success and has a 6 as his target number for the rest. He rolls three dice because of his Forces 3 rank. The dice come up 7, 4 and 10. Two successes!! With his Willpower, he achieved a total of three successes. The General Magickal Results Chart defines this as six potential damage levels to the Man in Black.

The Storyteller describes the blue bolt of electricity as it cracks from Trevor's fingertips. It strikes the Man in Black. He makes a soak roll, but the Storyteller decides to make a second Stamina roll for the Man in Black to see if he is stunned by the sudden jolt. If the Man in Black was standing in pool of water, the bolt might have done an extra two damage levels.

Trevor gets an automatic point of Paradox for using vulgar magick, but doesn't much care, and he flees into the darkened streets.

Failure

AAAAUUUGGH!!!

— Charlie Brown

When a mage fails her roll, nothing occurs. If she botches that roll, she incurs Paradox. Rolling for Paradox Backlash every time a player botches, however, can slow things down. As a general rule of thumb, troupes may assume that Paradox will not kick in unless the mage in question has more than five points of Paradox before she botches, or earns more than five points in a single botch. The metaphysical waters of reality are rippled, but are not disturbed enough to crash suddenly back upon the mage. Apply whatever Paradox the mage accumulates to her usual total. After she exceeds five points of Paradox, things start to get hairy. This provides a beginning mage an incentive to keep her nose clean.

An exceptional amount of coincidental magick used in a short period of time, however, could stir up a larger Paradox Backlash than any single Effect could (see The Domino Effect, below). This backlash might well affect everyone in the area, not just the poor mage responsible.

Difficulty

The base difficulty of a magickal Effect is that Effect's highest Sphere + 3. Not all manipulations of reality, however, are created equal. A mage who walks into a bar, spies an attractive Sleeper and decides to seduce him using Mind coincidentally, and a mage who clips a piece of his target's hair, waits until the stars are aligned and performs

a ritual using his focus shouldn't have an equal chance of success. A player character may perform magick without putting a lot of effort into the process, but a player who roleplays her magick use, adding to the atmosphere of the story, deserves a reward.

The difficulty adjustments for magick below reflect this, but no set of rules works as well as a good Storyteller. For game balance, we recommend that these modifiers not reduce difficulties by more than 3. (In addition, it's pointless to reduce a difficulty below 2.) As always, these are guidelines, nothing more. The important thing to remember is not to let game mechanics limit characters. Good roleplaying, the type that evokes the imagination of the entire troupe, should be rewarded for the real magick that it is.

Circumstance	Modifier
Uses focus without needing it	-1
Descriptive roleplaying of magick use	-1
Researches lore on subject before using magick	-1 to -3
Has item resonating with target's essence (sympathetic magick)	-1 to -3
Extra time spent on magick	-1
Mage distracted	+1 to +3
Spending a point of Quintessence	-1
Using Tass with appropriate Resonance	-1
Using Tass with opposed Resonance	+1

The Domino Effect

Q: When is a coincidental effect not coincidental?

A: After too many other mages have used static magick.

After the first use of static magick in an area, progressive use of static magick becomes more difficult. While causing a tire on a car to deflate lies within the bounds of possibility, causing the tires of every car that passes to go flat, having a sudden rainstorm start, an earth tremor occur, and a helicopter carrying Delta Force members make an emergency landing in the same intersection within five minutes causes reality to undulate. One extreme coincidence is one thing; weird occurrences after the first become much less plausible. This is the Domino Effect. Some coincidental effects are more probable than others. Opening a newspaper to a certain story, finding extra pocket change and having a taxi pull up just as a mage needs one may not trigger the Domino Effect.

As a general rule, every other use of improbable coincidental magick in a scene after the first increases in difficulty by 1. This effect is cumulative, so the base target number for the fifth static magickal effect rises by 2. Additionally, a Paradox Backlash, when it comes, can take some harsh all-encompassing form: a sudden rip in the

Gauntlet, a massive localized blackout, an invasion of pissed-off Paradox Spirits, etc. As always, the Backlash should advance the story, not clog the game while the Storyteller rolls dice or scans charts.

If you need more particular details for Paradox Backlash, then use this guideline: Paradox Backlash incurred during combat can cause one aggravated wound level per point of backlash; backlash brought about by indiscreet magick might summon a Paradox Spirit with a number of levels equal to the number of points of backlash; magick that grossly violates reality may shunt an offending mage into another Realm if enough successes are obtained on a Paradox Backlash roll. Let the story be your guide.

The Domino Effect is optional, and Storytellers can invoke it to keep magick from getting out of control.

Damage

There are two distinct types of damage in **Mage**: aggravated and non-aggravated (see **Mage: The Ascension**, Chapter 8, pg. 248). Most forms of magickal attack do regular (non-aggravated) damage, but there are exceptions. Some supernatural creatures, such as werewolves and vampires, take aggravated damage from attacks such as silver or fire in addition to the types below.

Aggravated damage for mages occurs from:

• A direct vulgar blast of Prime, or damage done from vulgar Life magicks. (Because vulgar Life magicks directly wound a target's inner life-force, they cannot be healed through normal means; hence, they are aggravated wounds.)

• Magicks, such as Forces, augmented with Prime (including weapon Talismans that utilize Prime in their damage). This does not include Forces, Life or Matter *created* with Prime, only attacks utilizing Prime to "energize" damage. (For example, Spawning Minor Forces does not incur aggravated damage, while the **Talons** rote in Book Four, which uses a point of Quintessence each time it hits, does).

• The natural weaponry of supernatural creatures.

• Spirit magicks that summon spirits to directly attack a target.

• Direct Entropic attacks on a physical body (see the **Bone Twisting Palm** rote).

In all other cases, damage is non-aggravated. Magick may heal the damage normally. As a special note, Mind magicks never do aggravated damage.

One clarification about damage and casting magick should also be made here: a character who is injured does have his Dice Pools for Attribute + Ability rolls reduced because of injuries (see pp. 160-161 of **Mage**). However, Health Level penalties should not subtract from rolls for casting magick (such as rolls against Arete). Using Arete is a state of mind, not of the body; having a broken leg or fractured rib will not prevent you from drawing upon your understanding of the Spheres.

Perception Magick and Awareness

Perception Magick, the first rank of any Sphere, allows a mage's senses to increase, not just for a moment, but for a length of time. Use the table in **Mage: The Ascension** (Chapter 7, pg. 175) for suggested durations based on successes (ignoring "Permanent"; Life magick is necessary to affect long-term bodily changes). During the duration of the effect, the extra-sensory abilities come as naturally to the mage as his regular perceptions.

The Awareness Talent enables a person to feel the magick in an area. A person with Awareness can sense the Awakened Avatar in a nearby mage or other supernatural being and may discern the differences of magick Sphere ratings of other Realms. Awareness also lets a character sense whenever magick is used in her vicinity. Depending on the number of successes, he may just feel bothered (1 success) or suddenly realize the truth about the mage (5 successes). At a Storyteller's discretion, Awareness can work almost like a danger sense. Animals and children have higher Awareness ratings than most adults.

Adjustments

At any time in the past, people have held a view of the way the universe works which was for them similarly definitive, whether it was based on myths or research. And at any time, that view they held was sooner or later altered by changes in the body of knowledge.

— James Burke, *The Day the Universe Changed*

Nothing is perfect. The following rules have been modified from the **Mage** rulebook for clarity, variety and game balance. If your troupe prefers the original rules, by all means use them. If the rules below make your game easier, feel free to use them instead. Again, as long as the Storyteller is consistent, the story will be consistent.

Foci

A focus is an object which helps a mage tap her Avatar's power. Foci make the process of magick easier, giving a mage an anchor when her thoughts stretch beyond reality. The relation of the mage to her focus is like the relationship of a subject under hypnosis to the gold watch spinning in front of her. The object helps a mage alter her state of consciousness. Once a mage completely accepts the metaphysic of magick, she no longer needs the focus.

Technological foci have a different use. In this modern age, people are willing to accept incredible events as long as they believe there is a scientific explanation. The Technocracy suffers less from Paradox, because in the case of their magicks, seeing is believing. Sleepers do not react to high-tech scanners or cybernetics with the same disbelief they would harbor while witnessing a Verbena use blood magick.

A creative cabal of Tradition mages in Los Angeles has learned from the Technocracy's example. Although none of the cabal's members are Technomancers, most Sleepers ignore their magicks. The reason: they always travel with a group of Acolytes, who set up video equipment and lighting and carry signs saying "Filming in Progress." Sleepers find the cabal's impressive special effects within the realm of reason.

Unique Foci vs. Universal Foci

As a general rule, unique foci work better than universal foci. Because the mage has invested so much of himself into the unique focus, difficulties for his magick are lowered by 1 (or more at the Storyteller's discretion). The disadvantage of a unique focus is not being able to perform magick if you lose the item (see **Mage: The Ascension**, Chapter 7, pg. 179).

Acquiring or Replacing Foci

One idea for a prelude would be to have the character's mentor take her on a quest for her foci. A Dreamspeaker might have to climb a mesa to reach an eagle's nest for a feather to use his spirit magick. Just because a focus is universal does not mean that it is easy to replace. Unique foci can never be truly replaced. Instead, the mage must relearn what she had learned (**Mage: The Ascension**, Chapter 7, pg. 179).

Quality of Foci

Some foci are better than others and enable a mage to cast magicks more effectively, lowering difficulty numbers. An Order of Hermes mage would no doubt discover that a circle laid out in silver with numerous intricate magickal symbols worked into it would work better than a circle drawn with a piece of chalk on the asphalt of an unused parking lot. Also, a Dreamspeaker using the feather of a pigeon he found in Central Park would have greater difficulty dealing with most spiritual magic than a Dreamspeaker who scaled a cliff to steal an eagle's feather.

Unnecessary Foci

A focus is an aid to a mage. If a mage decides to take a focus after his level of mastery has passed the point where he needs the focus for the magick, the Storyteller may still modify difficulty numbers to make his magick flow easier.

Types of Foci

Each Tradition teaches its Apprentices different Foci for each of the Spheres. However, within the Traditions, there are many variations on the acceptable types of foci. Some of these are spelled out in **Mage: The Ascension** (pp. 178-180, Chapter 7). Others are left to the troupe's discretion.

Foci need not be physical objects: song, dance, rune-carving and trance states may focus a mage's will as well. Alternative foci should be discussed beforehand— why does a certain focus work? Use this concept for flavor, not for rules-abuse. The key to judging a variant's suitability depends upon whether it has the same significance that makes the standard focus special. Flavor: Personalizing Magick (pg. 114) may inspire alternative foci for players.

Technomagick

Technomancer is the proper term for mages who focus their magick through some technological paradigm; that is, they believe that their science allows them to do magick. Although the term is commonly applied to Technocracy mages, it includes the Sons of Ether and Virtual Adepts. While the Order of Hermes has made a kind of science of their magick, it is a mystic science, not a technological one.

The upside of this mystic technology is Sleeper belief; the man on the street will sooner accept weird science than arcane miracles. Many technomagickal effects can be considered somewhat coincidental (within reason). The downside is an over-reliance on foci; without some kind of technology, many Technomancers cannot believe in their own magick. And without some kind of "scientific" theory to explain their actions, Technomancers risk greater Paradox (or outright failure) than their mystic counterparts. The Technocracy has "set" reality, but they do not own it. Depending on the Technomancer, magick attempted without a focus could either function as "vulgar magick with witness" (the skeptical mage himself!) or fail completely.

Through their contact with other magick theories, enlightened Sons of Ether and Virtual Adepts can eventually transcend the need for any type of focus, unlike Technocracy mages. However, Tradition Technomancers must reach a higher level of Arete (five, not two) before dispensing with any foci.

Tradition Foci

The standard foci for the Traditions are discussed below:

The Akashic Brotherhood

Do is the archetypal philosophy behind a number of martial arts styles in the World of Darkness. Some Storytellers may require an Akashic Brother to have an ability score in Do or Meditation equal to the Sphere level he wishes to access. For example, to use Mind 2, a member of

the Akashic Brotherhood must have Meditation 2. Do cannot be removed.

There are many rites of purification in the mystic world. They range from bathing in holy water to dressing in white linen or being anointed with drops of oil. The Storyteller and player should define the type of Purification an individual Akashic Brother must undergo. The ritual should be of moderate difficulty and require time or a special substance.

Each member of the Akashic Brotherhood has an individual sash which represents his knowledge of magick. Like belts in martial art schools, the sashes change in color and decoration as the mage increases in prestige and accomplishment. Storytellers may wish to reward players who describe their character's sashes. Belts, headbands or special robes are variants.

The weapon chosen by a member of the Akashic Brotherhood becomes an extension of herself. Most mages of this Tradition choose a staff, a remarkably simple, but very dangerous weapon. The many different styles and schools of the Akashic Brotherhood all choose different martial arts weapons. Instead of requiring a unique weapon for a member of the Brotherhood, a Storyteller could require a Melee skill equal to the rank of the Sphere to access the magick when using the chosen weapon type.

Celestial Chorus

Fire represents the sun, the original home of the One. Fire drives away the creatures of the night. For some factions of the Celestial Chorus, the light holds more meaning than the flame. Some groups use a lantern as a focus, trusting the light from the One to guide them. Fire is an incredibly ancient religious symbol, and the Chorus tends many eternal flames. Using an eternal flame as a focus reduces magick difficulties by a minimum of 2. If the flame dies out, the mage has no focus.

Depending on their backgrounds, each member of the Celestial Chorus has her own Holy Symbol. Different groups use the Star of David (causing confusion with members of the Order of Hermes), the Cross, the Ankh, the Crescent Moon and other symbols. Each of these has some religious significance in human history. A holy symbol is a unique focus.

Like the Akashic Brotherhood, the Celestial Chorus believes in cleansing. Pure water or holy water washes the impurities of evil from a site. They use this focus to bring luck and protection from decay. The water is usually sprinkled over the target of the magick. There are few substitutes for pure water, although some ancient groups used natural oils for cleansing.

Songs range from Gregorian chants to spontaneous poetry, depending on the philosophy of the mage. A song calls upon the power of the One to aid the Chorus member. A Storyteller may require a Chorus member to have an Expression Ability equal to the rank of the Sphere she wants to use.

Physical touch provides a connection between the mage and the subject of her magick. In rare cases, factions of the Celestial Chorus use touch as a focus for Life magick instead of song, "laying on their hands" to perform healing magicks. There are no substitutes for touch.

Cult of Ecstasy

Incense allows a Cult of Ecstasy member to alter her consciousness. Smell is the most powerful of the five senses, and the most memorable. Any breathable substance that can help an mage disconnect with the reality around him may work as a focus instead of incense.

Music, like incense, shifts a mage's perceptions of reality and shapes emotions. Any type of music may have this power, from classical to heavy metal. Most Cult of Ecstasy members use instruments to create music, but some have trained their voices. As in the case of the Celestial Chorus, an Expression score equal to the rank of the Sphere invoked may be required.

Every member of the Cult has a ring or piece of jewelry which represents the world. All rings are unique. Variants include necklaces, chains, bracelets and anklets. Cult members rarely remove this type of focus, except to adorn it.

"Vices" already vary from individual to individual. These odd foci provide a means to transcendence to the Cultist, but may raise eyebrows among his companions.

Dreamspeakers

The Dreamspeakers believe that the energy of Gaia collects in natural crystals. Uncut gemstones and other minerals hold special meanings for some groups of Dreamspeakers. Younger Dreamspeakers sometimes place their crystals or other stones in jewelry, but most carry a leather pouch filled with loose stones. Variants include bones, ashes, runes or sticks.

Music is a common focus for Spirit magick; drums are merely the most common type of instrument used. Depending on the chronicle, a mage's Expression rating may limit her ability to invoke Spheres with this focus, as in the case of the Celestial Chorus and Cult of Ecstasy.

Each Dreamspeaker gathers his own set of feathers to use for his magicks. Masters of Spirit travel deep into the realms of the Umbra, such as Pangaea (see **Umbra: The Velvet Shadow** for **Werewolf: The Apocalypse**) to collect feathers from powerful spirits.

Euthanatos

Bones represent the death that comes for each living creature. The remains of the dead contain a strange dark energy which the Euthanatos tap to help them focus their magicks. Other types of remains will work. The corpses of the recently dead and the ancient dead have tremendous power as foci, but tales abound of powerful ghosts appearing to protect fallen bodies.

The dances of the Euthanatos come from prehistoric funeral dances practiced by many early cultures. Some of these dances are the same ones used by ancient shamans to enter the Umbra to negotiate the fate of dead tribe members with spirits. Ritualized physical exertion with a symbolic death activates the magick. Some Euthanatos practice self-wounding instead of performing dances. After a point, the pain passes and the mage may use his Sphere. In some cases, the Storyteller may call for an Expression roll or a Stamina roll. A few Dreamspeakers claim that Euthanatos do not pass the Velvet Curtain, but instead use Spirit to follow the paths of the dead.

The essential purpose of dolls as a focus for a Euthanatos is to serve as a proxy for the target. Some mages use photographs or paintings of their victims as variant foci, burning or cutting them to invoke the desired magickal effect (sympathetic magick). To improve the quality of a doll, a mage may fill it with things associated with the target: hair, fingernail clippings, personal mementos, etc.

Rattles imitate the death choke of a final breath. Any soft noisemaker serves the purpose of a Euthanatos. Certain types of dark music work as well for foci. Some Euthanatos sing a soft lullaby or piece of poetry before giving the Good Death.

The weapon chosen by an apprentice of the Euthanatos is not a unique focus. Most Euthanatos have collections of weapons for magickal and mundane purposes. Personal preference and philosophies about killing help the mage choose a favored weapon.

Order of Hermes

In addition to the circle focus, mages may use other patterns, including inscribing a Seal of Solomon for their magicks. If a mage cannot spend the two hours needed to properly inscribe a circle, they may create a circle faster, but should suffer a major penalty to their difficulty numbers (increase by 3 or more).

The Order of Hermes maintains that words carry power, and language became the Order's major focus. The secret language of the Order has elements of the entire Indo-European family and Semitic tongues. Members of the Order still discover magick in patterns of letters, syllables and words. A mage using this focus should have a score in Linguistics equal to the rank of the Sphere she wishes to use.

The Seal of Solomon gave a wise king power over the spirit world. This symbol, also known as the Star of David, was changed to a pentagram by Christian mystics. Like most things in the Order of Hermes, different groups argue constantly over this focus. One side argues that the true symbol is the Star of David. Their opposition states that the pentagram has more traditional use and doesn't cause mages to be confused with the Israeli government. Whole Chantries have disavowed either symbol and use other ancient signs of protection, including the spiral, the triangle and the circle. Players may chose any favored mystic symbol as a focus, but they should remember that their fellow Tradition members will judge them by their choice.

Each member of the Order has a unique focus, usually a Showstone. The Showstones are gems, sometimes mounted in jewelry. As an option, other members of the Order just wear unique pieces of jewelry, such as signet rings or amulets.

Sons of Ether

A former Technomancer Convention, the Sons of Ether, still requires foci to use magick. After the Arete of a Son of Ether increases sufficiently, he no longer requires a specific focus to work magic. However, the Sons of Ether rarely escape foci completely, so they often carry around bags of odds and ends or wear lab coats with pockets filled with various tools and inventions.

The Sons of Ether avoid becoming trapped in systems of mathematics by not trusting completely in machines. Many of the Sons carry around an abacus to perform important calculations quickly. For a Son of Ether, the important part of the magick is to work the math by hand. Some modern Sons of Ether just carry mechanical pencils and memo pads instead of a portable abacus. Other Sons say pencil calculations are too imprecise. The paper mages claim that mistakes lead to the greatest discoveries.

Electricity provides the power for most experiments performed by the Sons of Ether. A few have turned to other sources, such as solar power, wind power or (be afraid!) nuclear energy. However, these are extremely rare. Admittedly, Sons of Ether are as likely to gather electricity from thunderstorms as wall sockets, but they all use electricity.

The Ether Goggles are the signature focus of the members of this tradition. Unfortunately for the Sons of Ether, there are no good variants for the goggles. Ether must cover the face of the mage. Some Sons use entire helmets filled with Ether, but this focus is easily one of the most recognizable in all the Traditions.

Any type of scientific meter will work for a Son of Ether, as long as it can measure some sort of environmental phenomena. Geiger counters, voltmeters, pH kits— these devices function to let the Sons of Ether collect enough information to use magick.

Verbena

Followers of the Verbena Tradition, some of the oldest practitioners of magick in the world, offer few options to their disciples for different foci. The ways of the Verbena have survived with little change from ancient times.

Blood contains the essence of life to the Verbena, and the blood of all beings has power. A Verbena mage may get blood from any source, although fresh warm blood has the greatest potency. Older sources of blood cause the mage to have difficulty using her magick (penalties of 1 to 5). Processed blood, such as that frozen in blood banks, is useless to the Verbena.

The Cauldron, one of the few Verbena foci that has variants, may be replaced by any large container where fluids may be mixed. A few Verbena try to get along by carrying small bowls (magick difficulties increase by 3).

However, even the best substitutes do not work as well as the cauldron (+1 difficulty).

Natural herbs are cannot be replaced as foci for Verbena magick. Artificial or chemical substitutes do not have the Quintessence needed.

The wand of a Verbena must be natural wood. Different Verbena may decorate or inscribe their wands. Some wands could even pass as slight walking sticks.

The weapon of the Verbena is always a dagger. These blades may be individualized with runes, but no other weapon can substitute for them.

Virtual Adepts

The Virtual Adepts need foci to perform all their magick, like their fellow Technomancer Tradition, the Sons of Ether. For most Virtual Adepts, this means their personal computer or laptop. The Adepts use a variety of peripherals and types of machine, but in the end, nothing replaces a computer, a network to connect it, and the electricity to power the whole setup.

Talismans

Even in Magick, we cannot get on without the help of others.

— Aleister Crowley, *Magick in Theory and Practice*

A mage who creates a Talisman leaves an enduring legacy. Often, the possession of one of these items can mean the difference between victory and defeat in the Ascension War. Talismans are the weapons of the Awakened. A few mistakenly believe that even the unawakened may use a Talisman, drawing on the item's Quintessence, but such accounts speak of artifacts, legendary objects more powerful than the greatest Talismans.

Any Talisman has an Arete rating and a Quintessence rating. A Talisman may hold a maximum of five times its Arete score in Quintessence. Talismans may possess a number of magickal powers, similar to rotes, up to its Arete score. A mage rolls her Arete against the Talisman's Arete to activate the item's vulgar magicks or to tap its Quintessence supply. A mage may burn up to the Talisman's level in Quintessence from the item in a single turn. Some Talismans require extra actions or the use of command words to activate. Other Talismans require an Attribute + Ability roll to use successfully. Each success on the activation roll increases the length of time that the Talisman remains active (see chart below). Talismans have a Sphere

Talisman Activation Chart

Successes	Duration of Activation
1	One turn
2	Five minutes
3	One hour
4	One scene
5	One day

rank equal to their own level. The wielder suffers the side-effects of all Paradox the Talisman generates.

A mage who uses a Talisman as a focus for magick may draw on its Quintessence or replace his own Arete score or Sphere level with the rating of the item as long as the Talisman stays active.

If a Talisman loses all of its Quintessence, it becomes inert. An inert Talisman may not be activated. Unless the Talisman is destroyed, a new flow of Quintessence will restore its power. Even a single stored point of Quintessence keeps a Talisman from becoming inert.

Creating Talismans

Mages usually go to Horizon Realms to make Talismans so that they can avoid confronting Paradox. Talisman creation requires an extended use of Prime 4 and other magicks. Any Paradox generated during the process destroys the attempt to enchant the item, and any Quintessence spent by the mage is lost permanently.

First, the mage must create or locate an item suitable for enchantment. This can be nearly anything, except for an artifact or another Talisman. Once an item is empowered, little can change its nature. The mage then takes the Talisman-to-be to her Chantry's Horizon Realm.

She starts the process by using Prime 4 to infuse the Talisman with a bit of herself. This is a vulgar magick (without witness) roll. She may reduce her difficulty number by 1 for each special circumstance she requires for activation, such as a gesture, command word or Attribute + Ability roll. She spends a permanent point of Willpower invoking this effect. Then, for every point of Arete she wishes the Talisman to contain, she must channel 10 Quintessence into the item using her Prime. The Arete possessed by the Talisman cannot exceed the mage's Arete.

The mage must then use her Spheres to create the magickal Effects that she wants the Talisman to perform. For every dot of a Sphere needed for the magickal Effect, she spends a point of Quintessence and rolls her Arete verses a difficulty of 8. If she succeeds, the Talisman gains the power. If she fails, she loses the Quintessence, but may try again. A botch means she loses her concentration on the enchantment, and nothing but Quintessence may be transferred to the Talisman. A Talisman may hold a number of magickal Effects equal to its Arete score. The mage then channels more Quintessence into the Talisman, up to five times its Arete score.

The creation process requires massive amounts of Quintessence, but the mage may take as much time as she needs, as long as the process isn't interrupted. Sleeping during Talisman creation is impossible, but the mage may renew herself during the effort by making Stamina + Meditation rolls. Anything that interrupts the enchantment process ruins the Talisman creation, leaving it complete only up to a point. Any Paradox gained during the creation destroys the Talisman completely.

Fetishes

Spirit Adepts may bind spirits into fetishes. These primal magick treasures resemble Talismans, but derive their power from spirits rather than channeled Quintessence. Most fetishes have one power; few have more than three, and these involve potent spirit-bindings. A fetish is not an inanimate object— its magick flows from a spirit. Fetishes, therefore, are picky, and may cause more problems than they're worth…

Fetish creation works like Talisman creation, with the following differences:

• The mage need not travel to a Horizon Realm to create one.

• Spirit 4 is used instead of Prime 4.

• Fetishes have one Effect for every *two* points of Arete.

• The mage need not transfer Quintessence into the fetish, although doing so may maintain a good relationship with the spirit.

• Botching does not result in Paradox; it results in a pissed-off spirit.

If you are using a fetish from the **Werewolf** rules, substitute Arete for Gnosis.

Talismans: New Background Rules

With these expanded Talisman rules, Storytellers should change the Talisman Background in **Mage: The Ascension**. A single Background point no longer buys one level of a Talisman. Background points must now be spent for the Arete, Quintessence and Effects possessed by a Talisman, as per the chart below. Continue to indicate the level of the Talisman by filling in the dots on the character sheet, but the player must record the other information as well. As an option, a player may give the Storyteller a number of background points to create a Talisman for her. This adds an element of mystery to the strange item that falls into the hands of the beginning mage.

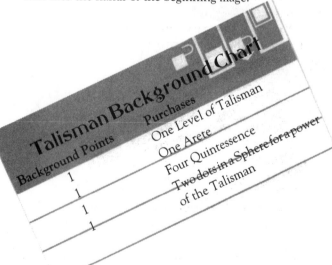

Talisman Background Chart	
Background Points	Purchases
1	One Level of Talisman
1	One Arete
1	Four Quintessence
1	Two dots in a Sphere for a power of the Talisman

The mundane uses of a Talisman and any special activation requirements are left to the discretion of the player and Storyteller. A gun may seem more useful than a ring for a Talisman, but mundane authorities may confiscate the gun. Also, activation requirements may prevent others from stealing and using a Talisman, but they also make it more difficult for the owner to tap into the item's powers.

Direct Magick and Hitting Your Target

I don't care if he does look like Rambo in power-armor— he can't hurt what he can't hit!

— Job Lightfoot, Cult of Ecstasy

Opponents don't always stand still; the targets of direct magickal attacks should, therefore, have some chance to dodge incoming attacks. Direct attacks— lightning bolts, explosions, transformation spells, magick bullets, blasts of holy light— are often vulgar and usually visible. If an opponent can see or sense an incoming magickal Effect, she can elect to dodge that Effect as if it were some normal missile weapon, falling building, etc.

Mind attacks may be likewise "dodged" with a Willpower roll in place of the usual dodge if the subject is aware of the attack. The difficulty to resist is 6 (yes, this is a change from the rulebook); each success removes one of the mage's successes.

Physical dodges roll against difficulty of 6 and subtract successes as usual. The magick, therefore, can still have an effect, but it may be much less than what the caster intended. Some Effects may be dodged completely with a good roll, i.e. a falling boulder, an attacking spirit, etc. Willpower cannot be used to actively "disbelieve" physical attacks.

Any attack that does physical damage can be soaked. Attacks that do *direct* mental damage cannot be soaked.

This set of rules makes aggressive magick more challenging for the caster and less lethal for the recipient. Mages fighting a HIT Mark with a Force cannon now have options other than countermagick. Likewise, a mage attempting to turn a vampire into a lawn chair would be better off trying some other tactic…

Countermagick

There are many ways to combat another mage's mystical abilities besides basic countermagick (**Mage**, pg. 177-178). A mage does *not* need to know the Sphere her attacker is using in order to attempt countermagick. Prudent use of almost any Sphere may disrupt a magickal attack. Difficulties for countermagick are based on the highest attacking Sphere + 3. Countermagicks, remember, disrupt incoming magicks; they do not damage their targets.

The suggestions below offer some creative possibilities for countermagick:

Correspondence

By altering another person's perceptions of space, a mage can prevent her opponent from using her magick accurately. Any of the Awakened with Rank 3 in Correspondence may stack scenes in the mind of an opponent, causing him to lose his ability to perceive his enemies.

Entropy

A mage with the ability to alter probabilities has many ways to affect a rival. Using Entropy 2, a mage may increase the difficulty of any coincidental magicks tried by his opponent, raising them by 1 for every success rolled. Directly attacking an enemy with Entropy, especially rank 4 or 5, may completely disrupt magicks, but a Storyteller must judge this on a case by case basis.

Forces

Forces are not subtle. To stop other mages, blast them before they blast you.

Life

Mages are only human. Like all other living things, a Master of Life can mold and shape them, causing nerves to misfire and blood clots to block arteries. Rank 3 in the Life Sphere should prove sufficient to distract most targets.

Matter

As with Forces Effects, attack first.

Mind

The secret to stopping magicks is to keep another mage from concentrating. With Mind 3, a mage can effectively cloud another's perceptions long enough to ruin magick use. A strong subconscious suggestion from Mind 2 may also work, depending on the circumstances.

Prime

The Sphere of Prime has a special use in battles between mages. See Anti-Magick, listed below.

Spirit

If a mage can cause her opponent to perceive events in the Umbra and the physical world, she may disrupt their magick use. Three dots are needed in Spirit magick, with at least that many successes on the magick role. Some powerful Umbrood, such as Incarna, have the ability to counter some magicks in their Realms.

Time

As with Mind and Correspondence, causing a mage's perceptions of the timestream to alter can disrupt magick. Rank 3 of Time may stop most Effects.

Anti-Magick

A mage with Prime 2 or greater may use his stored Quintessence to defeat another mage's magicks. This is a special defensive magick that requires an entire action. It never generates Paradox, since the mage tries to *stop* the disruption of reality. The defending mage rolls a number of dice equal to her Prime rating against a difficulty of her opponent's dice pool +3 (maximum of 10). Quintessence may not lower the difficulty number of this special Prime magick. Each success allows the defending mage to spend a point of Quintessence to raise her opponent's target number by 1 (again, to a maximum of 10).

The defending mage does not have to spend as much Quintessence as she has successes. The attacking mage gets a chance to spend Quintessence and Willpower immediately afterwards. This Prime magick may counter a spell that is not directed at the defending mage.

Anti-Magick Disruption

Bethany, a member of the Cult of Ecstasy, sees a Technomancer preparing to incinerate a crowd of Sleepers with a plasma projector. She decides to use her Prime 3 to stop this magickal weapon. The Technomancer has a coincidental magick Dice Pool of 4, because the Sleepers consider his weapon "secret military technology." The Storyteller declares the difficulty to be a 6. Bethany acts to counter his magick and spends a point of Willpower. She rolls her Dice Pool of 3 for her Prime score. The results are 7, 9, and 10. She receives three successes, and the Willpower point makes her total 4. She spends 4 points of Quintessence, raising the Technomancer's difficulty from 6 to 10. The Technomancer spends a precious point of Quintessence to lower the difficulty back down to 9 and burns a Willpower point as well. He rolls, but only succeeds due to the extra success from his Willpower. Still, Bethany saved many Sleepers from instant incineration.

Abilities and Magick

Magick does not exist in a vacuum: magick is an extension of the mage. Therefore, it is only fair that certain Abilities of that mage should affect the magick that he or she works. The following rules are suggestions to add flavor to a **Mage** chronicle, not new ways to mini-max magick difficulties. The Storyteller will have the final say as to how (or if) a given Ability affects a character's magick, or if the rules are used at all.

We recommend that Abilities come into play when appropriate, that their effect be limited to +/- 3 on difficulty modifiers, and that the player give some reasonable and creative explanation for using the Ability. These optional rules should provide opportunities to spice up a story, not provoke 40-minute arguments.

Abilities Enhancing Magick

In some circumstances, mundane Abilities can improve a mage's chances of successful magick use. If a mage has a Talent, Skill or Knowledge that applies to the specific use of magick, he may use that Ability the turn before he uses his magick. The difficulty should be the same for both Ability and magick, notwithstanding any Quintessence spent for the magick. Each success that he makes on an appropriate Ability roll can reduce the magick difficulty by 1, up to a maximum modifier of -3. (Note: this should not be cumulative with other modifiers to the casting difficulty except for the expenditure of Quintessence.)

The Storyteller may rule that certain Abilities are essential to using an Effect; channeling Forces through a blast-cannon might require Firearms, while fixing a generator with Matter could require Technology Skill. Other beneficial effects, like an extra success on the magick for every two on the Ability roll, are also an option, depending on the situation and the whims of the Storyteller.

Magick Enhancing Abilities

A mage may use magick to improve her chances of success with her Abilities. As with the rule above, every success using magick drops the difficulty number for the Ability roll by 1, to a maximum modifier of -3. Entropy has numerous applications for enhancing Abilities.

Note that the magick must be cast in the turn before the Attribute + Ability roll is made. Casting the magick and rolling an Attribute + Ability must be done as two separate actions. The mage must concentrate and cast the Effect as his first action before channeling his magick into his second action. Splitting Dice Pools (which requires "fasting-casting") is possible, but is highly ineffective. Also note that one way to get in extra actions during a turn is by using the **Accelerate Time** Effect.

Examples

Enhancing Magick

Oh Soon Hai works much of her magick through ecstatic dance. While using a Life Effect to kill a worthless yuppie, she dances wildly, using her Expression 4. Her Effect is difficulty 7. Although she spends two Quintessence, her dance difficulty is still 7. She rolls two successes, bringing her magick difficulty to 4.

Gregor Shadowmoon, a haunted Euthanatos mage, tries to summon a demon from the netherworld. The Storyteller allows him to make an Intelligence + Occult roll before he calls for the fiend to arise. Deciding that this event has a high chance of causing Paradox, the Storyteller gives Gregor an extra magick success for every two successes on his Ability roll instead of cutting the difficulty numbers.

Enhancing Abilities

Kayla Dare's car breaks down on a country road located in the territory of a pack of werewolves. Before she even opens the hood, Kayla decides to make life a bit easier. Kayla uses her Matter 3 to make certain that nothing crucial is broken. She rolls her Arete of 5 as a Dice Pool because her kind Storyteller considers this use to be static magick. She gets 2 successes, then opens the hood. The Storyteller drops the difficulty of her Wits + Technology roll from 7 to 5. With 4 dots in Wits and 3 dots in Technology, she rolls 5 successes. She finds a loose wire and slips it back into place as a howl echoes from off in the distance.

Explanations

The following sections may shed some light on aspects of **Mage** that seem unclear. Some offer new possibilities, while others expand or illuminate old ideas. For further explorations of some concepts of the mage's existence, see Book Five: The Fragile Path.

Resonance

Verily all things move within your being in constant half embrace, the desired and the dreaded, the repugnant and the cherished, the pursued and that which you would escape. These things move within you as lights and shadows in pairs that cling.

— Kahlil Gibran, *The Prophet*

According to some mystic scholars, just as a mage shapes her magicks, the flow of Quintessence influences her. Mages first documented these effects in Horizon Realms, but a few scholars of the Order of Hermes claim that resonance is universal. They say that every magickal effect leaves a stain on reality.

All Apprentices learn that Masters of the Spheres receive certain benefits from their knowledge. A Master of Life, for instance, never gets sick and retains his youthful vitality long past his prime. These side benefits result from the resonance left by years of mastering a Sphere.

Furthermore, some mages claim that even psychic emanations left at Nodes are part of Resonance. When Sleepers experience intense emotion or trauma, they transmit their feelings to the area around them. The Euthanatos believe that vampires can see this emotional residue and that wraiths feed on it.

In the latest issue of *Paradigma*, the noted Son of Ether, Dr. Solaris, claimed to have distilled a dark resonance out of Tass collected from the Civil War battlefield of Antietam. This influence "lends itself to violent magickal effects," according to the article. Unfortunately, no further information on Dr. Solaris' experiments are forthcoming, because shortly after publication, unknown spirits of the dead attacked Dr. Solaris. His acolytes claim they dragged the doctor into an unknown part of the Umbra. Most mages say Dr. Solaris' experiment was a massive hoax.

The greatest supporters of the resonance theory, members of the Order of Hermes and Verbena, say that all mages have definitive proof that resonance exists. Quiet, they claim, is the residue of Paradox.

Quintessence

Few things are more important to mages than Quintessence. Chantries, cabals, even Traditions have fought wars over Nodes, the primary reservoirs of Prime. Inexperienced Apprentices often don't understand the importance of Quintessence because they don't know how to use this power effectively.

Even the most unenlightened learn that possession of Tass makes magick easier. A mage who focuses her supply of energy can warp static reality to her will. However, among the Orphans, many Apprentices regard Tass as a luxury, hardly a necessity. They say if a mage has the power, he doesn't need Quintessence.

The true value of primal energy lies not in creating magickal effects, but in sustaining them. Horizon Realms depend on Quintessence to maintain their reality. Creating Talismans requires large quantities of magickal energy. Anything with a supply of Quintessence flowing through it is metaphysically stronger than something without that energy. Quintessence Awakens objects and people.

Mages may also spend Quintessence to reduce the difficulty of their countermagick rolls. The mage burns energy to strengthen reality against her opponent.

Using Prime to Gain Quintessence

A mage with Prime 1 may magickally draw Quintessence directly from Nodes. This is a coincidental use of magick. For each success she obtains, she gains a point of Quintessence. This is cannot exceed the number of dots she has in Avatar. Excess Quintessence bleeds off into the surrounding area.

With Prime 3, mages may draw Quintessence from Tass. This process works the same way as drawing Quintessence from Nodes. However, unlike a Node, Tass does not replenish itself.

When a mage masters Prime 5, he may tap raw Quintessence from anywhere. However, unlike drawing magick from Nodes or Tass, this is a vulgar Effect. Otherwise, the process works in the same manner: each success equals a point of Quintessence. Since the world is filled with raw Quintessence, this magick has few detrimental effects. Sometimes the air will grow cold, lights will flicker, and mirrors may crack, but that is about all. A Sleeper is a poor source of Quintessence, and typically has one to three

points of Quintessence in his pattern. Werewolves and vampires are richer sources of Quintessence, but woe to the mage who actually tries to tap it! This kind of life-force theft would be considered the worst kind of insult. The offending mage might have to deal with his "wellspring's" friends as well as the vampire or werewolf itself.

Paradox

Paradox is a puzzle. The key to Ascension is to unlock this puzzle.

— Marcus Triliox, Order of Hermes

Paradox is an immune system; its spirits protect Gaia from the disease of reckless magick.

— Heasha Morninglade, Verbena

Paradox is Jimminy Cricket with a chainsaw.

— Zerox, Orphan

Paradox is the curse of the Technocratic plunder of this world. When we're rid of them, we'll be rid of Paradox!

— Dr. Volcano, Virtual Adept

Paradox is nothing more than our lack of faith in ourselves.

— Oh Soon Hai, Euthanatos

What *is* Paradox? No one is quite sure, exactly. There are many theories, but no real answers. Perhaps in a world where belief shapes reality, there can never be one real answer. Teachers of magick recount parables, stories and myths about Paradox for their pupils. These tales tell of strange spirits linked to the Spheres who come to enforce reality on magick-abusers. Sometimes the spirits even kidnap mages and carry them off to a strange reality until they've made up for their crimes. A mage, it is said, never escapes the consequences of her actions.

Tradition members rarely talk about their own personal Paradox, except to close members of their own cabal. Some believe Paradox is the price of failure; having others discuss your private struggles with Paradox is humiliating, even mortifying. Mages at ancient Chantries, like Doissetep, use their knowledge of other mages' Paradox flaws and spirits to blackmail their enemies. In recent years, rumors of an underground movement dedicated to removing the stigma of accumulated Paradox have started, but unless mage society changes radically, such a movement is doomed to fail. Of course, this socially-imposed silence only increases the difficulty of a mage's personal struggle to stay on the path of Ascension.

Few of the Awakened honestly understand Paradox, its forms and how to combat it successfully. Young Apprentices ask their mentors annoying questions about Paradox. Why does Paradox only affect mages, and not other supernatural creatures, such as vampires and werewolves? Aren't Masters powerful enough to destroy Paradox spirits? How can Paradox spirits always find a mage? Did mages have to struggle with Paradox in the Mythic Age? Why doesn't Paradox destroy all the Marauders instead of ignoring them? Most teachers ignore these questions or give their students cryptic answers, such as, "You'll find out soon enough, young mage." Sometimes the teachers themselves do not know.

Theories

There are as many theories about Paradox as there are mages who have studied it. Some feel that Paradox stems from the Avatar's quest toward unity. The Avatar, then, summons Paradox to crush mages who dare too much or stray too far. This explains why werewolves, vampires, psychics and hedge-magicians do not suffer from Paradox. This does, however, leave other questions unanswered. Others speculate that Paradox manifests out of Sleepers' fear of the unknown, fueled by their sleeping Avatars; that vulgar magick, an insult to creation, is punished by God or the great Earth-Spirit; that Dynamic change is harnessed by natural law from going too far, lest reality be unraveled; that powerful Technocracy mages "programmed" reality to except certain things but reject others; that the world is winding down and the power of imagination itself has turned back against the visionaries; or that natural and physical law cannot abide a vacuum and will fill it by force if necessary. All of these ideas have validity. Not one of them, however, answers all possible questions.

According to ancient accounts, there has always been some degree of Paradox. Its effects were more localized in the past, and the degree to which reality could be stretched was far broader. The original Technomancers were apparently on the receiving end of Paradox until the rise of the Age of Reason. Early Sleepers would sooner believe in demonic gliding-winds or mental levitation than in flying machines. With the spreading of the Technocratic vision, mass communication and extensive mapping and exploration, one set paradigm was more or less established. Thus, the borders of Paradox were reestablished. Paradox occurs when reality is altered beyond those borders.

How and Why

The constraints of Paradox do seem to vary; the paradigm of real and unreal shifts a bit from place to place and group to group. Clever mages can take advantage of Sleepers' flexibility of belief (see the **Blatancy** Ability in Book One). Static reality would be more firmly set at a banker's convention than in an aborigine village. Nevertheless, consensual reality has only so much give to it. Herein lies the paradox of Paradox: reality has no bounds because it is constrained only by the belief of sentient beings, but because those beliefs set limits, consensual reality is *not* boundless. Changing the limitations of those beliefs, and thus the limits of reality, is the mage's task. Ascension transcends those limits, and the War is waged around them.

Some sages use the metaphor of a large air-bubble to describe Paradox, magick and reality. Reality, they say, is like water; magick displaces this water—slightly and gradually in the case of small coincidences, quickly and radically

in the case of vulgar magicks or ridiculous coincidence (see The Domino Effect). Given time, this metaphysical "water" seeps back into place, redistributing the weight of consensual belief. If the bubble pops, however, the water rushes in…. Paradox flaws, they say, are lasting ripples of this effect that center around the one who "broke the bubble." Paradox Spirits and their Realms are said to be creations of the subconscious mind made manifest.

Belief is critical to magick. A momentary faltering of belief can spell disaster. "Seeing the wires," "looking down," and "losing your faith" are some terms that describe the split-second doubt (a "botch") that brings reality crashing back in on you. This effect can cause Paradox even when there are no Sleepers around if the reality-displacement is profound enough. Horizon Realms have little problem with Paradox, but vulgar enough magick can disrupt even those ecosystems. Perhaps, then, any form of reality can stand only so much tampering before it lashes back in whatever fashion it can.

Paradox is an enigma. Perhaps with universal Ascension, this limitation of reality will cease to be.

Flavor: Personalizing Magick

Boil, boil, toil and trouble
Fire burn and cauldron bubble!
— William Shakespeare, *Macbeth*

Mages do not all share the same view of reality. The rules have been set down, and the various Spheres have been labeled and explained, but this is just as artificial as anything created by the Technocracy. The magic system of **Mage** is merely a construction of subjective reality (and, for the Traditions, political necessity) designed to facilitate easy game mechanics and smooth storytelling, not to become a body of dogma in its own right. Mages of each Tradition, and of each Tradition's sub-groups, conceive of reality differently. Even the more unified Traditions have their own heresies and internal disagreements.

It is very useful in game terms to speak of "Pattern magicks" and "perceiving an entity's life pattern," but each Tradition will have its own way of conceiving of these things and its own particular buzzwords associated with them. A groups of mages skilled in the Sphere of Life (which is a subjective term anyway) can all perceive an entity's pattern, but each will define it differently. A mage of the Order of Hermes would speak of having discovered a creature's "True Name," and would use this verbal representation of the pattern in incantations. He might also use numerology to derive the creature's "number" or graph the True Name as a magical sigil. One of the Sons of Ether, on the other hand, would proudly hold up her latest gizmo and announce that she has "read the DNA sequence" of a subject, while a member of the Akashic Brotherhood will have "perceived the physical nature of his Do." All of these terms mean roughly the same thing, but there are still shades of meaning between them.

Short of compiling a separate book for every magick style known to man, there is no way **Mage** could duplicate the bewildering variety of real-world practices and beliefs. All the same, portraying every magickal Effect as just another die roll robs the game of magick's rich flavor. Players should develop a definitive style for their characters with the help of the Storyteller.

Magick flows differently from each Avatar, and each mage has a distinctive style of magick. Sometimes this style is subtle—a few tendencies only noticed by mentors. Other mages use magick to make an individual statement, slapping a calling card down even with coincidental effects. These styles can range from a breeze incidentally blowing after an Effect to a mage twitching her nose every time she manipulates reality.

A well-developed style may also lower difficulty numbers. Perhaps a Cultist of Ecstasy's style involves loud music. The Storyteller decides that music follows the character everywhere. If this mage wanted to deafen a Technomancer in a nightclub, coincidentally changing volume control on a speaker next to her enemy, the Storyteller may give her a bonus. By the same token, she might incur a penalty trying to silence an area.

Each Tradition views magick differently. If a member of the Celestial Chorus calls upon Forces, the magick may appear as a beam of intense holy light called from the heavens, while a Son of Ether might have electricity fly from her scientific meter. These descriptions are more than atmosphere — they provide the reality of the game. Each character should have a unique flavor of effects to season her magick. A Dreamspeaker might have difficulty determining the frequency of radio transmissions, but a Virtual Adept would be hard-pressed to call upon the spirit of the land to answer his questions. Special effects may limit a mage's magickal abilities, but they enhance them as well.

Players should think carefully about their characters' personal beliefs and styles as well. If a Verbena wishes to cast a spell, the player should devise some ritual keeping with the beliefs of not only the Verbena Tradition, but of the individual practitioner as well. An English village witch and a Mexican *bruja* both make complex uses of herbs, and might both belong to the Verbena Tradition. However, the herbs they use differ, and their methodologies as well; the modern English village witch might have a statue of the Goddess of Willendorf on her altar, while the *bruja* or *curandera* would be lighting candles before a representations of the Virgin of Guadalupe. A Norse skald might carve runes beneath his World Tree. Pagan Goddess worshipers wouldn't buy into the standard definitions of "good" and "evil," but a *curandera* whose folk magic involved Our Lady would be very careful to observe the Catholic virtues. One Tradition, different practices.

Players and Storytellers should consider a mage's Chantry and cabal as well as and the cabal's purposes when considering a character's style. If that character spends most of her life at a Horizon Realm resonating with death energies, she will have more difficulty healing a comrade than a mage belonging to a Chantry focusing on renewal and regeneration. By the same token, a cabal focused on attaining knowledge might have an easier time penetrating the networks of the Digital Web than a cabal dedicated to violent conflict.

Storytellers should emphasize different styles, and players should help, even to the extent of imposing limits on their character's magicks based on their philosophies. All the same, remember that enlightenment and willpower outweigh material concerns. In **Mage**, anything is possible with some hard work, knowledge and a touch of creativity.

Different Spheres, Same Result

The Spheres of Magick overlap in **Mage**. Player characters can accomplish the same effects using different Spheres. There is nothing wrong with this overlap. **Mage** rewards creative use of magick.

If Job wanted to make a Sleeper walking across a carpet in a store trip, he could do it using a number of Spheres. Job could use Matter to create a previously unnoticed seam where his victim was about to step. He could use Life to cause the woman to have a sudden muscle spasm in her leg. He could use Mind to distract her, so she would be more likely to stumble, or Forces to cause the sunlight to reflect into her eyes in mid-step. There are even more alternatives just using the Spheres mentioned so far.

One of the most important secrets to effectively mastering magick is to determine exactly what result you desire and then considering how to use magick to achieve that result. If you don't have the Spheres or can't think of a way to manipulate them to achieve your goal, then you have to redefine your method. Sometimes the actual result you desire may not be what you first decide. In the above example, Job's goal is to trip the woman. However, he may be doing this simply to get an opportunity to introduce himself. If this is the case, Job might be better off just starting a conversation with her by asking a question. If he wants to steal her credit card, and hopes to trip her and filch it while picking up her items, he might just use Mind to make her absent-mindedly leave it somewhere. And if he wants to move her out of his field of vision, a handy mirror used to spot shoplifters might let him see around her.

Apprentices often use magick when it isn't needed. An experienced mage uses magick subtly to augment his other abilities, never to replace them. Discretion keeps Paradox and the Technocracy away.

The Fatal Embrace

"Think of it, wizard," says the vampire, eyes gleaming in the fireplace glow, *"eternity to chase your 'Ascension'. Eternity to rise above the others, perfect your craft and gather power of the shadows for your own."* He holds out a wrist already dripping with vitae, and bares his fangs. The Euthanatos' face sparkles with sweat. He licks his lips, weighing the greatest decision of his life.

"I accept," he says finally. His shirt falls to the floor. The vampire's skin is ice against his own, and the bite is a brand, drawing poisoned mortality from his veins.

Sudden starvation wracks him, ripping upward from gut to throat, replacing lost blood with gasping, drowning need. He reaches through darkness for the vampire's wrist, grasps it, and sucks the immortal fire.

Sweet brimstone/The walls shatter/Reality screams…

"Fool", the vampire mocks, licking his lips. At his feet, the young mage feels his Avatar shred. Bitterly, he howls…

Werewolves and vampires cannot become mages.

Mages cannot survive the Kindred's Embrace and retain their ability to use True Magick. While some mages have experimented with vampire blood, and some rare Garou Kinfolk work True Magick, the paths of the Awakened often lead in different directions.

Some wizards speculate that a vampire's Embrace destroys the essence of the Avatar that gives a mage his power. Others believe that the Avatars of vampires are set upon a certain predetermined Path that does not include magick. Still others maintain that vampires, being damned, are shut out forever from the light of the One. Whatever the reason, it is generally agreed that vampirism and magick don't mix. Vampiric thaumaturgy, say the mages, is only a pale shadow of True Magick and does not work outside the static bounds of conventional reality.

Awakening does not prevent the dreaded "Blood Bond" of the undead, as many mages have discovered. Powerful mages sometimes hunt down vampires for their blood, but this is chancy at best. More than one mage is said to have fallen into eternal Quiet after drinking from one too many Kindred, and vampires make very bad long-term enemies.

The Dreamspeakers claim that werewolves share a common Avatar, the soul of Gaia Herself. Sons of Ether dabbling with Matter state that there are properties of the changing blood that preclude magick outside the spirit-gifts of the Garou. This may be why some Kinfolk can grasp the Spheres, while werewolves cannot.

It bears noting that mages, werewolves and vampires don't collect trading cards of the other Awakened. While most Awakened beings are aware of each other's existence, they usually have their facts all wrong. It's a rare mage who holds real insight into the politics of the Camarilla or the workings of the Thirteen Tribes. Likewise, most supernatural beings see mages as modern-day Gandalfs and wouldn't know an Akashic Brother from a Technomancer. There are exceptions, but most supernatural entities know nothing about the Ascension War. Most of them couldn't care less.

The Rule of Shade

And if there rise among you a prophet, or a dreamer of dreams, and giveth thee a sign of wonder,

And the sign or the wonder came to pass, whereof he spake unto thee, saying, "Let us go after other gods, which thou hast not known, and let us serve them;"

Thou shalt not hearken unto the words of that prophet, or that dreamer of dreams…

And that prophet, or that dreamer of dreams, shall be put to death…

So shalt you put the evil away from the midst of thee.

— Deuteronomy 13: 1-5

Mortals, when confronted with things they cannot comprehend, tend to either worship those things or destroy them. Some do both. "Witch-hunters" are well-named; while the Inquisition (**Mage**, pg. 277) carries the most visible torch in the witch-hunting mob, all cultures have Sleepers who would defend their blindness or belief with deadly force. A hunter with True Faith (see Book One) is a dangerous foe. The Sons of Ether and Verbena are particularly aware of this threat.

The Rule of Shade

Seek not in the Darkness, for fear of corruption;
Seek not in Daylight, for fear of discovery.
Ascension walks the Middle Path of Shade
That Awakened may lead
And Sleepers follow without fear.

An informal Tradition Protocol—the Rule of Shade—puts further constraints on careless magick; flashy mages may find themselves betrayed to the hunters or Technocracy by would-be allies if they put mage society as a whole in danger. Though the Rule of Shade is not a hard-and-fast law, mages expose their true natures at their own peril. All too many Sleepers would be willing either to throw themselves at an unwitting savior's feet, or throw self-same savior into the nearest bonfire if he proved to be anything less than the answer to their prayers.

The Umbra

"What IS this place?" Jennifer asked as the cabal passed through the Barrier. The silver barrier had parted to reveal a misty half-mirror of the room they had just left. "Look," she continued, pointing to where the computer had been. In the Umbra, the pattern of the device could be seen clearly. It shimmered in the Umbral twilight; tiny phosphors of Quintessence danced throughout its frame. Jennifer grinned triumphantly. "I KNEW that was no ordinary deck!"

"No," the owner replied, unfolding from the shadows. "It isn't…"

The Umbra is a catch-all term for the spirit worlds that lie just beyond the consensual reality of Earth's "real world." Its apparent structure is so fluid and so dependent on individual perception that all attempts to "map" it fail. Most highly enlightened mages claim that by mapping something out, you fix it in place (a practice the Void Engineers use to limit the spread of "random elements"). The Umbra, they say, refuses to be set.

The Three Umbral Worlds

Most agree that the Umbra has a three layers: the "high" Umbra, a realm of ideas made manifest, the "middle" Umbra, the spiritual reflection of nature, and the "lower" Umbra, the land of decay and the dead. These locations are more like labels of understanding than "physical" locations; the Umbra is nebulous, and travel within it is guided by intent rather than by direction.

Certain aspects of the Umbra remain constant:

• The Periphery, where the pulse of the spirit world can be felt faintly in material reality. Even Sleepers can pass into this state, which is the natural home of the Awakened. This is less a state of "place" than of "being"; many mages become so attuned to the Periphery that they cease to feel the wonder of it.

• The Gauntlet, or Barrier, which blocks the world of the spirit from the world of physical form.

• The Penumbra, a shadowy reflection of the world as we know it.

• The Three Worlds, where concepts of abstract thought, the soul of nature and the shadow of death shape the Realms an Umbral traveler encounters.

• The Near Umbra extends from the Penumbra into the Realms of the three layers. These layers, connected by the Penumbra, contain Realms of various sorts—Domains, Spirit Realms, Dead Zones and other locations.

• The Realms themselves are locations where Umbral reality has taken on some set form, either as a reaction to some powerful phenomena on Earth, magickal patterning, or the will of some Umbrood entity. The nature of these Realms varies between the Three Worlds.

• The Horizon, or the Membrane, divides the Deep Umbra from the Near Umbra. Horizon Realms, as places of spirit patterned by human will, reside in the Horizon.

• The Deep Umbra extends into infinity beyond the Horizon. The Shard Realms and Paradox Realms spin endlessly in this cosmic void. The Nephandi and Marauders (and, many believe, worse things…) dwell in the outer space of the spirit world.

• The Zones are places which permeate the Three Worlds and transcend the boundaries between them. These include the Net, also known as the Digital Web, the Mirror Zone, the Dream Realms, and possibly others. These places drift between the Realms but do not truly belong to them.

The Near Umbra

Everything is more vivid in this spiritual reflection of Earth. Although it takes on an alien cast, forms appear more like their "true selves" here. High-tech research labs appear in the Umbra as a series of crystalline caves covered in webs of wire, crackling with electricity. A toxic waste dump grows darker, with spirits of mutated insects flying about it. An untouched spring glade seems more beautiful and serene than in the physical world. In places where the Gauntlet is thin, the Umbra and the physical world bear a strong resemblance. A few mages claim that on the right nights when the moon shines down on the caerns of the werewolves, the Umbra and the physical world become one.

Each traveller experiences the Umbra differently, coloring it with his own perceptions. The Umbra gives form to a place's meaning. A sterile antiseptic uncomfortable hospital might have walls and floors of metal in the Umbra. It might have no spiritual manifestation, no meaning to the world's collective unconscious. Only Awakened items, objects containing Quintessence, have form in the Umbra. This includes any area touched by magick or possessing a strong emotional significance to a Sleeper. This Prime energy sparkles in its patterns, and many mages see them differently. Mages may see them as glowing webs, shimmering graphs, dancing spirits or any number of things.

Items in the Umbra and the real world affect each other. If a physical change is made to a place, its appearance in the Umbra may change. An abandoned house getting fixed up as a home for terminally ill children will take on a new spiritual meaning. In the Umbra, the house may go from a dank place reeking of decay to a bright sunlit site filled with as much joy as parents and volunteers can give.

If the spiritual nature of a location changes, the Storyteller must decide whether the physical world shifts as well. Spirit magick affects everything in the Umbra, even things that cannot be recognized as spirits. Many mages, such as the Dreamspeakers, believe that the Umbra and physical world are intertwined, and neither can exist without the other. The Umbra gives a location atmosphere. Without a spiritual manifestation, a grove of trees might die. If a Nephandus infected the spirits of the grove, the area could become a site of violent crime.

Travel

We followed the Dreamer through the
Purple hazy clouds,
Felt we could control our sense of time.
We thought we were lost, but
No matter how we tried
Everyone was in peace of mind
— Judas Priest, "Dreamer/Deceiver"

Travel through the Near Umbra is more a matter of intent than of distance. A mage simply walks into the Umbral mists and arrives where he wants to be. Hopefully…. Through these mists wind paths into the various Realms. Many of these paths (called "airts," "high roads," "moon paths," "byways," "dream trails," and other names) are often guarded by spirits and are quite dangerous.

Mages travel easily to the Realms of the High Umbra; their Dynamic natures and inquisitive minds lead them on the paths to the Abstract Lands more easily than to the Primordial Forms of nature. Only the dead may venture into the Dead Lands. Although some Euthanatos and Nephandi are said to have walked the Dead Road, few are powerful enough to have returned from such a journey.

Primordial mages wise in the ways of nature can pass into the natural Realms (detailed in the **Werewolf** supplement **Umbra: The Velvet Shadow**), but most mages travel to the upper Realms shaped by ideas: the Heavens, Hells, tessaracts and metropoli constructed by human concepts. In between lie Domains, places where the Umbral reflection takes on a particularly strong form: "Blights," where dark passions or toxic wastes poison the spirit shadow; "Glens," the polar opposites of blights, where purity shines through; "Trods," where the ancient aura of Arcadia lingers in the Umbra, and other variations. These Domains are not Realms in the truest sense— they shade the Penumbra with their influence, but have no borders.

Technomancers, with their strong ties to the material world, have a hard time in the Umbra. Mages without some knowledge of either Cosmology or the Spirit Sphere get utterly lost in the Umbral mists. Adepts or Masters of Spirit, on the other hand, glow like beacons with the power of their knowledge (this is not always a good thing…).

The Deep Umbra

The Deep Umbra is a mystery, and a dangerous one at that. Few Tradition mages venture into this void and return to tell of it. The Sons of Ether (and their Technocracy counterparts, the Void Engineers) build vessels to travel into this endless space, but are hard-pressed to reveal the wonders they have found there. Many return from their voyages somehow changed; perhaps the Nephandi or their nightmarish masters corrupt these travelers. Maybe the secrets beyond the Barrier are too great (or too foul) for the human mind, even the mind of a mage, to comprehend…

The Umbrood

But though there is much to be learnt from a cynical devil, I really cannot stand a sentimental one. Señor Commander: you know the way to the frontier of hell and heaven. Be good enough to direct me.

— George Bernard Shaw, *Man and Superman*

"Umbrood" is a general term describing the Umbral beings called "spirits." The Technocracy (and some Tradition mages) equate these entities with alien life-forms, while more mystic mages see the Umbrood for the spirit-things they are: reflections and incarnations of aspects of the material world (or are we a reflection of them? The debate continues…).

Magick

These spirits have odd powers that equate to magick in some elemental fashion. They, like so many other supernaturals, are unaffected by Paradox on their home ground, perhaps because so-called magick is their natural state. Human mages must still contend with Paradox here, although all magick here is coincidental. Nevertheless, mages have an edge when dealing with these ephemeral beings. Mages are often more inventive, while spirits tend to follow more predictable patterns. A clever mage can outmaneuver even an Umbrood Lord.

Damage

Paradox, in the material world, actually damages Umbrood. Magicks other than Spirit inflict normal damage on Umbrood. Spirit Sphere Effects, however, do aggravated damage to Umbral beings. Thus, the Master of this Sphere is accorded great respect, fear and hostility in the Umbra.

Materialization

Many Umbrood manifest in the physical world, taking on physical forms. In the past, a few mages, including the Progenitors, speculated that all of these spirits had some rank in Life magick. The truth of the matter, as proven by members of the Dreamspeakers, is that Materialize is a special Effect of Spirit 3. Mages who step sideways transform their physical bodies into spiritual ephemera and then back from spirit stuff to physical forms again. The spirits use the same technique, but in reverse. They start with the second part of the transformation, turning their spirit bodies into flesh. Spirits and their manifestations are not truly "alive" on the physical plane. When killed, they dispel, reforming later elsewhere in the Umbra.

Part Two: New Rules

The following entries give new rules for a variety of things:

• **Child Mages:** Not all mages are "grown-ups." These brief rules cover young mages as characters for both players and Storytellers.

• **The Art of Do:** New rules for the Akashic art of The Way.

• **Familiars:** Details about the traditional mage companions.

• **Certamen:** A formal duel system approved by the Council of Nine.

• **Computers:** Some brief rules for normal computer use and hacking. **Digital Web** has more details about computer technomagick.

Child Mages

"Huh!" said the Starling contemptuously. "Look at 'em. They think they're the World's Wonders. Little miracles — I DON'T think! Of course you'll forget—same as Jane and Michael."

"We WON'T," said the Twins, looking at the Starling as if they would like to murder him.

The Starling jeered.

"I say you will," he insisted. "It isn't your fault, of course," he added more kindly. "You'll forget because you just can't help it. There never was a human being that remembered after the age of one— at the very latest— except, of course, Her." And he jerked his head over his shoulder at Mary Poppins.

"But why can she remember and not us?" said John.

"A-a-a-h! She's different. She's the Great Exception. Can't go by HER," said the Starling, grinning at them both.

John and Barbara were silent.

— P.L. Travers, Mary Poppins

Most Orphans Awaken as adolescents. A few, however, are born Awake, or just never go to Sleep. Indeed, there are those who believe that all babies are Awakened, and it's only after some time in the world that they go to Sleep. People spend their lives trying realize things with the clarity and simplicity that they did as children. A few children never forget.

Children instinctively know ritual and magic, and those with sufficient imagination can accomplish some of the most amazing feats. They also know of the forces of Paradox and why not to do magick around Sleepers. Almost all grownups— and children who act like grownups— think they know everything. Magic zap-guns and so on tend to turn back into ordinary toys when grownups are around, but by the same token, the bogeyman in the closet has to hide when mommy's around because she doesn't believe in him. Sleepers do have their uses.

Children are among the most powerful and the most dangerous of all mages. Some believe that children lack the necessary willpower for magick. These people obviously have not been around many children, or have forgotten what it is like to be a child. Most *adults* lack the willpower to be mages. What children lack is experience and interest: experience in what is and is not supposed to be possible, and interest in changing the way of the world. A child who has had the spirit crushed out of her is not going to believe herself capable of changing the world and will consequently go to Sleep. Conversely, a child filled with self-assurance generally lives in a situation quite to her liking and will see no reason to change reality. Sleep will come slowly and gradually, and the child will realize she is a mage only if there is some abrupt and drastic change which makes her need to use her power. Then there are children who are just so weird and willful that they never buy into the Technocracy's lies in the first place, and continue their lives as mages...

There are some children who are born with knowledge of their past lives, often even knowledge of their past lives as mages. These are often the most dangerous, as they know something of the world and of the importance of magick. Enlightenment can be a dangerous burden, but such children usually know what to do, and can be quite adept at hiding vulgar magick from grownups and other Sleepers. Usually, such children go to opposite ends of the Karmic equation, being either blessed and holy Golden Children or wicked and evil Children of Darkness. Then again, some may simply be very strong-willed mages who haven't forgotten their previous lives and intend to pick up where they left off.

On the other side of the equation are the Innocents, children so pure and naive that they are in fact, enlightened. By some philosophies, innocents are new spirits in their first incarnation, and hence have no memories of anything, not even phantom wisdom. Innocents know little or nothing, but do magick instinctively. Many lose the facility as they lose their innocence, replacing it with knowledge. Even these children will eventually lose most, if not all, of their purity. Innocents are also protected from many types of harm, but as they need it, it generally isn't much of a problem for game balance. Roleplaying such a character has great dramatic potential.

Awakened children can be a challenge to play, but the experience can also prove very rewarding. Finding out that the mean old neighbor lady is a Nephandus can make for an exciting adventure, and the Hermetic Order can have an interesting time when they discover that Awakened nine-year-olds have snuck into the Masque of the Sacred Mysteries. Child mages also are among the most unusual foes characters may face, whether it's a case of Chantry being pestered by Awakened brats, or an encounter with some evil sorceress in her latest incarnation.

Child Mages as Player Characters

Young mages begin with the Flaws: Short and Child: they start with only 10 freebie points (to reflect their lack of experience). Child mages cannot spend more than six points in Physical Attributes and cannot start with a Strength higher than 2. (Children can be quite dexterous, and they do get amazing bursts of stamina.) They begin with two points of Arete instead of one, can begin with any one Sphere, and will almost always have a Mentor, Destiny, and a strong Avatar. Innocents may start with one to three points of True Faith, though this will be sorely tested.... Reincarnated mages will often have a strong Dream rating. Another possibility is the child possessed by the soul of a dead mage. Simon Hawke's Wizard of Whitechapel has an amusing example of this. This type of character would be built with the Flaws above, but would have normal beginning Traits and a real identity problem!

The Art of Do

The animal grinned, a wicked smile, but —— —— was not sensitive to the divine vibrations. He did not quiver with delight on hearing a few words from the mystical Book. Instead he spat on the outdoor carpet of the truck floor and cursed.

— Stephen Billias, *The American Book of the Dead*

The human body is made to bend and twist in many ways. The Way of Do (pronounced the same way as "dough") seeks out the natural motions of the human form: which motions conserve the most energy, which produce the most force from the smallest effort, and which allow the body to remain strong and healthy. These exercises cover the whole of the body both internally and externally. Stamina, speed, strength and accuracy are chiseled into the stylist's body, mind and spirit.

Proper execution of Do allows the stylist to lock into the Flow of the Cosmic All and thus become an unstoppable force or invulnerable target. Akashic Brothers may also augment such moves with magick when necessary, achieving truly amazing feats of awe-inspiring beauty and devastating destructive potential.

The Master of Do moves without thought of convention or style. The body, mind and spirit must all flow naturally like a rolling, babbling stream. The water laps over a muddy, stone-covered pathway to make its way back to a larger source. The being needs to be as supple as a willow, hard as a rock, sharp as steel, strong as a river, and as peaceful as a rolling meadow.

The secret of Do is to be everything at once and nothing at all.

Do as a Skill

Do is the most basic of martial forms, and, it is said, the basis for all other arts. Primitive, yet refined, it stems from the very basis of human hand-to-hand combat: punching, kicking, dodging and throwing. The Do master punches, kicks, avoids or redirects all blows; other maneuvers are the easy man's way out of a fight.

The secret of the Do is that it is the truest and simplest method of applying, transferring, absorbing and redirecting the Pattern known as intrinsic internal energies, also known as Chi or Ki. This Pattern runs with the flow of the Prime. That is to say, it is not in itself the Prime, but it is a Pattern that attempts to duplicate the flow of the Prime. Practitioners learn to ride along the currents of their intrinsic internal energies.

The Masters of the Do can perform acts with the use of intrinsic internal power that are very similar to a standard mage's usage of Quintessence. However, this intrinsic internal power does not come in readily physical forms like Tass and cannot be transferred. The Akashic mage merely uses what is already there to its fullest extent. Intrinsic

internal power can be drawn out by merely practicing Do maneuvers; this is called "cultivating" one's intrinsic internal energies. The use of intrinsic internal power has been known to produce incredible effects. By augmenting these effects with magick, Akashic mages can use traditional rotes that no one else can (see the special Do rotes in Book Four).

Do Skill (Pg. **XX**) must be purchased during character creation by anyone playing an Akashic Brother. Characters already created may exchange their Brawl skill for Do by dividing Brawl in half, rounding up (Brawl 3 becomes Do 2, etc.). This may seem unfair at first, but Do is a far more intricate and powerful Skill than Brawl. *Anyone* can be a good brawler; only the wisest artists may master Do. Brawl never carries over into Do, even when that Skill represents some martial art. Even the most accomplished fighter must start at the beginning when learning the Way. Whenever an Akashic Brother fights another martial artist, Do is always used instead of Brawl, as a matter of honor. The Way cannot be learned just anywhere— one must train vigorously under a Mentor to learn the Skill and its special powers.

Do stylists tend to have high ratings in other Abilities, although the Skill itself adds nothing to those ratings. These skills may include Alertness, Athletics, Dodge, Melee, Stealth, Enigmas and Medicine. The Ability ratings will vary from character to character, but many Akashic Brothers have at least one dot in most, if not all, of these Abilities.

The Powers of Do

A great warrior feels no pain!
— Barbarian, *Oriental Heroes*

Do has two primary functions. The first is to link the body into the flow of intrinsic internal energies; the second is to direct this flow to enhance the abilities of the body. Do, in many ways, is the study of one's own being. Through this mastery, Do masters can perform amazing feats without vulgar magick. These powers are magick of a sort, but affect the inner being rather than external reality. One need not become a mage to utilize these effects— they require intense training and will, but not the Tapestry-reweaving powers of True Magick.

Because these abilities have been so ingrained in human belief that they do not invoke Paradox. Quintessence, however, cannot be spent to reduce difficulties.

The Basic Maneuvers

These moves are efficient variations on normal fighting strikes. Any Do stylist can use all of these strikes with a roll of Dexterity + Do. Each of the four basic maneuvers of Do utilize the human body to its ultimate potential. Through perfection of the art, Do warriors add their successes to the damage of these maneuvers. Because the strikes depend more on focus than on strength (and for simplicity's sake), base damage remains constant.

Example: A mugger attacks Sara Lynch, Akashic warrior. With grace and speed, Sara's body moves like the wind, slamming the bottom of her foot into her target with ultimate precision. Sara rolls for her Dexterity of 4 and her Do of 3, gaining three successes. She adds these to her kick damage of 4, for a total of seven Health levels of damage.

Maneuver	Difficulty	Damage
Punch	6	3 + Successes
Kick	7	4 + Successes
Flying Kick	8	5 + Successes
Throw	8	3 + Successes

[Opponents trained in Do may roll a Dexterity + Do roll versus 6 to land on their feet rather than attempting to Dodge a throw. If this roll is successful, no damage is inflicted.]

Energy Sources

Do stylists directs their inner Chi one of two ways: internally or externally. Do practitioners tend to employ one of these energy sources, though great masters (level 4 or 5) can utilize both quite effectively. When the stylist attains a degree of skill (three or more dots), he may declare a specialty with his energy source (for details on specialties, see **Mage**, pp. 145-146).

Internal

The internal stylist directs intrinsic internal energies through the body directly by motioning with the energy's flow, and, thus, following the way of the currents in the Prime. The practitioner learns to direct this flow through meditative motions and studies of the intrinsic internal energy he channels within his body.

Internal style energy transfers from the practitioner's body in motion (potential energy) to the target's body in relative non-motion as kinetic energy. Although the Brother seems to move very slowly, his blows are difficult to dodge. Specialists in the internal style may reroll 10s on rolls to hit and often have high Dexterity scores.

External

The External Stylist forces intrinsic internal energies to coalesce within her muscles, bone structure, skin and tendons. This method is learned through repetition of exercises. In this method, the energy of the Do releases as physical kinetic energy. Specialists in "external" style reroll 10s for damage and usually have high Stamina.

Exercises and Body Control

There are millions of exercises for Do. Each set of exercises is linked to one of four main goals of the Brotherhood and, in turn, to one of the four Avatar Essences: perfection of the body (Questing Style), perfection of the mind (Pattern Style), perfection of the spirit (Dynamic Style), or perfection of being (Primordial Style). Most of these exercises overlap categories of distinction. For one to find perfection in any, one must achieve a grasp of the cosmic all. These exercises have no real application in game mechanics, but add roleplaying flavor to stylist characters.

Precise bodily control is of primary importance to the true Do practitioner, control not only of movement and perception, but of internal processes and structures as well. These skills allowed many Brothers to escape Euthanatos death squads by playing dead during the great Himalayan Wars of 900-600 B. C. This control can be measured by the level that the stylist has in Do and allows her to manipulate her bodily functions to a degree. These non-magickal effects take a roll of Dexterity + Do or Stamina + Do, difficulty 8. The effect lasts for one scene.

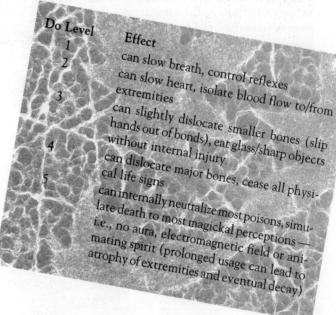

Do Level	Effect
1	can slow breath, control reflexes
2	can slow heart, isolate blood flow to/from extremities
3	can slightly dislocate smaller bones (slip hands out of bonds), eat glass/sharp objects without internal injury
4	can dislocate major bones, cease all physical life signs
5	can internally neutralize most poisons, simulate death to most magickal perceptions — i.e., no aura, electromagnetic field or animating spirit (prolonged usage can lead to atrophy of extremities and eventual decay)

Special Maneuvers

Through the art of Do, stylists may learn a number of special moves. Characters with more than two dots in Do may learn one of the following maneuvers, in no particular order, for each point of Do over the second (e.g. a Do of 3 confers one Special Maneuver, a Do of 4 bestows two Maneuvers, and so on). Those initiates new to Do (i.e., with one dot) do not yet have the skill to master these maneuvers.

Return Melee Attack

Roll: Dexterity + Do

Difficulty: see below

Damage: special

Primarily used against opponents attacking with either swords, knives or clubs, this maneuver allows the defender to redirect the energy of the attack around and back into the attacker. The practitioner rolls a resisted roll against the attacker's Dexterity + 3. If the Do artist wins, he does his Do + successes in damage; this reflects how well he redirected the blow. This action must be declared before the Attack Stage begins.

Deflect/Catch Missiles

Roll: Dexterity + Do

Difficulty: special

Damage: none

Do practitioners are often trained in barehanded methods of defense against weapons which can be thrown or shot through the air. Deflection may be attempted as long as the defender has an arm (or leg) free, and can see the missile coming (or has Correspondence 1). Catching, however, requires full concentration, so the defender must be initially aware of the attack and must take no other action that turn. This skill does not work against any form of magickal missile, although a mundane object propelled through coincidental magick can be deflected normally. Below are difficulties for the most common missiles (a number in parentheses indicates the number of successes required):

Missile	to deflect	to catch
rock, thrown	4	
rock, slung	5	5
knife	6	6
shuriken	6	7
spear	5	8 (both hands)
hatchet	8	4 (both hands)
arrow	7 (2)	7
crossbow bolt	8 (2)	8 (2)
bullet	10 (3)	9 (2)
		10 (5)

Kiai

Roll: Stamina + Do

Difficulty: 6

Damage: none

When struck, the Brother emits a loud yell which expels all air from the lungs, tightens the stomach muscles, and draws the testicles up into the abdominal cavity (when applicable). This maneuver allows an Akashic Brother to focus his Ki (or Chi). Like a dodge, the Kiai must be

Optional Rule: Training Flashback

On occasion, an Akashic Brother's player may wish to perform some extremely complex or specialized maneuver for which the Storyteller must demand a difficulty of 10. With this optional rule, the player may call for a flashback to her early Do training, and through it, negotiate a lower difficulty by means of brilliant roleplaying. The Mentor Background is usually involved, and both the player and Storyteller should work out the master-student relationship(s) in some detail.

A time limit of two or three minutes should be set (this usually happens in the middle of combat, after all), and the Storyteller may discount the entire flashback if anyone involved says the word "grasshopper."

Example: Sunila is attempting to free her companions from a Nephandi dungeon, despite the fact the she is suspended by one leg (and a looped sash) from a ceiling vent as she foolishly tries to swing across the hall and lift the dungeon key from the nose-ring of the slumbering guard without waking the guard or damaging herself on its acidic dermal secretions. (whew!) Her highly trained and focused mind drifts back to the time she spent with the Old Man, and how the Old Man liked to nap while forcing Sunila to pick the flies off his face without waking him..

Frequent abuse of the Training Flashback can lead to powerful Quiet. Brothers have been known to stare in blissful reverie while combat is resolved around them by their companions. Brothers who have witnessed the deaths of teachers, family or friends can become plagued with unwanted flashbacks of the event, and become prey to vengeful obsessions.

declared during the attack phase of a turn, but other actions may still be taken (the Dice Pool must be split, as usual). For each success on this roll, one extra die may be added to a regular soak roll or an Intimidation roll if the character desires.

If Kiai is used as a prerequisite for a Do Rote (see Book Four), the stylist rolls his Arete instead of Stamina + Do. The task is a manifestation of his enlightenment rather than a display of power. The roll may be done the turn before the rote is executed to avoid splitting a Dice Pool.

The Final Blow

Roll: none

Difficulty: see below

Damage: normal

The long history of the Akashic Brotherhood is replete with many examples of the superhuman capabilities of Do practitioners, including the ability to sustain and yet temporarily ignore massive amounts of physical damage. Few high-ranking Brothers die in combat without either delivering one last blow to their killer or giving a prolonged explication of the final secret of her style to a tearful student. Once during his lifetime, a Brother may, if the Storyteller allows it, completely ignore all Health Level

penalties, including death, for a number turns equal to his Do.

If this capability is used at any time other than the moment of death, the Storyteller may tell the player that an amount of permanent Willpower equal to the Health penalty overcome in this way is lost; this dramatic action may even result in a coma or permanent handicap.

A famous demonstration of this power is the final battle of the Weaponless Defender Nichiba, who was disemboweled by the warlord Hakai but used his own dangling entrails to strangle his slayer.

Familiars

Spirit
making a passage
for himself
Spirit
making a breath
for himself
out of me
out of me
— Eskimo Shamaness Hiwuna

Familiars are the companion spirit-creatures-made-matter who work with mages. The exact nature of these intelligent and powerful beings is unknown, although members of the Celestial Chorus have asserted that familiars are actually fragments of Avatars shattered by Marauders or other powerful creatures. The Dreamspeakers, on the other hand, insist that familiars are merely Awakened spirit-beings whose true homeland lies somewhere in the Deep Umbra. Some Dreamspeakers even go so far as to say that mages in the deepest throes of Quiet may themselves be familiars in that homeland. Whatever the truth behind these ideas, familiars are truly alien creatures whose true motives for joining with mages remain uncertain.

Familiars come in a variety of forms, from the golems of the Sons of Ether to the black cats of the Verbena, from the ferrets of the Cult of Ecstasy to the hyper-advanced AIs of the Virtual Adepts. It is said that even some Technocracy mages have familiars, though they would never refer to them as such. Familiars can take the form of almost any creature, even robots and golems. They often have some form of mobility, and thus rarely take the form of, say, a crystal ball or staff. On rare occasions, however, mages create familiars in the form of animated broomsticks, mushrooms, cars and the like. The Sons of Ether and Virtual Adepts are most likely to create such familiars. Be warned though: these familiars may cause Paradox to accrue to the mage if any Sleepers see the familiars behaving in a manner "impossible" in their reality!

The Familiar-Mage Bond

The familiar is a spirit foreign to the reality which the mage calls home. Its perceptions, the layers of its mind and the nature of its perversities are far different from those of its mage. The relationship between a mage and his familiar is incredibly deep and complex. It is not the relationship of a master and a servant. Rather, it is a melding, and through melding, the empowering of two distinct and diverse individuals. Mages who believe they will control their familiars are quickly disabused of this notion.

The bond between a familiar and a mage is almost always an exclusive one, although a few mages have been known to have more than one familiar. Usually, however, the familiars will not agree to this arrangement. Even if the mage can get two or more familiar spirits to agree to bond, most mages cannot keep more than one familiar fed and happy. Thus is demonstrated the extreme rarity of such a multiple bond.

Familiars often accept a physical form because they wish to conduct their own experiments on Earth, which they find to be a bizarre and fascinating place. A spirit may also become a familiar in order to hide from its enemies, find a particular tome or discover a way to have some fun. The reasons are as diverse as the familiars themselves.

Although mages and familiars are known to bicker amongst themselves (especially the Hollow Ones and their familiars), the bond between such individuals is strong. A familiar will always look after the interests of its mage, whom the familiar may refer to as *its* familiar (which may lead to a certain amount of confusion and jokes on the part of a mage's buddies), so long as the mage does the same for the familiar. It is a compact that is rarely broken deliberately by either party. Certain familiars have been with their mages for centuries. When the compact is broken, it is almost always due to either a outside interference, or the mage himself screwing up.

Familiars are sensitive creatures who can take offense easily if they are not fed the proper amount of Quintessence or given something they view as truly important. This is not to say that a familiar will drop the mage simply because he doesn't buy it the Barney doll it finds so fascinating, unless, of course, stuffed animals are part of the compact made between the two parties. Regardless of their many peccadilloes, familiars are generally loyal and can provide their mage-familiars with incredible amounts of information and power.

Finding the Familiar

There are a variety of ways in which a mage can seek a familiar. The most common way for a mage to seek out a familiar is to first use the Life rote **Imbue Flesh** to prepare an appropriate vessel which a spirit-being may take up residence as a familiar. However, the Sons of Ether and certain Virtual Adepts are known to use a different rote to prepare a suitable physical form for a familiar. These mages use the Matter rote **Pygmalion's Paradigm** (Book Five) to prepare a physical vessel.

The mage must decide beforehand how much power she wants to seek when searching for a familiar. This decision is usually determined by two factors: how much Quintessence the mage thinks she can manage to feed her familiar and the level of the mage's Arete. The desires of the familiar, of course, play some part in the equation…

It is not wise for a mage to attempt to bond with a familiar which she cannot properly feed. Since a familiar can only feed upon the Quintessence of its mage while bonded to her, it needs to have a steady supply of Quintessence. The more powerful the familiar, the more Prime Force is required to initially attract it and keep it fed.

A mage can only call a familiar spirit up to that mage's level of Arete. Thus, a mage with an Arete of 3 can attract a level three or lower familiar. More powerful familiars will simply ignore the mage's call, viewing the mage as unworthy of their attentions.

The Search

Preparing a vessel suitable for a familiar to inhabit is only the first step in finding a true familiar. Familiar spirits are powerful, Awakened, self-willed beings who actively choose whom they will accept as their own "familiar," or master, as most mages prefer to think of themselves. Finding a familiar involves going on some form of a quest. This quest most often involves reaching into the Umbra, although certain Virtual Adepts have successfully found familiars within the Digital Web. Members of the Akashic Brotherhood are said to have attracted familiars by remaining in a state of such profound serenity while meditating beside the familiar shell they have created that spirits enter the shells in order to begin a discourse with the mages. In most cases, however, the mage must seek out the familiar himself.

Each Tradition has its own method of going on such quests. The members of the Dreamspeakers search the world of their dreams looking for the allegorical clues that will tell the mage how to approach the spirit he seeks. Eventually a challenge intrudes on his dream. If the mage can successfully overcome the challenge that is presented in the dream, the spirit will present itself to him.

The Dreamspeakers' quests are far different from the beautiful and elaborate hymns a member of the Celestial Chorus will compose and sing during a nightlong vigil. A hymn will tell of her desire for a companion to aid the mage in her mission to remove the evil scourge from her world or to bring back the knowledge of true spirituality to the arid world of the Technomancers. If the song is intricate and powerful enough, a spirit may present itself to the mage during her vigil.

The Bargain

When a familiar spirit presents itself to the mage, it does so by entering the body prepared for it. At this point, the mage must give the familiar an amount of Quintessence equal to the spirit's power level. Thus, a three dot familiar requires three points of Quintessence, or else it will immediately leave the mage, never to return. In addition to this initial amount, the mage must agree to provide the familiar with the same amount of Quintessence every seven days. The mage will probably also have to bargain with the familiar about certain other preferences the creature has. These preferences vary widely from familiar to familiar. The range of demands can encompass just about anything, from a special bed to access to a new magickal tome on every third new moon. Familiars will almost never explain the reasons behind such demands, usually asserting that the reasons are obvious.

In return for the demands of the familiar, the mage may also request favors of the spirit. Such favors can take a variety of forms, but the most common are given below.

Advantages

Familiars provide mages with a variety of powers and services. Certain powers such as **Paradox Nullification** and **Information Font** are possessed by all familiars to one degree or another. Other familiars have additional powers that can be of use to a mage.

On the average, familiars of each power level will grant the mage the following advantages for so long as they remain with the mage.

- •   One dot in a Knowledge Ability
- ••   Two dots in a Knowledge
- •••   Two dots in a Knowledge, acts as level one Mentor
- ••••   Three dots in a Knowledge, acts as level two Mentor and provides one temporary point of Arete
- ••••• Three dots in a Knowledge, acts as level three Mentor and provides one temporary point of Arete

The Mentor function allows the mage to learn from the familiar; the other attributes of the Mentor Background are beyond familiars. Powerful familiars can even add to their "pet" mage's enlightenment. This benefit disappears if the two are separated for more than a day or so.

Paradox Nullification

Familiars can absorb and subsequently nullify a certain amount of Paradox energies. Familiars themselves seem immune to those same energies. Although the reason for this ability is a mystery, some theorize that familiars can somehow absorb Paradox energies into themselves and then channel or carry that energy through the Deep Umbra back to their homeland. It is also said that in the familiars' homeland the Paradox energies are somehow disbanded or transformed. As no one is known to have travelled to the familiars' homeland, the nature of this process is an enigma. When asked, familiar spirits merely respond in seeming non-sequiturs, act huffy, sharpen claws on furniture, and so on.

The amount of Paradox a familiar can absorb and nullify depends upon its power level. A one dot familiar can absorb up to one point of Paradox per month, a two dot familiar eats up to one point biweekly, one with three dots consumes one point per week, a four point familiar munches on two points per week, and a five dot familiar can absorb one point of Paradox per day.

Information Font

All familiars have access to information not normally available to the mage. This power manifests itself in a variety of ways. All familiars will occasionally spout pieces of information at various times. Such information is almost always cryptic in nature, although often extremely useful. The familiar does not necessarily intend to puzzle the mage, but the minds of familiar spirits are peculiar things. It is perhaps the nature of the familiar's mind that both allows it to discover such pieces of floating knowledge and causes the knowledge gained to be so damned confusing.

In addition to random pieces of information tossed at the mage from left field, a familiar also provides the mage access to the knowledge stored within its mind. The exact nature of this knowledge and its benefits to the mage vary somewhat with both the nature of the familiar and its level of power.

Other Powers

Certain familiars have other powers peculiar to the particular familiar or type of familiar. These powers often seem to result from some combination of the nature of the physical body the spirit inhabits and the peculiar nature of the spirit itself. Of course, more powerful familiars have a greater variety or depth of powers, while relatively weak familiars may only be able to do one or two unusual things.

Some common powers include: being able to use a few Spheres of magick; the ability to travel in the Umbra at will; the ability to sense danger; and the occasional power to demand respect from the strangest places— Umbrood, old mages and, occasionally, werecreatures.

The Familiar Dilemma

Although familiars confer a number of advantages and powers on the mages they accompany, they also make that mage more vulnerable. The most obvious disadvantage of keeping a familiar is that the creature must be fed a steady diet of Quintessence. Mages value Prime Force greatly and do not have an unlimited supply of this all-important substance. If a mage does not supply its familiar with the necessary Quintessence for more than two or three weeks, the familiar may leave the mage, taking all its advantages with it. Familiars starved by their mages often view such treatment as a betrayal of the pact between the two parties. Betrayed familiars have been known to go on rampages, ripping away Quintessence from other creatures and people close to the mage. Other familiars have rechanneled the Paradox energies they have most recently absorbed back into the mage with disastrous effect. Occasionally, such a familiar can be mollified by feeding it an exorbitant amount of Quintessence, and perhaps gifting it with a Talisman or magickal tome for good measure.

Rival mages, Marauders or Nephandi may also capture or destroy familiars. Marauders are particularly fond of ripping apart familiars and feeding on the raw Quintessence of their bodies. In such a way, the Marauder can gain an amount of Quintessence equal to the power level of the familiar.

The destruction of a familiar causes the mage to immediately lose double the familiar's power in Quintessence. However, the capture of a familiar is a far greater danger to the mage. A mage gains new Knowledges from his familiar through his intimate connection to the familiar's mind, and this intimacy is not a one-way street— the familiar also gains access to the mind of the mage. This is often an advantage to the mage, as the familiar can hear a summons from anywhere in the Tellurian and knows when the mage is in danger. However, the enemies of a mage may be able to gain access to his secrets, and perhaps even his mind, through a captured familiar. It is rumored that betrayed familiars have occasionally sold such information to others for a few points of Quintessence.

A wise mage treats her familiar with great respect and will come to the familiar's defense whenever it is endangered.

Certamen

Thou hast become the path and the way
That leadeth to destruction
Be thou accursed
Be thou abolished
Be thou annihilated
— Christian Death, "Path of Sorrows"

A Transcript from a conversation with Kjarl Hamarskald, of the Order of Hermes:

You come to me, an old and weak man, to learn about dueling, do you? Heh. Shows how much you know. Still, I'll tell you a few things. And you can decide whether they're true or false, eh? Or perhaps you'll find out too late. Heh. Back in the days before even the Mythic Paradigm was in place, the Pure Ones dueled through storms and rain, wind and sun. They boiled up great lava flows from the earth and summoned down huge mountains from the sky. Their conflicts formed oceans, raised glaciers, birthed islands, and, some say, started an ice age. Who would blame the Sleepers for their thinking these warring Pure Ones were gods? Many times whole tribes of humans were wiped out by the battles of these gods.

In the early Mythic Age, I know there were many kinds of magickal contests: the shapechanging duel (some fought in their new forms, some didn't), the contests of Will (where a great bell was hung between two Adepts and the first to cause the thing to ring won), the contests of Fate (where two mages would leap off a high cliff, each holding an eagle's egg— the winner would be the one who landed alive with the egg intact), and the Duels Arcane (where a single Spheres was the focus, and the mage who could demonstrate a greater facility and understanding of a particular area of magick was considered the winner). It was not until the grand and glorious Order of Hermes turned its thoughts to dueling that we were given a means of true testing!

That's right, boy. What I'm talking about is certamen! Evolved from an ancient contest put to members of the old Cult of Mercury, certamen was a true testing of the full measure of a mage, done without possible harm to Sleepers nearby or the mages themselves. Now we can settle our conflicts on the field of honor, just like knights in the old days, without dragging the locals into it.

When the Council of the Nine put out the question of how they might solve disputes, it was the Order that suggested their way of dueling. There was an uproar among the more dynamic Traditions: they complained that certamen with all its forms and formality was too rigid and structured— too much like the Technocracy. But even they soon learned that there was a subtle wildness in the play of Aegis and Gladius. When all is said and done, it is as swift and as strenuous as any video game of the Virtual Adepts or shapechanging combat of the Verbena. Did your Mentor teach you how it works? He did? Care to take on an old goat like me? No? Why am I not surprised?

Certamen Unveiled

"I am anti-life, the beast of judgment. I am the dark at the end of everything. The end of universes, gods, worlds...of everything. Sss. And what will you be then, Dreamlord?"

"I am hope."

— Neil Gaiman, "A Hope in Hell", *Sandman* #5

Certamen has been updated and revised since the days when the Order of Hermes first created it. It was adapted to the Tradition's Spheres and had to be revised to function in (or rather, outside of) the new reality paradigm that the Technocracy had asserted. The greatest minds of the Traditions, including the imaginative Ahl-i-Batin, joined forces to translate the dueling system into something that all the Traditions could use. The present day system is not perfect, but it does accurately and objectively test mages against each other.

Setting the Stage

An Adept of Prime, called the Marshall, must be present to enact the ritual. A certamen circle, created in exacting detail, must also be present. This circle gathers magickal energy into literal Spheres, which hover and crackle with power. These Spheres epitomize the energy which creates them: Life Spheres pulsate organically while Forces Spheres bristle like balls of Saint Elmo's Fire. The exact form the Spheres take on varies from Tradition to Tradition, but their nature remains clear to all who see them. Each combatant summons her Spheres into being, then chooses which ones to use in the upcoming contest.

Many Chantries have a certamen circle inscribed in a special room that is kept protected. The act of inscribing the circle requires Adepts of each of the Spheres, and is a costly activity as well. A Chantry will often have only one, although it is rumored that Doissetep has many, including one that is said to be inscribed by Verdi himself. If you are using the Chantry Creation Rules from **The Book of Chantries**, a certamen circle costs 3 creation points. Certamen is highly vulgar and cannot be utilized on Earth without serious repercussions.

The Certamen Marshal enacts the setting ritual, then watches the conflict and makes sure that safety and honor are maintained. The two combatants stand within it in a prescribed place and must stay put until they are given leave to move. When the ritual is complete, a bubble of Patterned Quintessence surrounds the two mages, enabling them to fight without fear of damaging the outside world. This bubble also prevents outside effects from interfering with the contest. Even if the Marshall is slain, the certamen will continue until there is a winner.

During the Summoning, when the two mages each draw forth their Spheres, the mages draw forth one Sphere per point of Arete that they possess. Any Spheres not summoned cannot be used. A mage's rank in a certain Sphere is not important— if she has any knowledge of an element, she may summon the appropriate Sphere. Combatants must draw the Prime Sphere first; this Sphere enables them to utilizes the others. They may not summon the same Sphere twice (i.e., two Life Spheres, or two Forces Spheres). The Spheres form glowing balls of light as they rise up from their appropriate symbols from the certamen circle. Summoned Spheres may not be used for magickal Effects: the form they take is an Effect in itself.

The next phase of certamen is called the Arming — when the combatants form the Gladius (or weapon) and the Aegis (or shield) for the upcoming combat. They do this by mentally visualizing the Sphere morphing into a dagger and a shield, respectively. They must choose which Spheres to use for their Gladius or Aegis. It is customary for the challenger to call out his Gladius Sphere upon challenging, and it is customary for the challenged to call out his Aegis Sphere at the same time. It's bad form to change your Gladius or Aegis, but it's been known to happen.

During this phase, they also take all of the other Spheres they Summoned in the first phase (including the Prime Sphere) and leave them hanging in reserve behind them, to bob and weave until summoned with a mental command or utilized in the fight (in which case they glow brightly for a moment). Of course, the maximum number of current active Spheres (including the Spheres for the Gladius and the Aegis) can never be more than the mage's Arete rating.

Before proceeding, each mage form a Locus, or Center. The Locus is made up of a pool of Quintessence, and represents the true target of any attack in certamen. Combatants need not use their full pool of Quintessence on the Locus, but it's considered polite to do so. Many consider holding onto Quintessence to use in battle as cheating. When all preparations have been made, certamen can begin.

The object of certamen is to rob your opponent of all her Quintessence. The Gladius is used as a tool to move past or pierce an opponent's Aegis, which forms a channel between the Attacker's Locus and the Defender's Locus. Through this channel, the attacker strives to siphon the defender's Prime Force away.

Viewing a certamen from the sidelines is quite exciting. The Gladius forms a jagged dagger-like shape, while the Aegis generally forms a round shield-like effect. Both these tools fly around, propelled by the craft and skill of their makers. More elaborate duels are performed in circles that can cast illusions illustrating a metaphor for any conflict in progress.

One "round" of certamen lasts for a very short period of time, objectively. Each round is usually over in less than a minute. Many certamen duels are over before you can even see the movement of the Spheres, and actually take longer to set up than they do to conduct.

Certamen Rules

Or art thou a dagger of the mind, a false creation, proceeding from the heat-oppressed brain?

— Shakespeare, *Macbeth*

Both mages roll initiative each round. On a tie, the person with the highest Wits goes first. Otherwise, the winner may either attack or wait her opponent out, saving her action until the other moves. Certamen combats are then played out like normal fights. An attack is a roll of Wits + Sphere. Attackers roll the rating of the Gladius Sphere against the defender's Aegis Sphere + 3, rather than the usual Dexterity + Brawl or Melee roll against a difficulty of 6.

If the attacker fails, her attack has been blocked by the Aegis. A successful attack hits the Locus, draining one Quintessence per success. Loci can soak drain damage: roll the defender's Prime score against difficulty 6.

A defender may use part of his Dice Pool for that turn to block an incoming attack entirely by rolling Wits + Aegis against the attacker's Gladius + 3. If he succeeds, the Gladius gets nowhere near the Locus. He can also try a Locus Dodge, rolling his Wits + Arete against difficulty 6, but cannot attack on that round if he does. Each success takes away one of the attacker's successes.

Victory Conditions

When one mage's Locus is drained, the battle is usually over, unless both agree to "refuel" and try again. The winner then dissolves her Locus and the Quintessence is stored in her Pattern.

A draw occurs if both mages drain each other's locus simultaneously. Draws are rare, but they have occurred, especially with particularly adroit warriors.

Optionally, a combatant may yield to his opponent. He does this by intentionally dissolving his Locus (but this may be a prelude to a terrible attack, as well...). The shield which protects the contest will only drop when both parties' Loci are dissolved. At that time, the Gladius and Aegis of both participants vanish.

Stakes vary with the mages concerned. Often, a simple apology or retraction from the loser will suffice. Other times, the winner may claim some payment or service from the loser. In extreme cases, losers of certamen may be exiled from their Chantry or cabal. The winner usually keeps whatever Quintessence she wins in the contest. Refusing to honor the outcome of a certamen duel is a serious breach of etiquette, but it happens more often than the Traditions would like to admit.

Permutations

You call that hard? I used to bull's-eye womp rats in my T-16 back home. They aren't much bigger than two meters.

— Luke Skywalker, *Star Wars: A New Hope*

Different Spheres and maneuvers can have various effects in certamen. The suggestions below should guide these effects. As always, keep the combat tense and dramatic through character interplay. Don't let rules permutation slow you down. Ultimately, certamen is a battle of skills, wits, magick and honor, not of rules-hacking and chart-consulting.

Maneuvers

Botching: A botched roll means the mage has lost control of the Sphere; he "fumbles" it and it disappears. See "Re-arming."

Disarming: A mage can try to disarm his opponent by attacking either her weapon or shield with his own. This desperate maneuver is at a difficulty of 9, but success will disrupt the opponent's Sphere for one turn per success. Four or more successes destroys the chosen Sphere for the duration.

Re-arming: A combatant may find himself without a Gladius, an Aegis, or both. He must then either form a new weapon or shield by drawing on one of the Spheres he has held in reserve or, if he has no appropriate Spheres in reserve, by summoning a Sphere anew. Forming a new weapon or shield from a reserve Sphere takes only one round, while summoning a new Sphere and forming a weapon or shield from it requires two rounds. During this time, devastating damage may be done to the combatant's Locus.

Changing Weapons or Shields: It takes one round to form a Gladius or Aegis out of one available Sphere and discard the previous Gladius or Aegis (the Sphere does not vanish when it is discarded; it becomes a Sphere in reserve).

Neither forming a new Gladius or Aegis nor summoning a new Sphere requires a roll. Both are automatically built into the certamen circle.

Refueling: It is possible for a mage to carry Tass into a duel in order to refuel the Locus. If this is not agreed upon ahead of time, it can be a form of cheating. Still, the tradition of carrying Tass into certamen originated with the Order of Hermes and it still goes on today.

Refueling takes one round. It is necessary to have the Prime Sphere active and in reserve. The Sphere must be at least 2 and a normal Prime effect must be cast. The difficulty for the effect is 6. The number of successes equals the Quintessence points that go to refuel the Locus.

Technically, it is possible to Refuel from a Node during certamen, but this is truly bad form.

Sphere Special Effects

Different Spheres do different things. The optional effects below reflect the pro and cons of the magickal Spheres. A combat Sphere may be used as either an Aegis or a Gladius; reserve Spheres don't work as weapons, but allow the mage access to some special maneuver on the round(s) that they are tapped. Tapping a reserve Sphere takes a half-action, splitting the Dice Pool for that round in half. No roll need be made.

Correspondence (Reserve): A glittering and disorienting Sphere, Correspondence can be tapped for extra dice, which can be used either for Attack or Defense. They must be committed at the beginning of the round and cannot be changed until the start of the next round.

Entropy (Combat): The scintillating blade of an Entropy Gladius adds one success to drain rolls, but consumes one point of any Quintessence gained while transferring the rest to the attacker's Locus.

Forces (Combat): Force often appears as a crackling ball or shield of fire or electricity. On a roll of "10", a Forces Gladius forks, giving the attacker one extra die per "10" to roll against the Locus. Forces shields give no special benefits.

Life (Combat): This robust Sphere grants no special effects in attack. Defending Life Spheres, however, add +1 to an attacker's difficulty.

Matter (Combat): Matter often takes on the form of a stone shield or a giant hammer. When used as an Aegis, Matter adds +2 to the difficulties of incoming attacks. Matter Gladii gain no bonus but are as intimidating as hell.

Mind (Combat): Mind weapons and shields are nearly invisible. All attack or block rolls against them are at a +3 difficulty.

Prime (Reserve): This blazing light Sphere allows a mage to expend Quintessence to lower his difficulties for both attacks and defenses, and to refuel the Loci.

Spirit (Combat): The smoky gray Spirit Gladius adds one additional drain success for every "10" rolled.

Time (Reserve): Like Correspondence Spheres, coalesced Time Spheres are difficult to gaze upon. The air seems to warp in and around itself for several feet in either direction. For each point of Time expertise after the first, a mage tapping this Sphere may make one extra action — attack, defend, re-arm, refuel or summon— by spending a point of Quintessence per extra action.

Certamen and Essence

A mage's Essence can affect his or her strategy. Knowing the nature of one's opponent is useful.

Dynamic mages are known for their inconstancy and seemingly random choices of strategies.

Pattern mages are the opposite: they have set strategies that they often use, and they are very methodical certamen opponents. They are, however, excellent at analyzing weaknesses and exploiting them.

Primordial mages are very base in their strategies and attacks. They seem to have a driving energy which underscores their consciousness.

Questing mages focus on one goal and move towards it unerringly. Of course, this means they are not incredibly adaptable, and can be somewhat predictable.

"Don't Call Me Mary Lou!"

While visiting the Euthanatos House of Helekar, Hollow Ones "Bitch Queen" Vannoy and "Hutch" Hutchenson have a spat (Hutch called Vannoy "Mary Lou" one too many times). Much as the Euthanatos would like to see the two Hollows tear each other apart, courtesy prevails, and the two mages are shown the way to the certamen circle. The winner gets the Quintessence; the loser does dishes for a month.

Vannoy has an edge over Hutch in the Arete department: she has 4 to Hutch's 3. Once in the circle, she summons up all four of her Spheres: Entropy, Forces, Matter and Prime. Hutch turns swirling balls of Forces and Matter into her Gladius and Aegis, respectively, while her Prime Sphere hovers in reserve. Both mages create Loci out of their meager Quintessence stores and the fight begins.

The Bitch Queen wins initiative and attacks with her Forces sword. Her Wits 2 and Forces 2 combine into a total pool of 4 dice. Hutch's Matter 1 gives Vannoy a total difficulty of 4 to succeed. Neither mage has Quintessence to spare, so the Bitch Queen blows a Willpower and wins a total of 2 successes. "Goddamn it!" howls Hutch as the Gladius slips past her and hits the Locus. Hutch's soak roll fails, and two Quintessence flow from Hutch to Mary Lo…uh, the Bitch Queen.

Hutch counterattacks with a blazing ball of Forces (Wits 3 + Forces 3 = 6 dice); she rolls three successes against Vannoy's Matter shield (difficulty 6). Two of those dice come up 10s. "Hiding behind a rock won't help you, bitch!" she growls as her Gladius forks into twin tongues of lightning. The two extra dice she gains turn up one more success, for a total of four. Vannoy curses and tries to soak. She has only one die to roll, and blows it. Four Quintessence charge Hutch's Locus into a blazing ball of bluish fire.

Next round, Hutch elects to Locus Dodge Vannoy's expected attack. Vannoy obliges by shifting her Gladius from Forces to Entropy. "You cheat!" Hutch spits, but Vannoy only laughs; "All's fair in love and war, fashion victim!" When Hutch wins the next initiative round, she plunges her Gladius straight at Vannoy's own. Spending a Willpower, she rolls against difficulty 9… Two successes! Vannoy's Entropy dagger scatters as she screams with rage.

The incoming bolt of Forces strikes Hutch's Locus dead center. Vannoy's 4 dice are augmented with 2 Willpower. She rolls well — an additional three successes — and Hutch soaks only one. The air turns blue with Quintessence and profanity. Hutch strikes back, but the Bitch Queen counters. Round three ends.

Both mages score devastating hits on the next round. Vannoy drains Hutch's last two Quintessence as Hutch's Gladius, aided by a Willpower point, spears the Bitch Queen's Locus. The scattered Quintessence settles into the Circle and the Marshall smiles; "Draw!"

"That was cheap!" Hutch snarls.

"You're cheap, fashion victim," the Bitch Queen retorts.

"I guess," says Chantrymate Alvin Locke, "you're both doing dishes this month."

They pummel him without mercy.

Cheating

There are many ways to cheat at certamen. Some are considered merely bad form and a few are considered grounds for sanction against the mage employing them.

Forming a "backup" Gladius before you release the current Gladius is bad form, and attacking twice using the Time Sphere with both of them is a Foul which might indicate a penalty. Mages who stash Tass on themselves without indicating so to their opponent can face a Foul or even a Forfeit if it is discovered, but this is a common way of cheating at certamen. Serious offenses include altering or affecting the certamen circle itself, bringing in Talismans which aid in the manipulation of certamen energies, or calling in outside help from outside the certamen circle. These offenses could lead to censure.

Differences and Respect

By fighting each other through certamen, each mage is treated to a very personal exposure as to how each mage sees the Spheres, for they form in accordance to their own beliefs and knowledge. For example, a Virtual Adept's Spheres might appear computerized or digital; a Hollow Ones' Spheres may appear gray or dull; a Son of Ether's Spheres may arc with energy or flux for one reason or another.

By being forced to see how each mage views their own Spheres through certamen, a Tradition mage gets a peek at another's viewpoint of Ascension. Instead of dividing the Traditions further, certamen is a conflict resolution system which reveals the ultimate unity of vision in the Traditions. Even if they do not come away enlightened, however, certamen exists because it does not harm Sleepers, it is a true test of skill and knowledge of the Spheres, and it is the best system the Traditions have.

Players are encouraged to make their certamen duels contests of creativity and storytelling. Rather than mechanically rolling dice and assessing damage, the players may describe the contest however they see fit. Illusions can easily spring up within well-prepared certamen circles. An Akashic Brother might assume the form of a giant serpent or a raging tiger, a Euthanatos might make the circle appear to fall away, revealing a yawning cosmic void, and so on. It is quite possible to "lose" certamen and still put on a good show. Feel free to use the circle to tell a story.

Variations

I hear Their laughter
I'm not alone but I fear
That laughter is my own
— Liers In Wait, "Torture Chamber"

The Duels Arcane

Not every Tradition mage uses the formal certamen to solve their disputes. Each Tradition has its own "house" method of solving problems, and there are still the old ways to consider. Generally, in order to provide some structure and to try and not endanger many mortals in their machinations, two mages often agree upon a certain set of goals which they are both striving to attain.

Two Euthanatos may decide to duel to see which one can kill the other first. Cultists of Ecstasy have been known to have sensory overload duels with music, drugs, sex and cinema (the infamous Movie Crawls of Manhattan); the first Cultist to drop loses. The Verbena return to the shapeshifting duels of old. The Akashic Brotherhood has a rote which allows two Brothers to challenge one another simply by gazing into each other's eyes. The first mage to blink loses. The Virtual Adepts have constructed wargames in the Digital Web to solve their disputes, although "flame wars" are also common.

Some of the enemies of the Traditions also know and can use certamen, particularly the *barabbi* mages of the Nephandi, who often like to certamen for the soul of a mage. Even some Technomancers know the use of a certamen circle, if only for the purposes of "blending in" with other mages.

Marauders disdain any such formal system, and often have very dangerous, Paradox-ridden contests. (See **Loom of Fate** for some of their favorite kinds of challenges.)

The Ultimate Duel: Reality Shaping

As the Traditions grow in power and the Technocracy clenches its fist over reality, it is ultimately the greatest test of any Tradition mage to shape mundane reality according to its view of Ascension. For this reason, one of the more popular of the "new" dueling practices is to take a specific facet of reality and shape it into something new, preferably something more towards Ascension.

For example, the city block at Sanford Street and Hairston Road is a run-down area of the city, full of crime, drugs, and poverty. A Celestial Chorus mage is confronted by a Man in Black, who demands that he leave the area. The Chorus mage challenges the Man in Black to a Reality Shaping duel, and names as his goal 100% attendance in the local elementary school. Thus, through hard work, coincidental magick, lots of social manipulation and some judicious bribes to truant officers, the Celestial Chorus mage tries to collect hundreds of children and get them back into school without much trouble and win the Shaping. Of course, the Technocracy might bring in big guns, slap court orders on the Chorus mage, destroy his Chantry and suborn the school. The Technocracy is under no obligation to "play fair."

Although it is deadly serious, ultimately the battle that the Traditions have with the Marauders and the Technocracy is not a moral one, but a war of ideals and ethics— a war for and about Reality.

Computers

The new literacy is computer literacy. Those who can use even the lowliest computers have access to information machines of vast potential. The Virtual Adepts are the masters of this new language, but any mage can use a computer. The following rules are for normal computers; magickal decks are covered in **Digital Web**, while some examples of the Adepts' Trinary computers can be found in Book Four.

A computer is a tool for accessing information, analyzing the information and acting upon that analysis— all at the same time. Computers in the real world are very complex. For the sake of simplicity, we describe four types of normal computers and offer some rules for using them in a storytelling game:

Laptop: The smallest of the computers, laptops are designed primarily for portability. Although small, these computers will still run most software. **Cost:** $2000.

Personal Computer: A desktop computer like the type found in most offices today. These computers are quite powerful and may run a wide variety of supplementary software to accomplish many different tasks. **Cost:** $1000.

Minicomputer: Typically used by a smaller office or organization, minicomputers have multi-user capacity (more than one person can use the computer at once). **Cost:** $10,000.

Mainframe Computer: Used by banks, governments and large institutions; mainframes are like minis, only much larger and more powerful. **Cost:** $100,000+.

Computers Equal Information

Computers normally become involved in a game because information is on someone else's computer and the characters want it, although computers do have other uses (writing and addressing form letters, for example). The characters may be keeping information of their own on a computer (this should give a healthy bonus to a recollection roll).

Computer Security

Computer security comes in two forms: physical security and "software" security. Physical security is the denial of physical access to the computer— no access, no data, no data theft. A physically secure computer is one that is not connected to the phone lines. Turning a computer off is a good way to bolster physical security.

Software security is any program that keeps unauthorized people from looking at certain information stored on a computer. Unless the person using a computer has purposefully hidden or encrypted information, anyone with **any** Computer Knowledge will be able to retrieve **all** information on that computer— given enough time.

In the real world, someone hiding information on a computer either does it right or doesn't. If information is hidden correctly (and that means using security software), then getting the information without the correct password is very difficult. This makes passwords a valuable commodity.

In order to use (or abuse) a computer system, a character must have both physical access to the computer (in person or by telephone), and software access to the information desired— whether through the correct password or a Computer roll to break through ("crack") the security system.

Before introducing a computer into the chronicle, a Storyteller should decide the following things:

• What information on the computer is relevant to the chronicle?

• What other information is on the computer (for descriptive purposes)?

• How well (or poorly) organized is the information?

• Was any attempt made to hide information? If so, how much time/difficulty will this add?

• Taking all of the above into account, how many successes must the characters score to retrieve the information?

In order to write a security program, make three rolls (Intelligence + Computer, difficulty 7). The total number of successes accumulated from the rolls is the difficulty of the security program. Security software can push the difficulty rating over 10. The only way to crack such a system is to use "cracking software" (created the same way) to reduce the difficulty to 10 or lower.

Poor Organization will never push the difficulty rating over nine. It is time-consuming, but not more difficult, to find information on a poorly organized computer. Also

Hacking Chart

System	Time(Hours)	Difficulty
Laptop	1	5
PC	2	6
Mini	3	7
Main	4	8
Security	+1 to +6	+1 to +6
Poorly Organized	+1 to +6	+1 to +3 (9 max)
Cracking Software	-1 to -8	-1 to -8

Time: The number of hours each roll takes.

note that "poor organization" may be a perfectly logical filing system the characters do not understand!

Example: A laptop (1) with moderate security software (3) will require four hours for each roll to crack its system; the difficulty of such a feat is 8. The number of successes must be set by the Storyteller.

Computer Uses

Dedicated Computers: A dedicated computer system is a computer designed to do only one task. A bank ATM machine is a good example, as are the fire-control systems on modern naval vessels. These computers are normally PC or mini-sized systems, but breaking into one is usually very hard. Add 2 to the difficulty to break into one. Matter or Forces magick can disrupt such computers, but affecting one without wrecking it requires a roll of Intelligence plus Technology, Computer or Computer Hacking.

Dedicated computers store a record of everything that the computer does. For example, an ATM stores a record of all its transactions, and it also stores a record of its communications with the bank's other computers. Naval fire-control systems keep a record of every target that they track.

Example: Bank automatic teller machine (ATM)— PC system with added security and security software (difficulty 10, time 6).

Typical Office Computers: Word processors and spreadsheets account for more than 50 percent of all computer use. Databases account for another 25 percent.

Typical Home Computers: Games account for about 80 percent of home computer software and word processing accounts for 15 percent.

Programming: This classic computer operation requires a number of successes determined by the Storyteller (generally 10-25) rolled against a difficulty set by the Storyteller (generally 7). Each roll normally requires two hours, although Time or Mind magick can speed things up (at the Storyteller's discretion).

Book Four: The Magick Toybox
Rotes and Equipment

Magick is not supernatural. If our entire universe came about either as the creation of an intelligent being or beings, or merely as the result of chance events, we still must come to the same conclusion: everything in the universe is natural!

— Donald Michael Kraig, *Modern Magick*

This Book presents new rotes and Talismans for **Mage** adventurers. It should be stressed that magick is *not* bound to these Effects, nor are certain rotes the only possible way of accomplishing results. These are suggestions and guidelines only, not absolute lists of "spells" or "magic items." While the rituals of vampiric Thaumaturgy have some static form, True Magick is far more fluid. As always, guide the magick by story intent, not nit-picking. Reality is subjective, magick moreso. Reality shaping is an art, not a science.

Rotes

The power of magic should not be underestimated. It works, often in ways that are unexpected and difficult to control. But neither should the power of magic be overestimated. It does not work simply, or effortlessly ; it does not confer omnipotence.

— Starhawk, *The Spiral Dance*

Mage magick is not static. Lists and books of "spells" are not the rule in the World of Darkness, at least not among True Magi. All the same, some static Effects— rotes— exist as tried-and-true ways to get things done. When a mage pulls off a particularly useful or spectacular Effect, other mages inevitably ask, "How did you *do* that?" Hence, rotes become a sort of commodity. You show me yours, and I'll show you mine.

While some rotes "belong" to a certain Tradition, they get passed from hand to hand between allies, and are sometimes even stolen. Many of the rotes below have changed over the years as others have improved on their original forms. For simplicity, signature rotes have been grouped by their specific Traditions (the Hollow Ones and Ahl-i-Batin are also represented here); common "free" rotes follow in the General category. Specific rotes for Do round out the rotes section. These rotes are extensions of Do maneuvers and may not be used alone or by those unversed in the art.

Tradition Rotes

The value of a tradition, of any sort, is that it gives us some framework within which to interpret events that happen during the stages of psychic transformation. Without the tradition… we may lose sight of the way and linger far longer than we need in any one stage or state of consciousness. In times of extreme difficulty, it is possible to use the tradition … as a lifeline.

— R.J. Stewart, *The Way of Merlin*

Akashic Brotherhood

Peace of Buddha (•• Mind)

It is said that Ah Mu could calm anyone or anything with a simple hand gesture and the words "Buddha bless you." The members of the Akashic Brotherhood who utilize this rote uphold that tradition. By gesturing with a peaceful hand posture and uttering "Buddha Bless you," the Brother projects peace and tranquillity upon his target. All but the most bloodthirsty individuals will immediately become calm and cease to perform further hostile actions.

[The mage forces a feeling of peace into the opponent's psyche. If the number of successes equals or exceeds the opponent's Willpower, the caster will drain the subject's will to do harm for the rote's duration. The individual is unlikely to do things that he wouldn't normally do. This

rote functions as coincidental magic as it resembles a blessing, not an attack.]

Avatar Form (••• Life, •• Prime, •• Mind)

Vibansumitra could look back in time through his Avatar, even before his Awakening. One of his greatest feats was his ability to project the true form of his Avatar into this physical Realm. His skin would turn a bright sky blue and become immune to the effects of natural temperature changes. Instead of two arms, Vibansumitra now had six. Each hand was constantly busy fiddling with something of importance to him; yet one always remained clasped in a position of respect for his Avatar.

All who saw Vibansumitra gazed in awe at his heavenly form.

[This rote hardens the skin so that it can take exposure to intense temperature extremes, from chilling arctic wind to the heat of a lava flow. It might, optionally, harden the skin like armor (**Mage**, pg. 269), adding one level of Armor per success. This latter Effect slows the mage down, applying the normal penalty of actually wearing armor of that type. The Brother may decide the level of Armor after the success of the initial magick roll.

[The mage grows four additional arms. He may add four dice to his Dice Pool for manual tasks, but must split that pool between the various actions he performs. Difficulties for each action might increase, due to the concentration involved in using six arms. The skin of the practitioner also turns blue. While in this form, an overwhelming feeling of awe projects into the minds of everyone viewing the caster via the second Rank of the Mind Sphere. A simpler form of this rote, Iron Body, toughens the mage's body but confers none of the other effects. The simpler rote uses Life and Prime to harden the body like armor and does not require Mind.]

Ahl-i-Batin

Eagle Eye (•• Correspondence, • Life)

While Shalitza was going through a maze in Cairo, she projected her senses up into the sky to look down upon her surroundings. Through the repeated use of this rote, Shalitza finally burst through the barrier holding her from attaining the Third Sphere of Correspondence. This rote is one of the first lessons taught to new initiates of the Batini, even if they are not yet versed in the Spheres necessary to perform it.

[The mage looks into the sky and focuses her senses so that she is looking down from that point in the sky. This is often used for tracking opponents across rooftops and through crowds of people. It has also been used to help mages escape from mazes and detect approaching individuals.]

Sneaking Shadow (•• Forces, •• Mind)

Ali By-yam set about to drive his opponents mad by playing subtle tricks on their minds. Many rotes used during battles in the Ascension War have been taken from his notes. Ali By-yam would locate his opponent and cast magick on his enemy's shadow, giving it a frightening appearance. The shadow would dart about as if it were attacking the target, causing the individual to become subconsciously paranoid until he realized that his shadow was "attacking" him. This realization was enough to drive many to eventual madness.

Ali By-yam claimed that he first used this rote to drive a sultan insane. Whether a sultan's vizier would be stupid enough not to realize what was going on is another point entirely.

[The Sphere of Forces is used to manipulate light waves from available lighting so that the target's shadow will shift about in a disturbing manner. The shadow is often manipulated to take on the form of a monster or known enemy of the target. The shadow can be made to appear on the opposite side of its natural location or even upside-down. The Sphere of Mind is used to keep the target from intentionally looking at her shadow; this does not stop the target from staring directly at the shadow, but it affects the target's comprehension and suggestibility. To avoid creeping paranoia, he must make a Willpower roll and exceed the number of successes the mage obtained when the rote was cast. If the target cannot shake off the effects of the "lurking shadow," he may make a Wits + Alertness roll to realize that the shadow is behaving strangely. If the second roll is unsuccessful, he will be at a -2 to his Dice Pool for the duration of the rote, and he will become increasingly irritable and neurotic. Others may notice that the shadow looks odd, but will not suffer the Mind Effects.

[Mages, if they notice the odd shadow, will immediately be able to detect the magick. Sleepers who notice, on the other hand, must make a Willpower roll versus a difficulty of 8 in order to maintain sanity. Those who fail will be haunted by the shadow. If the duration of the spell lasts long enough, the Sleeper will be worked up into such a state that he will become catatonic after a number of hours equal to her Willpower. Sometimes it is better not to see the bogeyman that lurks right over your shoulder.]

Celestial Chorus
Sense Corruption (• Entropy, • Spirit)

Antonius, an ancient Celestial Chorus mage, allied himself with some Garou, creatures otherwise known as werewolves, Lupines or lycanthropes. These Garou believed that the One was plagued by a force known as the Wyrm. The Wyrm was a great source of corruption and wished to bring about the end of the Realm. Antonius recognized the common nature of the Wyrm and his own Adversary and sought to detect corruption the way the Garou did.

Seeking first for tainted spirits in the Umbra, he was unable to detect them as they were perceived by the Garou. Next, he tried searching for sources of great entropy. Linking his search in the Umbra with his search for chaos enabled him to identify the Garou-termed "Wyrm spirits".

This is a dangerous rote, one known to drive mages crazy; there is only so much that can be done in the face of eternal corruption.

[The first Spirit Sphere is used to pan through the Umbra while the first Sphere of Entropy is used to focus on random fluctuations of decomposition. There is usually a low-level underlying current of Entropy and an increased level of Pattern corruption in Wyrm creatures that can be detected with careful analysis of one's perceptions. This allows the mage to understand the difference between an "evil" spirit and a Wyrm-fettered one.]

Wall of Mirrors (•••• Correspondence, ••• Force)

The **Wall of Mirrors** was designed by Sister Marcella of the Roman Chorus to protect her from unexpected attacks as she ministered to the pagan hordes of Dark Age Europe. This rote is strictly defensive and cannot be used in conjunction with any attacks, but can prove devastating as a defense.

[The **Wall** subtracts successes from any attack directed at the mage, moving the assault through space in a different direction than that which was originally intended. The direction is completely random and normally appears as if the attacker simply missed, or as if the attack was "coincidentally" deflected. For example, a bullet might ricochet off of a pendant, bouncing harmlessly off of a wall. Each success deducts one die from any attack Dice Pool used against the mage. This rote does not defend against indirect attacks, such as strong winds that buffet an entire area.]

Cult of Ecstasy

Tune Psychic Radio (•• Forces, • Mind)

Jenny "Songbird" Logan, the notable 1960's protest singer, was cornered by several Progenitor agents. She barely escaped with her life, and a chase ensued. As she fled, she began to scan the radio waves for the signal band the Progenitors were using. Once she had homed in on the signal, it was easy for her to begin to use their own intelligence network against them. First she found the "bug" that they were using to track her motion. Then she locked her mind into the radio communication between the Progenitor agents. Eventually, she was able to flee through a crowded store and lose enough of her clothing so that her Progenitor followers abducted a groupie look-alike instead.

Unfortunately for Jenny, she had not progressed to mastery of the third Sphere of Forces. If she had, she would have been able to produce her own signals as well…

Of late, Cultists have used this rote to listen into police, fire, rescue, news and entertainment transmissions. Some members of the Cult believe that this rote can be used to lock onto voice patterns so that conversations can be heard across crowded rooms and recognized the next time the Cultist is exposed to them.

[Using the Sphere of Forces, the mage tunes into any radio frequency that he wishes. The Sphere of the Mind is used to translate the radio signal into a form that can be understood. No actual sound is produced; all interaction is within the mage's mind.]

The Trip (•••• Mind, •• Correspondence, •• Time, • Entropy)

Members of the Cult have always sought ways to alter the minds and bodies of themselves and others. This rote causes the mind of another individual to extrapolate on events in the past and the present in a highly structured yet chaotic fashion.

Tim "Doc" Pere first utilized this rote to stimulate women. Acting as a hypnotist, he would lock his mind into the woman's mind and search for parts of her past that were sexually gratifying to her. He would locate moments of chaotic pleasure within her mind as well. Once he had this information, he would merge his perceptions into her own. As this infusion of pleasure flooded into her, he would reveal the moment in the past that she experienced as it was happening.

When attacked by a member of Nephandi, "Doc" was forced to utilize this rote offensively. Opening up the woman's mind, he locked into the moments of confusion in her life. He linked these moments back into her body via sensory input, but instead of linking the same moments in time back into her mind, he began to flash alternately forward and backward in time with as little relative relation as possible. As her will began to break, he bombarded her with the good times that had happened during her life, then projected images of the evil things she had performed. The woman was left a babbling vegetable.

[Using the fourth Sphere of Mind, the Cultist takes control of the target's mind. Any delusions or misconceptions that the target has within his mind are detected by the first Sphere of Entropy and manipulated by the Sphere of Mind. Once these areas of the target's memory have been located, they are fed into the target's waking mind as sensory input. Once the time and place of the memory have been revealed, the Cultist locates the place via the Sphere of Correspondence and the time by the Sphere of Time. The actual time and place of the incident are then revealed to the target.]

Dreamspeakers

Scrying (•• Correspondence, • Spirit)

Dreamspeaker mages developed this rote to "dream" of other locations. This is mostly used for spying and exploration. The Dreamspeaker goes into a drumming frenzy and allows her senses to wander out away from herself until they come to some point on which the Dreamspeaker wishes to concentrate. Dreamspeakers are known to use this rote quite frequently; it is not only useful, but highly entertaining.

Dreamspeakers have been known to send their "dreaming" into the Umbra as well. This gives a different insight to the spirit world than one would normally achieve. Since the point of view is within the Realm rather than the Umbra, the senses coming out of the spirit world make the spirits appear more like patterns of the Realm than they normally would. This can gain the mage insight into the nature of spirits that would otherwise be concealed — not that spirits are any good at concealing their true nature.

[This rote allows the mage to view other locations. It is usually limited to familiar locations or those that have been purposefully memorized, but this can be used to slowly "drag" one's Sphere sensing across an area by moving the point of Correspondence around within sensing range. This takes time and can be blocked by (and is visible through) other magicks. This is coincidental magick, as it appears that the shaman is completely immersed within her drumming frenzy. Others do not know what she is doing.]

Sucking Gate (•••• Spirit, •••• Forces, •• Prime)

Facing an ever increasing number of HIT Marks, Water Rhythm decided to take a wild chance. If her idea succeeded, she would take care of all her opponents with one blow; if she failed, the Paradox might kill her. She drew upon what Quintessence she had at her disposal and tore through the Gauntlet. The Umbra sucked everything into its gaping maw. Water Rhythm was drawn in as well, but unlike the HIT Marks, she possessed the ability to control the gate. As the gate ceased to draw upon the Realm, Water Rhythm rushed back through and sealed the gateway behind her.

Water Rhythm swore never to utilize such dramatically vulgar magick again, but, of course, once Destiny begins her drumming, there is no way to stop her.

The Dreamspeakers have held this rote in reserve for times of great emergency. It is not taught to all students of magick. In fact, the Dreamspeakers take great pains to erase all traces of its use with the higher Spheres of Entropy.

[The fourth rank of the Spirit Sphere is used to breach the Gauntlet. Once the Gauntlet is breached, the fourth rank of Forces alters the direction of gravity so that it draws everything within its area into the Umbra. The second Sphere of Prime supplies the necessary Quintessence supply to maintain the gate and manipulate gravity.]

Euthanatos

Random Impulse (•••• Mind, •• Entropy)

Cathi Marisha, a Euthanatos specializing in indirect mayhem, conceived this rote. By controlling the random impulses of her targets, Cathi was able to impel them into random acts of chaos.

[The mage using this Effect may control her subject's actions to a certain extent, but entropy rules the target's mind for the most part. For each success the mage scores, she robs her target of conscious control over his own actions for one five-minute increment (one success, five minutes, three successes, fifteen, etc.). She may direct one action of her target for every success she scores, but the target may resist this control with a successful Willpower roll, difficulty 7.]

Bone Twisting Palm (•••• Entropy, •••• Life, ••• Prime)

Developed by the Euthanatos mage Ho Chow Fan, the Bone Twisting Palm technique mutates an opponent's bones upon themselves until they finally shatter from the strain or become horribly malformed. Ho took extreme pleasure in employing this attack; it was one of his favorite rotes to cast on failing adepts.

Many of the other Traditions claim that Ho Chow Fan was secretly *barabbi* and that this rote had no place in Euthanatos' teachings. The Pedagogues of the Euthanatos refuse to discontinue the teaching of this rote.

[This rote can only be cast on one opponent and one limb at a time. It is usually employed by touch. The Sphere of Life is used to bend and twist the opponent's limb, while the Sphere of Entropy begins to work the real damage upon the bone and marrow structure. Knowledge of the Sphere of Prime channels Quintessence to mutate the opponent's Pattern.

[If causing damage instead of crippling, this rote inflicts aggravated damage. If the mage is seeking to cripple the opponent, the crippling causes normal damage, but twists the limb for the duration of the Effect. There is no method of naturally healing such damage; the only method of recovery is to use the Sphere of Life to return the bones to their natural state. In either case, the rote is quite vulgar.]

Hollow Ones

Be Cool (•• Mind)

Wendy "Spider" Jones always needed to feel hip to whatever scene she indulged in at the time. Once she became Awakened, she realized that being cool was only a matter of conforming to the views of others and that their moods and attitudes could easily be drawn out of them.

"Spider" started by feeling out people by reading their surface emotions. Next she began to implant the feeling that she was "cool" into the minds of others around her. Finally she decided that she wanted to stop wasting time casting the magick each time she went out; it was bringing her too much Paradox. "Spider" found it was best to permanently cast the rote on a given bar or club. In this way, she was able to "be cool" at these magicked locations whenever she returned to them.

The Hollow Ones jealously keep this rote hidden from the members of the Cult of Ecstasy. Let 'em find their own way to be cool!

[Using the second rank of the Mind Sphere, the Hollow One probes the emotions of others to see when he is considered "cool." Once the mage hits the right train of thought, he continues along it, using the same Mind rank to implant the impression that what he's saying is cool, no matter what he might be babbling.

[Hollow Ones have been known to cast this rote on places that they frequent. However, this leaves mystickal residue that can be detected by other mages. This practice is strongly discouraged by tutors, but many Hollows don't know any better. Such residue has lead members of the Technocracy to many Hollow One hang-outs.]

Lecherous Kiss (•• Mind, •• Life, •• Prime)

Howard "Rex" MacNesh practiced this rote while travelling the world in search of the perfect tutor. In his Awakened state, he quickly realized that he could easily augment his already proficient seduction skills. "Rex" studied pheromonal releases in humans. With practice, he was able to produce a pheromonal chemical on his lips that would amplify his own pheromones and increase the impact of the endocrine that he was releasing within the targets' minds.

[This rote is utilized to stimulate an individual into a state in which he will accept sexual advances or will make sexual advances himself. Using the second Sphere of Mind, the mage sways his or her target into thinking sexually. The second Sphere of Prime fuels the work done by the second Sphere of Life, producing both endocrine within the target's mind and a pheromonal compound on the caster's lips. A kiss seals the Effect.]

Penny Dreadful's Bright New Penny (••• or •••• Matter, •• Prime, •• Time)

One Hollow One, Penny Dreadful, devised this rote to restore sticks of old rubbish into the beautiful furnishings they had once been. By perceiving them in their heyday, she returned them to their former splendor. Moreover, an antique tablecloth allowed her to conjure every meal that had ever been placed upon it, gathering a fortune in vintage china and silverware. After tiring of Paradox, she devised several non-vulgar applications. After all, one never knows exactly what treasures you might find in the attics of abandoned houses or locked inside that antique hope chest willed to you by your Great Aunt Martha.

[Time 2 allows the mages to look back across the "life" of her focus. The Third Rank of Matter reshapes old articles, while the Forth recreates them entirely. Prime fuels the created pattern.]

Order of Hermes

Unseen Nomenclature (•• Mind, •• Matter, •• Prime)

The Order of Hermes used this rote to disguise most of their teachings during the Inquisition. It allows information to be implanted into a text in an non-alphanumeric form. This rote is usually employed to impregnate the pages of a book with information in a non-standard order.

For example, a mage wants to implant a message into a book so that others won't happen upon it. She uses the

rote to put the message into the book so that if it is read backwards, the information is transferred into the reader's brain. These messages work on a primal level. If someone happens upon the method of activating the impulse, she may not recognize what she has stumbled upon, as the messages tend to be loosely connected images or feelings.

[The Sphere of Prime is used to power the Spheres of Mind and Matter to place an emotional or subliminal message into the Pattern that makes up the book. The closer that message is to the original concept, the fewer success a mage needs to place a hidden message "between the lines." Putting a completely different message in a book can take five or more successes. The message can be stored in any sequence the mage wishes. Of course, variation from linear implantation will mean that a student wishing to learn from the material must read the text in the proper order.

[Mages can detect that printed materials have been effected by magick, but they will not know what sort of magick was used. Even if they do, they won't be able to figure out how to draw the information from the book if they fail a Wits + Intelligence roll versus difficulty 8.]

Unraveling the Text (•• Entropy, •• Matter, •• Prime)

This rote makes it impossible to read a book. No matter how hard the individual tries to concentrate on the words, the words themselves will not allow the information to be transmitted into the reader's brain.

[This forces a person reading a text to start jumping around the page instead of being able to read it normally. This can be very frustrating to the reader. Most people will stop reading the book altogether. If a mage realizes what is going on, she can take magickal steps to thwart the rote in order to understand the written words.]

Sons of Ether

Jury Rig (•• Matter, •• Prime, •• Correspondence, • Mind)

Ruf Argonholf was an Orphan who could fix machinery without taking it apart. By sensing inside the machinery, he could fix the problems by use of his mental powers alone. It wasn't long before members of the Sons of Ether approached him and asked him to join in their scientific experiments. This rote was too much for the Sons of Ether to pass up and was added to their tutoring manuals for new initiates.

[A successful Wits + Repair or Intelligence + Science roll must be made versus the state of the machine's damage. The number of success required depends on the condition of the machine:

- 10 — Totally smashed (vulgar magick required)
- 8 — Obvious damage that should stop the machine from operating
- 6 — Outside of the machine looks fine

• 4 — Electronics that can't be checked for actual functioning just by looking (i.e. computer chips, diodes and batteries.)

[The Son of Ether can temporarily (for the duration of the rote) return a machine to a functioning condition by analyzing the damage and magickally mending the Patterns that are damaged, disconnected or completely missing. First, the mage uses the Sphere of Correspondence to look inside of the machine. His innate scientific or repair skills are then augmented by the Mind Sphere. Lastly, Prime fuels Matter to repair or to replace any damage to the machine. When the duration of the rote expires, the machine returns to its previously broken state.]

Supporting the Brain (•••• Life, •• Matter, •• Mind, •• Prime)

Great scientists throughout the ages have struggled to extend the lifespan of humanity. The Sons of Ether often try to transplant the brain into another body— human, composite human, cyborg or robot. Some means of supporting the brain after death had to be created.

Doctor Gustov Finney created of the newest version of this rote. Having successfully decapitated a Man in Black, Dr. Finney was struck with a sudden bolt of enlightenment. "I will keep this brain alive! It will be an invaluable source of information for decades to come!" Finney quick-froze the severed head with liquid nitrogen, carried it to his lab, and began his work.

Carefully, he sawed open the skull and skillfully removed the brain, eyes and remaining spinal column. These organs were set into a suspension fluid filled with special nutrients and supersaturated with oxygen. Once this process was completed, Finney hooked electrodes into the brain and spinal column to check for response.

"Eureka!" The experiment achieved the desired results and eventually the brain was sapped of its information concerning the New World Order and the tactics of the Men in Black.

[A brain severed from its body needs two main things to stay alive: another life-support system and the will to live. The life-support system is created by use of three Spheres of magick. Matter is used to create the supportive fluid, the nutrient bath, and the supersaturation of oxygen within it. Life is used to keep the electrical current running within the brain and to insure that there is no decomposition or damage before the brain is placed within its "new body." Both of these Spheres require the use of Quintessence to accomplish their tasks; the Sphere of Prime is necessary to insure the success of his rote.

[Mind magick is used to stimulate the subject's will to live. This urge is subconscious; it is extremely hard for a person to fight against such a primal brain function. Of course, if you're a mage, there's always magick...]

Verbena

Shadows in the Mist (•• Forces, • Spirit)

Within any quantity of mist, fog or smoke (such as from a bunch of herbs thrown in a charcoal brazier, or a bundle of incense sticks lit at once), Verbena mages can manipulate the vapors to conform to the shapes of objects in the Umbra. Whether or not this is vulgar magic depends on a viewer's opinion and credulousness. Members of the Celestial Chorus use a variant employing incense.

[In the absence of any proper amount of smoke or fog, it is possible to create it via Matter 2 and Prime 2.]

Spirit Wounding (•••• Spirit, ••• Matter)

This ancient fey rote allows a Verbena to translate physical matter into spiritual matter without entering the Umbra. War-witches use the rote to inflict psychic wounds which cause traumatic Pattern leakage at the same rate as normal physical wounds. The advantage of such wounds is that once arrowheads or poisons lodge in a person's spirit, they will not heal unless a physician can see and reach into the Umbra to remove them.

[The Fabricate Spirit Effect allows the mage to gather and solidify spirit energies, while Matter magick grants this spirit-form shape. A mage reaching into the Umbra may remove such missiles with ease.]

Virtual Adepts

Adrenal Rush (••• Life, •• Prime)

No one is sure who was the first to realize that the Adrenal Rush from playing video games could be utilized as a rote to hype an individual, but the Effect is known to many Sleepers as well. This rote is considered coincidental magick.

The Virtual Adept merely begins playing a video game. Within a short amount of time, her body begins to secrete hormones and chemicals that not only increase the body's alertness and energy, but also flush toxins from the mage's system.

Some Virtual Adepts believe that this state is achieved by locking into the Net and allowing the pristine nature of perfectly coded programming to flow through their beings, locking them deeply into the very core of the subroutines constantly called upon to carry information. Others believe they are just excited by the thrill of destroying things without the fear of death getting in the way.

[This rote allows the Adept to refresh his body and cleanse it of all toxins. Any poisons, foreign chemicals, diseases or viruses within the mage's body are flushed out through his sweat glands. With three successes, the Adept also gains an additional dot of Stamina, Strength and Alertness for the duration of the rote. The Life Sphere stimulates the body to release the necessary by-products and purify the body, while Prime fuels the reweaving of the Pattern.]

**Override Signal (•• Forces, or sometimes ••••
Life)**

The Men in Black were signaling for back-ups. Ken Javlin was wedged into a tight spot. Using his laptop, Ken sent out a narrow beam signal from his wireless modem to jam the MIBs' call. Once he was sure that the MIBs would be unable to call in support troops, he called in the rest of his cabal. The MIBs were easily killed by the group of novice mages, as they were unaccustomed to being cut off from their organization, the New World Order.

Over the years, Ken's rote has evolved to include the jamming of modems, both wired and wireless. In fact, some Virtual Adepts called Reality Hackers have gone so far as to jam only certain wavelengths of energy that correspond to the electrical current that passes across neural synapses. It is extremely hard (difficulty 10) for even a mage to pinpoint such a small variation in frequency, but in-depth studies on one individual can lead to learning the exact frequency necessary to put an individual into a coma; the subject will remain in the coma until bombardment by this frequency ceases. This variation requires Life magick.

[The Virtual Adept blocks any transmitted signal that he wishes to jam using the Sphere of Forces. Most Adepts use this rote to jam radiowave, microwave and infrared transmissions. This requires a Intelligence + Technology or Wits + Investigation roll. The difficulty depends on the mage's familiarity with the sort of technology being used:

- 10 — Alien
- 8 — Heard about it once
- 6 — Seen it work before
- 4 — "Have one right here"

[An Intelligence + Computer roll may be substituted if the target device is a computer. An Intelligence + Medicine roll may be exchanged when attempting to jam medical equipment (or people). Roll Intelligence + Science if the rote is applied against scientific research equipment.

[Once the basic knowledge is discovered, a casting roll determines the degree of success (of course).]

General Rotes

*We lift and we keep turning
the same few figures;
we can almost understand
why they don't perish—
but we're meant only
more deeply and wonderingly
to cling to what once was
and smile: a bit more clearly
perhaps than a year before.*
— Rainer Rilke, "Tanagra"

Ariadne's Thread (• Mind, • Correspondence)

Virtual Adepts have made the most recent use of this ancient rote, whereby a mage may fix any particular spatial

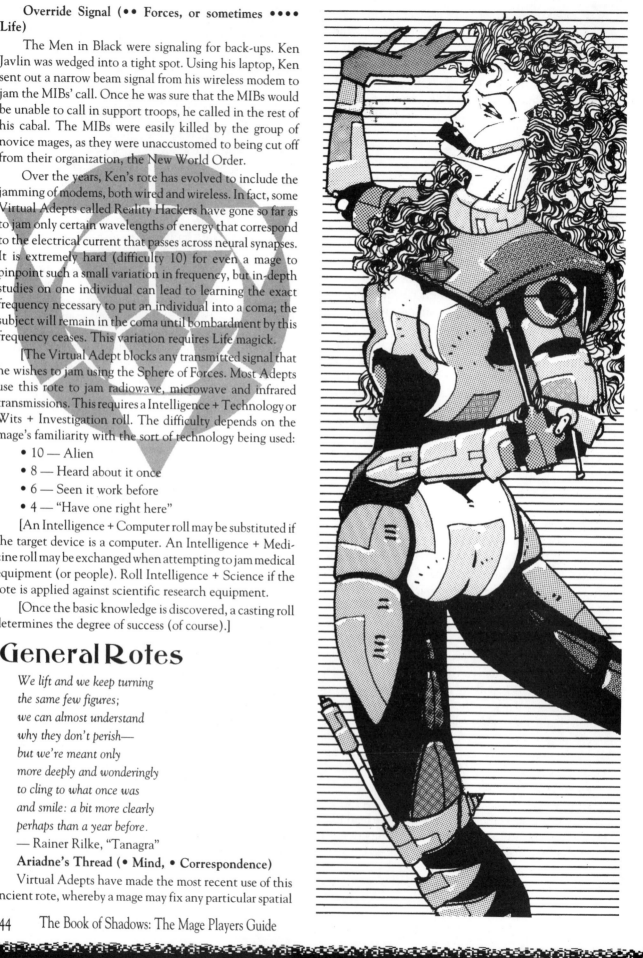

location in her mind, then play out a mental line, memorizing her progression through space. A mage can thus memorize the pattern of any maze, labyrinth, freeway interchange or virtual reality flowchart sequencing routine. Landmarks may change on the way back, of course, and roadblocks may be erected, but the mage will not be confused by any illusions or detours off the beaten path.

[Used in conjunction with the **Seven League Stride, Ariadne's Thread** guarantees a return to one's previous location with even the slightest degree of success, although there are Effects to counter this...]

Detect the Dream Gateway (• Correspondence, • Spirit)

Dreamspeakers use this rote to inspect their immediate vicinity for spots where the gauntlet is weaker. This is especially important in the inner city, where a Dreamspeaker may detect that the archway of the Public Library (built by Masons) has a gauntlet of 3, compared to the 5 of the surrounding blight, while the jungle gym in suburban park may have a gauntlet of 2 in one particular corner. This is not so much a rote as it is a roll of Perception + Awareness to notice such features. However, a casting roll is still required to augment the mage's awareness.

Prime Location (• or •• Correspondence, • Prime)

The old joke in real estate is that the three most important selling points of a house are location, location and location. Mages know about the importance of locations, as the most valuable spots in any area are the focal points of magical energy called Nodes. Just as the temporal junctures often coalesce at times of transition and at the midpoints of certain cycles, Nodes tend to appear at borders and centers. The edge of a forest may have one, the middle another. The deepest part of the deep blue sea has a third, while a far more accessible spot forms at the constantly shifting shoreline. Generally speaking, they occur in the center and at the transition of the elements.

In Oregon, one of the most spectacular sights (and sites) is Multnomah Falls. Behind the curtain of the falls is a grotto, and in the center, just above the line of the water, is an altar-shaped stone. If you were to stand on the stone, the wind would blow spray through the curtain of the falls into your face, while the mountain would be directly over your head. It is an ancient sacred site, the meeting of water, wind and earth. The Node is there, despite the tourists, few of whom know or care enough to find the spot. The point of transition forms the Node, the intersection of lines of magical force.

Western lore refers to these paths of energy as ley lines, while Eastern traditions refer to them as Dragon Paths. Yin paths follow the course of valleys and the low places on the ground, while Yang paths follow the courses of mountains and hills. A mountain pass between two valleys would contain a prime Node, though the exact location would depend on minor geological features. Mountain passes are also areas of high wind and geological activity (which is formed by fault lines).

Nodes, however, shift, as do the elements, and human handiwork can affect a change in a Node's position. For example, some of the most magically charged sites are crossroads. Folklore tells us that ghosts, devils, vampires and witches all travel to crossroads for power (especially at the juncture of midnight). The power is obvious and the Node at a crossroad is well-marked. The psychic energy and stresses involved with the road keeps the existing ley lines fixed in place, or causes new ones to form (or old ones to shift). The excess energy Prime Force collects at the crossroads, forming the Node.

[By use of the **Prime Location** rote, mages may find the precise spot of a Node, and may roll Perception + Awareness to notice spontaneously created Nodes if they appear.]

Burn Out (•• Forces, • Entropy)

By randomly locating the most delicate part of an electric circuit or IC chip, the mage can surgically create and direct a small energy surge and cause the device to fail without totally destroying the whole device. This disrupts the device's function for one turn per success. (Note that technomagickal devices typically have an Arete or countermagick to resist this.)

Hallmark (•• Mind, • Prime)

A mage's magicks are as distinctive as his handwriting or fingerprints. With this rote, a mage may examine a magickal working and gain insights into the personality and identity of the mage who made it, including the techniques and affiliation of the caster. With a roll of Perception + Awareness, he may attempt to match it to other magical workings or auras of mages he knows. Sometimes this is very easy, as some mages who know this rote (typically the Order of Hermes) use it to blazon an elaborate seal at the end of all their workings. Such hallmarks are visible to those looking with only the first dot of Prime, though it requires Mind to detect the personality behind the magic. Hollow Ones refer to this technique as "tagging" and sometimes scrawl psychic graffiti over things for sheer amusement value. Such seals and tagging are easily visible from the Umbra.

[If a mage wishes to conceal his identity as the author of any particular Effect, he may roll Wits + Subterfuge versus the difficulty of the Effect being attempted. Partial successes will leave an indeterminate or smudged hallmark. If a mage wishes to forge the hallmark of another mage, he should roll Manipulation + Expression at the difficulty of the Effect being cast, with additional penalties for forging the impressions of mages he is unfamiliar with or the techniques of other Traditions. The Verbena and the Virtual Adepts use very different methods, and the style of magickal handwriting is equally distinct.]

Pixie Lead (••• Mind, •• Correspondence)

This rote changes a subject's perceptions such that he easily gets lost, following one path while perceiving an-

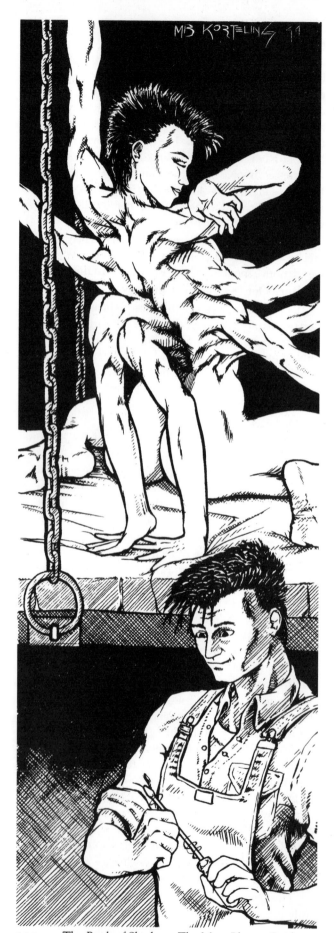

other in his mind. This is particularly useful when confusing pursuit in a large city, where wrong turns are a common occurrence. Virtual Adepts use a similar routine, called **Confuse Pointer File**, relabeling any given path to the point where the subject becomes hopelessly lost.

Talons (••• Life, •• Matter, •• Prime)

The origins of this rote have been lost to antiquity; its popularity with Euthanatos, Verbena and Akashic Brothers can not be denied, and Iteration X uses a variant of it in their cybernetic enhancement programs. The mage in question extends the bones in her fingers through the skin, hardens them into steel-like claws, and fuels the resulting blades with Prime energy. The result, a gauntlet of blazing blades, is highly vulgar, but very effective in a knock-down drag-out fight.

[The claws enable the mage to do her Strength+2 in aggravated damage, with a difficulty of 6 on rolls to hit. The claws last for two turns per success scored and drain one Quintessence from the mage's supply with each successful strike.]

Pygmalion's Paradigm (•••• Matter, ••• Life, •• Prime, •• Spirit)

This rote was supposedly developed by the ancient mage, Pygmalion, in an effort to create another being who would understand his bizarre conception of Reality. Working with ivory and gold, Pygmalion transformed matter into a receptive vessel for a spirit-being. The result of Pygmalion's experiment was the familiar he called Galatea (see Book Three for rules detailing familiars).

Pygmalion is said to have originally intended to create a whole community of such familiars, but became so jealously protective of Galatea that he could not bear the thought of any other creature distracting him from the profound link with Galatea. Some mages, however, maintain that Galatea soon became the dominant personality in the relationship, and simply told Pygmalion she would leave if he created another golem. These mages also insist that Pygmalion went into a state of deepest Quiet when Galatea eventually tired of this reality. The truth is a matter for debate, but legend claims Pygmalion became extraordinarily powerful following Galatea's creation.

[The number of successes determines the maximum familiar power level the prepared body is capable of holding. The mage is still limited by his own capabilities to attract a powerful familiar, however. To create a familiar out of living flesh, see the Life Sphere description (**Mage**, pg. 197-201).]

The Poison Maiden (•••• Life)

The Euthanatos pioneered this rote as one of the most insidious forms of assassination. After conferring immunity to a particular poison, the mage then infuses the subject with the toxin, so much that it sweats from her pores and comes out with each breath. This lasts for a number of months equal to the successes; five or more successes make it permanent. While the maiden given to

Alexander the Great is the classic example, the subject needn't be a maiden, and the poison needn't be belladonna, although the Hollow Ones who have learned this rote find it stylish.

Song of Orpheus (●●●● or ●●●●● Life, ●● Matter, ●● Prime, ●● Time, ●● Spirit)

Dreamspeakers tell of Orpheus, who so loved his wife Eurydice that he journeyed to the underworld to bring her back. Orpheus failed, but other mages have succeeded in this Effect. The mage must have the body on hand, restore the fragmented pattern, revivify the corpse and summon the spirit back to its mortal shell. However, if the death was not recent, it may be difficult to contact the spirit, and the mage may only succeed in restoring the body, but not returning the soul.

[With the very recently dead (those still recognizable and without missing parts), Prime is unnecessary, while those mages who wish to give a nasty (or wonderful) surprise to a vampire have found no need for the Sphere of Spirit, as a vampire's spirit is already there to revivify the corpse (unless it has been sold or stolen...). The Sphere of Time is needed only if the body is missing, in which case the fifth level of Life must be used, while the second level of Matter is made unnecessary. The difficulty of this rote often depends more upon the circumstances than on the Spheres used. Also note that the revivification might not be permanent. Storytellers can, and should, make this rote as difficult as they like.

[Entire Chronicles can be based on attempting to use this rote successfully. After all, there are forces that attack mages who attempt such impudent magicks, and there can be very severe or bizarre consequences for mages who fail. (Remember the Monkey's Paw?)]

Call Forth the Forgotten: (●●●●● Life, ●● Prime, ●● Spirit)

This rote was created originally by the Marauders, but has since gained a certain popularity among the Tradition mages. **Call Forth the Forgotten** allows a mage to summon forth a creature of myth. While the beast is likely to be grateful for the summons, the mage has no control over the mythic creature, save deciding what type of creature appears.

While there is a obvious risk involving Paradox, the mages have learned that summoning a dragon into this reality while fighting the Technocracy is likely to at least buy the mage time to escape while the Technocracy tries to restore order. Each success on the roll allows the summoned creature to maintain its tenuous hold on reality for one turn.

[Spirit magick summons the (hopefully!) appropriate spirit from the Umbra while the Life and Prime Spheres build the spirit a body to inhabit. Without Forces or other Spheres, the creature has only physical powers. A dragon, for example, could not fly or breathe fire without additional magicks.]

Do Rotes

If one seeks to unravel his sensation from the mesh in which it lies caught, he will find the charm of the thing to consist, I think, in energetic rhythm.

— Percival Lowell, *Occult Japan*

Although the Akashic Brothers are the only modern practitioners of Do in its original form, legend relates that once all people, Sleepers and Awakened alike, practiced Do— not as some specialized meditative art, but simply as the Way in which they lived their lives. This could be considered the Mythic Age of Asia. The heroes of these ages demonstrate feats not only of martial prowess, but of physical and mental superheroics which could only be considered magickal in this day and age. Though this is generally attributed to practice of Do, the fabric of reality remains far more mutable in the Orient. The Western ideas of the Technocracy came late to this part of the world, although their foundations can be found in the perfection ethics of Chinese philosophy.

Miraculous powers have been attributed to martial art masters. Tales of their feats have passed through history virtually unaltered and unexaggerated, preserved in literature, dance, and most notably, in the evolution of Chinese street opera into the modern martial arts movie. Although western audiences tend to consider these films absurd, they may be taken as accurate representations of what an advanced Akashic Brother may be capable of in combat.

The magickal Effects below can be used only with certain Do maneuvers. Unlike special maneuvers (Book Three), these powers are True Magick, and are subject to the usual rules of Quintessence and Paradox. Most are extremely vulgar, but quite traditional. Depending on the circumstances, the Storyteller may consider many flamboyant Effects coincidental if the setting is appropriate (a martial arts tournament, remote Chinese village, late-night movie house, etc.).

Dragon Fist (●●● Life, ●● Prime, sometimes ●●● Forces)

Required Maneuver: Punch or Kick

This rote is credited to Slayer D, who stood resolute against a plague of vampires that swept across his lands. Realizing that his Do skills did little lasting harm to the undead, Slayer D focused his Chi into his hands and feet, making them blaze with concentrated power which burned the screaming bloodsuckers.

[By channeling Prime Chi behind his blows, the mage may do aggravated damage with his Do attacks. A variant on this technique causes the mage's fists to literally burst into flame, burning his target, but not himself. This vulgar attack allows the mage to add an extra die to his damage. Both attacks expend one Quintessence for every blow that lands, as the energy discharges against the target.]

Screech of the Owl (••• Mind, ••• Entropy)
Required Maneuver: Kiai

Much of the philosophy of martial arts involves avoiding physical conflict altogether, and few have embodied this principle better than Nichiba, who walked through thirty-six battles and seventy-two personal challenges without ever striking a blow.

[By augmenting his Chi in this way, the Brother can psychologically stun a number of opponents equal to his Stamina + Intimidation, rendering them incapable of action for a number of turns equal to his successes.]

Piercing Cry (••• Matter, ••• Entropy)
Required Maneuver: Kiai

Folktales tell of Cheng Sa, The Avenging Woodcutter, who would offer to split logs in exchange for millet, then carry the wood into the forest and emit a series of piercing cries. Afterward, the assembled crowd would marvel at the stacked cordwood and wonder how he did it all without an axe.

[By augmenting his Chi in this way, the Brother can shatter objects. All objects are not affected equally; double the successes of the magickal effect roll to determine the effective Strength to shatter. One success allows the Brother to break glass, while three or four may be needed to crack a wall or heavy door.]

Long Fist (•••• Correspondence, •• Prime)
Required Maneuver: Punch

A punch is no longer merely the impact which can be delivered at arm's length, but may be projected through space beyond the body's limits. Astute military scholars have noted that the Shaolin Monastery did not fall to the Manchu army until General Kwai Chien ordered his troops to attack in a staggered formation instead of their traditional straight-line marching order.

[By channeling her Chi force into her punch, the Brother can strike one additional target per success. This rote does normal Force damage (successes times 3), not the Brother's usual punch damage. Long Fist may also be used to punch a target at a distance (range equals 3 yards per level of Do), or to punch "through" an intervening object or person, such as walls, car doors, loved ones, etc., without disturbing it/them (+2 difficulty). The punch can only travel in a straight line, so multiple targets must be situated directly behind one another.]

Flying Dragon Kick (•••• Forces, • Correspondence)
Required Maneuver: Flying Kick

The Stone Sutra relates that Yu Fong initiated this maneuver from his monastery in the Himalayas to successfully attract the attention of Wao Mu Ling when that venerable hermit did emerge from the Thrang grotto at

Mount Taishan, over one hundred and eight miles away, for his yearly sip of water and breath of air. This may, of course, be a slight exaggeration…

[The Brother leaps into the air for a normal leaping kick, and remains in flight until target is reached, even if it involves several minutes of cross-country travel, so long as the target was in sight when the kick began and the mage travels in a straight line. Damage is equal to the number of successes times 3. Yes, this *is* vulgar as hell.]

Talismans

Shout, if you will, but that just won't do.
I, for one, would rather follow softer options
—Jethro Tull, "Flying Colours"

The Talismans given here are built according to the new rules given in Book Three. The Quintessence amounts listed are the maximum the item can contain; "found" Talismans may have much less. Storytellers are advised to tread lightly with Talismans; remember that they are tied to specific Effects, not to general Sphere magicks. Players are advised to use Talismans as storytelling devices, not world-destroyers.

Talismans are much more than "rotes-in-a-box"; they are objects imbued with the Prime essence of creation and shaped by sculpted reality. They are *not* common, even among the Technocracy. Mages respect Talismans as the product of hard work, vision and power. These magickal tools are never treated lightly.

The numbers of dots refer to a general ranking of the Talisman's power, *not* the total point cost for owning one. Storytellers who wish to calculate the point cost of a Talisman are referred to pg. 110 of Book Three.

•• Golden Walnut
Arete 3, Quintessence 10

This Talisman is a large walnut with a rich amber coloring that shines in strong lighting. When a mage grasps the walnut tightly in her hand and focuses her will upon an individual plant, she can call upon the powers of life to extrapolate the growth mechanism of that plant.

The surface areas of the plant, most notably leaves and roots, become gorged with Quintessence, and are able to draw in nutrients much faster than normally possible. Cells replicate at a greatly increased speed.

The Verbena tend to utilize Golden Walnuts the morning or evening before mystick ceremonies to insure that flowering plants are in bloom. They also call upon these Talismans' powers to make plants yield greater harvests, increasing both the number of successful blooms and the size of the individual fruits, vegetables, etc. A mage focusing his will for a matter of minutes can cause a seed to sprout, pass through the dangerous "days" of seedling growth and strengthen into a healthy plant that will surely reach adulthood. Trees can be made to sprout new branches, and fast growing plants like bamboo can be made to grow several feet nearly instantly.

•• Lycanthroscope
Arete 3, Quintessence 15

The Lycanthroscope was created to track down werewolves, more politely termed "Garou." Using the Spheres of Life and Spirit to look for known traits of werewolves, the Lycanthroscope shows higher readings in the general direction of the nearest werewolf. There is a meter on the box with a needle that indicates intensity and a flashing light that warns as the scientist gets dangerously close to the Garou in question. Variants exist for detecting vampires, wraiths and faeries.

[This device allows an additional + 2 dice to any Perception + Awareness rolls used to detect the being in question.]

•• Prayer Beads
Arete 4, Quintessence 20

The Akashic Brotherhood are known most for their devastating martial arts and superior powers of the mind. Yet the Brotherhood has always been an organization of peace. Throughout history, Adepts of the Akashic Brotherhood have worn such Talismans in order to keep peace around them.

The Prayer Beads generate peace by radiating thoughts of serenity; this is the second rank of the Mind Sphere at work projecting thoughts into other peoples' minds. While the Brother clutches the beads, he is also able to sense all animal life in the surrounding area via the Life Sphere. If the Brother ceases all motion, most animals will leave him completely alone (though a hungry tiger will not be turned away!). The Brotherhood wishes everyone to go through their natural flow, but causing someone to be peaceful is a better alternative than using Do to soundly trounce someone or something into non-aggression.

••• Cord of Three Winds
Arete 4, Quintessence 20

With this traditional Verbena magick, a particular specialist, called a "storm wife," uses a teakettle in place of a cauldron and whistles up a wind, binding a wind spirit into a knotted cord. When the cord is undone, the spirit is released and will blow a wind from whatever direction the mage summons. Traditionally, these cords will have three knots, the first holding a gentle west wind, the second holding a stronger east wind, and the third holding a furious north wind.

••• Fan of Kang Wu

Arete 5, Quintessence 25

An avid warrior-mage, Kang Wu, had a terrible reputation as a troublemaker. In order to conceal his weaponry, Kang Wu had a Talisman crafted to suit his needs.

This simple-looking silk fan has the power of the third rank of the Sphere of Matter. Through the use of the **Sculpture** Effect, Kang Wu was able to convert the fan into any melee weapon he could imagine. In addition, the fan has the power of the second rank of the Sphere of Force; the fan can become magnetically attractive or repulsive. The fan's final property is to sense Quintessence with the first rank of the Sphere of Prime.

During long sustained battles, Kang Wu would not only convert the fan from one weapon into another, but would also utilize it to find out what items the enemy mage possessed that were filled with Quintessence (Talisman, fetishes, Tass, etc.). Once located, Kang Wu would proceed to remove these objects from the opponent. He defeated many an unwary mage in this manner.

••• Glasses of Speed Reading

Arete 3, Quintessence 15

Wear this Talisman while reading and immediately begin to absorb information. The mind is rocked with the impulse to memorize, information is dumped into the brain paragraph by paragraph rather than word for word, and time is dilated so an entire book can be read in next to no time.

Size of the book and the level of complexity of information will rate the difficulty for comprehension and length of time necessary to "read" the text.

••• Herbal Plaster of the Ancients

Arete 3, Quintessence 15

These specially-treated pieces of cloth were developed by the Akashic Brotherhood to heal themselves quickly in times of dire emergency. The Talisman is activated as it is applied directly onto a wound. First, the Plaster analyzes the wounded area and figures out what needs to be done to cure the problem. Next, the Sphere of Prime channels energy into the wounded area. As the wound begins to coalesce with Quintessence, Life is used again to realign the person's Life Pattern to its natural state.

••• Master Remote

Arete 4, Quintessence 20

This Talisman is created to run any type of machinery that can be activated by remote control. The Talisman locates the method of information transmission— electrical, electromagnetic, etc.— and creates signals to activate the device.

The lettering on the top of the remote mutates as the Talisman is activated to label every function available on the accessed device.

••• Tonics and Potions

Arete n/a, Quintessence n/a

These herbal or alchemical mixtures have a variety of Effects, useful for one use each. The most common are medicines which prevent one disease or another. More useful are those which cure diseases. There are also tonics that raise attributes temporarily. Most, for safety's sake, contain coincidental magical Effects, as these elixirs may be used by Sleepers as well as the Awakened. One Life Effect, up to the third Rank, can be contained within a potion.

••• Wolf Link

Arete 4, Quintessence 20

The Talisman allows the mage take on the form of a wolf. As her Life Pattern is modulated to become a wolf, so too are her thought processes. This Effect will trick wolves and unwary Kindred or Garou as the mage is, for all practical purposes, a wolf. The Talisman blends in with the wolf-form during transformation; however, no clothing or other items will be transformed along with the mage.

•••• Carte Blanche

Arete 5, Quintessence 25

This is one of the most prized Talismans of the Virtual Adepts, though similar objects have been made by other Traditions down through the ages. The **Carte Blanche** is a small white credit card blank with a magnetic strip on the back. When inserted into any cash machine, pay point, electronic lock or such, it will act as a skeleton key, prompt the machine to greet John or Jane Doe, give him or her whatever cash is available, up to the regular transaction limit, or whatever access is usually permissible, and then erase the operation from the machine's log.

When given to a living being, **Carte Blanche** will appear as a driver's license, library card, or whatever form of identification the recipient expects, showing the name of whoever the mage says he or she is. **Carte Blanche** itself has an Arcane of 5 for purposes of people remembering the name on it, though it will not protect the mage's face. Spending one point of Quintessence will allow the card to function for a scene.

•••• Hand of Glory

Arete 5, Quintessence 25

One of the most celebrated of medieval Talismans, the **Hand of Glory** is also among the most potent. The Talisman is a mummified hand that has been taken from a hanged man and then soaked in various herbs, resins and the fat of a murdered man. The Hand is lit while the following charm is said: "Hand of Glory, Hand of Glory! Let those who are asleep, be asleep. Let those who are awake, be awake." The Hand then becomes a five-fingered candelabra of blue flame; the light thus shed highlights passages of magickal works being studied, while keeping the mage from falling asleep during such dry reading, and preventing the waking (and subsequent interruptions) of others in the same house who might be disturbed by midnight chantings.

The last Effect of the **Hand of Glory** is, however, the most famous and potent: any who see the burning hand will be paralyzed by fascination until the view is obscured or the Hand is extinguished. Mages, vampires and other Awakened creatures may spend a Willpower point to break this fascination, but regular mortals are snared by the Hand's magical light. The only substance which will extinguish this grisly Talisman once it's lit is milk. (The symbolism of this can be explained by the Verbena and Nephandi who create these artifacts.)

•••• Nine-Dragon Tattoos

Arete 5, Quintessence 30

Developed by the Akashic Brotherhood (with variations by the Cult of Ecstasy and Dreamspeakers), this Talisman is formed and endowed with its power directly on the surface of an Adept's skin through a mystickal tattooing process known to a chosen few. Though rumor has it that the tattoos still possess their power after a Brother's death, few would dare offend the Akashic Brotherhood by attempting to use the skin of a Brother as a Talisman.

As the tattooing inks are impregnated into the Brother's skin, the Patterns that make up the powers inherent in specific Spheres of magick are woven into the individual's flesh. These tattoos are not stagnant, but move about the body in very slow repetitive sequences when activated.

The tattoos work to sense life in the general surroundings, whether it is in the physical Realm by means of the Life Sphere or in the Umbra by the Sphere of Spirit. The three tattoos of red dragons make their way to the Brother's arms and face. The dragons, now emblazoned on each forearm, begin to roar and flick their tongues out in the direction of sensed life forms. If the sensed creature is within the Realm, the dragons' wings are held tight against the body. If the creature is within the Umbra, the dragon will unfurl its wings. Typically, the dragon on the right arm responds to the Tellurian Realm, while the one on the left responds to the Umbra.

The green dragon tattoos help the Brother to maintain order about himself by lowering the rate of Entropy in the surrounding area. One green dragon dominates the Brother's back with wings outstretched, while the second likewise fills the chest. The third green dragon darts about the body and spits out fire at any source of entropy. The Brother merely outstretches his arm toward Entropic events, and the third green dragon's use of the Sphere of Entropy will increase the amount of order present (**Control Randomness**).

The three white dragon tattoos function to open a gateway into the Umbra through which the Brother can pass. These dragons possess the knowledge of the third rank of the Spirit Sphere and enable the Brother to step into the Umbra once they have migrated as a group onto the Brother's chest. With their tails wrapped together and claws extended, they slowly shred their way through the Gauntlet and into the Umbra.

• • • • Thought Transference Device

Arete 6, Quintessence 30

This large Talisman takes up about half a room. It has two large seats and metal caps that fit over the two subjects' heads. As the Talisman is activated, the brains of the two subjects are literally teleported via the Correspondence Sphere. The brains are switched. The Life Pattern of each subject is altered. Even though each subject's brain is in the other subject's body, each can still function as if he was familiar with the motions of the other person's body.

Talents are specific to the body in question, so a person with a low Brawl skill can gain Brawling abilities by putting his mind into a professional boxer's body. Skills and Knowledges, however, require use of the mind.

This Effect only lasts for a day before the body will begin to reject the alien brain.

Silicon Servants

I'm your little friend
I'm not your only friend
But I'm your little glowing friend
But really I'm not actually your friend
But I am…
— They MIGHT Be Giants, "Birdhouse in Your Soul"

These computers exemplify the Trinary computers of the Virtual Adepts. These computers are unique foci (**Mage**, pg. 179), not Talismans, although magick goes into their creation. Trinary decks can store downloaded rotes for quick use later. Normal computers can do this, but only with rotes of the first or second Sphere. Though other mages may use Trinary computers, it's fairly difficult (an additional + 2 to + 4 to difficulties) due to the complexity of the machines. Virtual Adepts, it should be noted, are very possessive of their Trinary decks!

Alpha Series: "The First Name in Computers"

Alpha Computing creates Trinary computers for connected Virtual Adepts. Their output, obviously, is quite low, and prices are high, but their quality is superb. Alpha's current high-end model, the Alpha IX, has a Kevlar coating that allows it to double as an emergency shield and protects it from most damage. The IX has a built-in modem able to transmit at speeds well beyond 14.4s. Several gigabytes of storage space reside in the briefcase-sized machine. Also, Alphas have multiple processors. Each contains hundreds of megs of memory, making them able to do amazing multi-tasking. They also have tremendous processing speeds. The Alpha IX may read and write CDs as well as access the more common 5 1/4" and 3 1/2" discs, and can translate every type of mundane computer language.

An internal power supply allows the Alpha IX to function for days (or at least until a mage botches his Computer roll). Several serial ports and built-in connections let the Alpha interface with nearly any other system. Alphas also contain full multi-media systems, and have built-in scanners.

The key reason for Alpha's success is reliability. Alphas may run out of power, but they never break down. Once a mage owns an Alpha, she has a focus forever.

Elite Series: "The Name Says It All"

Second only to Alphas in popularity, the Elite Series laptops have limited artificial intelligence, and all come with Net On-Line Packages. As an additional feature, two knives are hidden on the underside of the computer, so the Adept is never unarmed.

Elites respond to their user's voice commands and do not have a traditional keypad. Like the Alphas, they contain gigabytes of storage space and tremendous memory. They are also full multi-media machines with the capability of doubling as cellular phones. The Elite even contains its own answering machine. Elites may connect to almost any interface, and they may read/write any type of storage device, even CDs. Elites come with headphones and have a five-CD holder for audio CDs as well.

As an option, the Storyteller may allow the AI within an Elite computer to have points in various Knowledges. If a player desires this type of AI, she must spend one Background point per Knowledge point in the computer. The points add to the mage's own score, but the mage's total Knowledge score may not exceed 5.

Elites suffer from only one major drawback: they break relatively easily. If a mage botches a computer roll while using an Elite, the machine breaks down. An extended Intelligence + Technology roll (difficulty 8, 10 successes) must be made to get it operating again. A botch at any point on this roll means that the mage needs at least a day of work

to repair her computer. Nonetheless, Elites remain popular; some Adepts claim that "if you're good, you don't mind living on the edge." To get an Elite, potential customers must perform a service for the Elite Cabal. Some say these services include terrorist-style attacks on Alpha Computing.

Grandmaster Computer: "The Key to Knowledge"

The Grandmaster series of computers are probably on their way out with the Adepts. They are the Trinaries that aren't completely portable. Grandmasters are barely luggable machines, weighing around 25 pounds. The machine folds into a large briefcase. Some Adepts joke that Grandmasters also make great bashing weapons.

A Chantry of Virtual Adepts manufactures two types of Grandmasters: the White Knight and the Grandmaster-1000. The White Knight has several terabytes of storage space, making it larger than the Alphas, and it performs almost all of the same functions as the Alpha IX. Though it doesn't interface nearly as well with other machines and doesn't have the Kevlar coating, the White Knight does contain a fast high-quality color laser printer.

The Grandmaster-1000 has the same features as a White Knight, with one additional function. Each Grandmaster-1000 contains a level 4 Talisman, a **Magickal Macro Keyboard** (Arete 7, Quintessence 30). The user prepares a magickal Effect and casts it into the board. He then designates a single key or sequence of keys to press to release the magick. When the mage uses the stored magicks, then Paradox is determined.

Sadly, the Grandmaster series has the same breakdown problems as the Elites. In recent years, some mages have returned Grandmaster-1000 models because "they weren't cool enough."

Book Five: Parables

Magical systems are highly elaborated metaphors, not truths... The value of magical metaphors is that through them we identify ourselves and connect with larger forces... But if we use them for glib explanations and cheap categorizations, they narrow the mind instead of expanding it and reduce experience to a set of formulas that separate us from each other and our own power.

— Starhawk, *The Spiral Dance*

Mage is a game of stories, of trials faced and choices made. Though elements of these tales, like Quintessence or the guiding Avatar, remain abstract, the mages depending on them feel the force of the indefinable every day of their lives.

Is the Avatar the soul, the mind, the self or something else? Does the Seeking take one into the spirit Realms, the inner self or another reality entirely? Does Quintessence form the foundations of Life, or does it spring *from* Life? The most enlightened mages have wrestled with these questions for centuries and seem no closer to real answers. Many argue that to quantify such ideas, setting them in stone, would press the magickal essence from them, like Void Engineers mapping the magick from hidden places. Better, then, to delve into concepts like Paradox or the Seeking in fables and read the lessons between the lines than to try to hammer them into dry text. The hard crust of fantasy seems more nurturing, in the long run, than dry and crumbling facts.

Stories provide guideposts to the Path of the Awakened. Follow with an open mind and a questing heart.

The Signposts of the Mage's Path

... Your pious English habit of regarding the world as a moral gymnasium built expressly to strengthen your character in occasionally leads you to think about your own confounded principles when you should be thinking about other people's necessities.

— George Bernard Shaw, *Man and Superman*

Mahmet,

For your edification, an excerpt from *The Book of Humours*, written by the Hermetic mage Livius (ca. 1352, my translation) and based loosely in the tradition of the medieval animal fable. Even though it is a dated set of allegories, it contains kernels of truth applicable today; read this and understand what you face on the Path ahead— and what you've left behind.

— Porthos

CHOLERA: The Farmer and the Mouse

Moral for Apprentices: Hunger for knowledge gnaws at those meant for the Path, but overzealousness kills those who indulge.

Long ago, on a small country farm, lived a mouse whose only desire in the world was to visit the city. It so happened that it was early spring, and the farmer, who owned the farm, was preparing to travel to the city to buy some seed. As he saddled the horse, he glimpsed the little mouse clambering into a small bag in the back of his cart.

"Ho there, little mouse! What be ye a-doing?" cried he.

Squeaked the brave little mouse, "I am travelling with you to the big City, as it appears that you are headed there."

"What be ye a-wanting to find there, Mouse?" asked the farmer, amused.

The little mouse, his eyes sparkling with anticipation, replied, "The answer to everything. Surely in the City there is one who can do justice to my quest, and I intend to find him."

The farmer shook his head. "The journey to the City is long. Is this Answer worth leaving your family and friends here on the farm?"

Replied the mouse, "It is worth suffering and dying for, Farmer. I would do anything to know the answer to everything."

"Well," said the farmer, a bit surprised, "I can't promise ye the Answer, but ye'er welcome to join me if ye carry ye'er weight."

The mouse perched precariously on the bag. "I will help you in every way I can!" he eagerly declared.

"Then," said the farmer, "I'll steer the cart, guide us to the City, and provide us with food along the way if ye will but scrape the horse's hooves clean o' mud, ensure the cart's axle-pins 'r in place, and wax my saddle."

"That I will, and more," promised the eager little mouse. And he got right to work.

When the mouse had finished, the farmer, who had been watching him, said, "Ye have a great deal of talent, Mouse. I'll be happy to have you with me on the journey to the City." Having said this, he mounted the horse and snapped the reins. The horse started off at a slow trot, and the cart jolted forward.

The little mouse had never ridden a cart before and was quite overwhelmed by the feeling of the wind against his fur. He climbed to the very top of the sack, right near the wall of the cart, and stood on his tiptoes, nose to the breeze. Just then, the cart hit a rut in the road.

The mouse, jarred by the bump, fell out of the cart, straight into a muddy puddle right in the path of the wheel. The farmer, hearing the mouse's frightened squeak, reined back the horse just in time.

Cried the farmer, "What be ye a-doing in that puddle there, Mouse?"

Angrily, the sodden mouse shouted, "You jolted the cart, and I fell out into this puddle. You should be more careful!"

"Would ye rather ye were back at the farm?" said the farmer.

The mouse replied irascibly, "Indeed not. Yet I would rather have my hand at the reins than let you continue to jolt me into mud puddles in this manner!"

"Then ye try, Mouse, and see how ye fare." The farmer climbed into the cart and rested his head against the sack, while the mouse climbed atop the horse's saddle, gathered the reins, and pulled as hard as he could on them. The horse, not feeling the slightest tug, blithely continued to nibble on the grass.

Finally, the mouse said to the farmer, "Would you pull on these reins so we could at least get started?" The farmer tugged on the reins, and again the mouse and the farmer were off.

After some hours of travelling, the mouse said, "The road to the City is much longer and more difficult than I ever expected, and I am beginning to miss my family."

The farmer laughed. "The path is much longer and more difficult than ye suspect even now, Mouse, and ye'll miss ye'er family even more. Is the Answer still worth the cost?"

Without hesitation, the mouse replied, "Yes! I would not abandon it for all the families in the world."

Some hours later, they came to a hill where the path rapidly descended into a rocky valley. As they began down it, the horse and cart sped up, and the mouse tightened his grip on the reins. Soon, the horse and cart were lurching down the steep path rather too quickly for the mouse's taste. The mouse pulled back the reins, but the horse continued just as fast as before. Desperately, he pulled on the reins, the cart now swaying precariously in the horse's wake. Then the farmer, who had been sleeping, awoke and clambered to the front of the cart. Taking the reins, he slowed the horse just before it came to a large stone in the road that would surely have overturned the cart and its occupants.

"Mouse, did ye not see this steep hill and the stones in the path?" the farmer asked angrily.

Replied the mouse, "Yes, but the horse would not heed my reins."

Said the farmer, "'T'isn't the horse's fault, but ye who have not the ability to handle the horse. I'll take the reins, and ye'll learn how to guide the horse by watching me."

And so the farmer did. As for the wise little mouse, for the rest of the day, and the rest of the journey, he carefully watched the farmer, took heed of the path to the City, and never again complained about who held the reins.

MELANCHOLIA: The Fish in the Pond

Moral for Disciples: Beware three things: your newfound power, your enemies who know how to use it against you, and, most of all, yourself when you discover that you will never overcome either.

Once, in a deep pond whose waters ran down to the sea, there lived a fish who could swim faster, farther, and longer than all of his schoolmates combined. The fish bragged grandly of his prowess to his family and friends, until everyone had grown tired of his boasts. His schoolmates, whom he had humiliated one too many times, wanted to kill him, but they dared not do so before all the other fish in the pond.

Thus, one day, one of the fish's schoolmates said, "Brother, we do not believe that you can beat us to other side of the pond. We want you to prove it to us."

Said the fish, "I have beaten all of you to the other side of the pond and back again many a time. Why should I again, when I know I will win?"

The fish's schoolmates, who had anticipated his response, replied, "You are right. You are a better swimmer than all of us combined. Perhaps we should change the game."

"Oh?" said the fish, "And how do you propose the game should be changed?"

Replied one of the fish's schoolmates, "Do you see the fly on that reed, just above the water?"

"Yes," said the fish, seeing a vague, black speck far above the surface of the water.

"One of us will jump out of the water and catch that fly. To beat him, you will have to jump out just as far or farther."

The fish, never before having beaten his schoolmates in this fashion, agreed. His competitor, who was to go first, swam to the very bottom of the pond, and then shot straight up, faster and faster, past all the other fish who had gathered

around to watch. And sure enough, the fish's schoolmate broke through the pond's surface, caught the fly in his mouth, and then plunged back into the cool water.

The fish was astounded and jealous. With all the power he could muster, he swam straight up, streaming past the onlookers, and leaped into the warm air. Up and up he sailed toward the hot summer sun. Thinking that he had passed over the top of the reed, with a flick of his tail, he turned and fell towards the water.

"I will show my schoolmates who is the best swimmer in the pond, and then they will never want to compete again!" thought the fish.

But instead of landing in the cool water as he thought he would, the fish landed hard on the packed earth along the pond's edge. Unable to breathe, the fish flopped about, trying to throw himself back into the water.

"Help me!" cried the fish desperately. He flopped some more, and then some more, but no help arrived. Soon, gloomy thoughts of death overcame him, and he rested quietly on the hot earth, tired and ready to die.

After waiting a while, his schoolmates gathered in the water around the shore. Having suspected that the fish would jump so far and so high that he would land on shore, they gloated, "We are sorry you have proven to us that there is no one here so strong and so fast that he can save you. But you have won."

The fish struggled once again, but, without hope, he soon died on the bank of the pond.

PHLEGMA: The Tortoise and His Shell

Moral for Adepts: Caring softens you to hard blows, but it also gives your life purpose.

One morning just before dawn, a wise old owl lit upon a branch near a pond, thinking it a nice place to sleep for the day. Beneath him, he happened to notice a young tortoise lying on the cold, leaf-covered ground. At first, the owl thought the tortoise was asleep, for the tortoise did not move at all. But then he began to wonder why the tortoise had not drawn his limbs into the safety of his shell for the evening.

"Perhaps Tortoise is just resting," thought the old owl. Then, a few minutes later, "What if Tortoise is ill?" and "What if Tortoise is dead?" The owl could no longer ignore the Tortoise, and so he flapped down to land on the ground beside him.

"Tortoise, are you asleep?" asked the owl.

The tortoise slowly lifted his head to look at the owl. "No," he replied.

The owl bent over to peer into the tortoise's face. "Then are you ill?"

"No," said the tortoise.

"Then, for heaven's sake, what is wrong?" asked the owl.

The tortoise, unconcerned, slowly lowered his head back to the ground. "Why should you care?"

"Because I am your neighbor." The owl stamped his foot. "What is wrong?"

Looking out at the pond, which was just beginning to ice over with the fall's chill touch, the tortoise replied, "If you care to know, Owl, then I will tell you. Snake is a powerful enemy, and he has killed my entire family and all my friends. I am the only tortoise left in this pond."

The owl was taken aback. "Why do you sit here exposed if Snake is so dangerous?" he asked.

The tortoise snorted. "Because I don't care if he kills me— I have nothing left to live for."

"Of course you do," the Owl encouraged. "You must work to improve the pond by ridding it of Snake. You must remember your friends and family who have died."

Said the tortoise, "But how can I when I do not care to live?"

The owl thought for a moment, then replied, "I know of a way, but you will have to trust me."

The tortoise yawned. "Do what you will. I do not care."

Said the owl, "Then I must ask you to crawl out of your shell."

The tortoise blinked. "Out of my shell? Why?"

"Ah, Tortoise," said the owl, "you do care what becomes of your hide. Don't worry— I only mean to carry you above the pond so that you can see where Snake lies."

The tortoise thought about the owl's offer, then sluggishly emerged from the warmth of his shell into the frigid dawn air. "We had better find Snake," warned the tortoise.

"Don't worry," said the wise old owl, "you will spot your enemy immediately." With that, he caught the tortoise in his talons and took off. Slowly, he flapped his great white wings and lifted them above the trees and above the pond. As they flew, the sun rose and the air warmed.

The tortoise looked down at the tiny pond and his tinier shell, abandoned, far below him and suddenly felt relieved of a great burden. "Owl," said he, "how can I ever thank you?"

Replied the sage owl, "Live like an owl, without your shell, for then you will remain strong, independent, and free of earthly burdens. Secondly, pursue your purpose, for then you will have reason to remain so."

The owl descended from the heights and put the tortoise back on the ground. Said the owl, "Did you spot your enemy?"

Then the tortoise realized that the view had been so beautiful that he had forgotten to look for Snake. "Truly," said he, "the only thing aside from the pond and the trees I remember seeing was my shell."

"Then," said the wise old owl, "you spotted your enemy."

SANGUIS: The Lion and the Mouse

Moral for Masters: Master hope, even in the midst of lost freedom, and a commitment to truth, and you will master your own life.

It is said that many years ago, there was a lion who lived the worrisome life of king of the jungle. While he had few

responsibilities and no one to look after, he had to watch his back, for treachery was rife in his court. All of the jungle animals were envious of him, for it seemed that the lion had everything: power over all the animals of the jungle and the freedom to live his life as he chose.

The lion, however, felt that he had little; the court over which he presided was corrupt. He had searched long and hard for happiness: he had bullied others, but that had only created enemies. He had tried to occupy his mind through study, but found theory dry. He tried to make friends, but they seemed only to respect his position. He had to give up family and friends to find knowledge; when he found knowledge, he found power; when he found power, he found enemies; when he found enemies, they destroyed his family and friends; in fighting his enemies, he thought he had discovered a purpose to life, but later found it dark.

Now, this lion had surrounded himself with the most learned advisors in the jungle, but none of them had been able to show him what happiness was. In fact, these very same advisors helped him seek happiness and plotted to kill him in the same breath. The lion, who once was convinced that he would someday find what he sought, was not so sure anymore.

One day, in the heat of noon, while his advisors were napping, the lion took a stroll in his garden and ran across a mouse.

"Good day, little mouse," said the lion. "How did you get inside the royal gardens?"

"I am sorry, your Majesty, but I had to sneak in here in order to find you," replied the mouse.

"To find me?" The lion laughed. "Do you not know that these gardens are private? I could have you killed."

Replied the brave little mouse, "Oh, please, hear me out. I have sought your Majesty far and wide, and I beg you to let me speak."

The lion, who did not intend to kill the mouse, was amused by the little one's bravery. "Speak on," said he.

"Thank you, Majesty," he said, and the little mouse bowed. "You see, I have sought the Answer far and wide; I have travelled from city to city, but I have not yet found what I seek. Now, I was told that you were knowledgeable and wise. I had dared to hope that you could guide me to the City I seek."

"Which City is that?" asked the lion.

"Why, the City that holds the Answer, your Majesty," replied the mouse.

"The answer to what, Mouse?," said the lion.

Said the mouse, "To life, Sir."

The lion chuckled in bitter amusement. Said he, "Life is but a series of failures, each one more desperate than the last. There is your Answer."

"Forgive me, Your Majesty, but you are wrong. Only those without hope would speak such foolishness. I am confident that there is an Answer, and I intend to find the City that holds it."

The mouse's frankness momentarily astonished the lion, for he was used to the cajoling lies of court. Said the lion, "Mouse, you are quite right. I am sure there is an Answer. I hesitate to take on the responsibility of showing you the way, but you have given me confidence in our eventual success."

Asked the mouse, "So you will show me the way?"

"If I can, I will indeed," said the lion.

Years later, the lion, remembering his adventures with the mouse, recalled their somber parting. Ranging far across the lion's kingdom, the mouse had not found his city. Finally, he had taken leave of the lion, who was sullen and gloomy.

Said the lion, "I am sorry you must go, Mouse. I know now that there is a City hidden somewhere in this realm, and I am determined to find it. I am sorry that you will miss it."

"Your Majesty," replied the mouse, "we have searched for many months now, and I grow weary. I long for my home."

"Seek your home, then, Mouse. Someday you will return here and we will continue our search."

"And will you return to court?" asked the mouse.

"Court? Heavens, no, Mouse. Court is a distraction from my seeking. I have never had as much control over my life as I do now. I intend to continue this way."

"Do you not miss your freedom?"

Said the wise lion, "Freedom? That was not freedom, friend; those years were a net binding me to my own self-indulgence. You have shown me freedom: your hope gave me wings, and my responsibility to you was the wind that lifted us."

The Mentor and the Disciple

The improvement of understanding is for two ends: first, our own increase of knowledge; second, to enable us to deliver that knowledge to others.

— John Locke

By learning, you will teach; by teaching, you will learn.

— Latin proverb

"You American kids think you know everything there is to know about teachers, no? Well, I teach you a thing or two."

Mother Francesca clutched her sun medallion and closed her eyes. For several long minutes, I shifted uncomfortably on my knees and watched the fragile old woman meditate. The room gradually grew hotter, until the walls seemed to shimmer with the heat of the Mediterranean sun. I found myself longing to be outside, bathing in the cool waters of the piazza's fountain.

Slowly, the Mother opened her eyes and gestured towards the shimmering walls. "Magick is wonderful study, no?" Her gaze slid towards me and her eyes narrowed. "I hear you try on your own? *E vero?*" The accusation hung heavily between us.

After a moment, I replied, "Yes, it's true."

"I tell you what's true. You're a fool—that's the truth." I sat there thinking that she had no right to tell me this, teacher or not. But before I could retort, she continued, "I tell you another truth: the Chorus keeps you in Roma until you learn to be less a fool. That lesson starts now."

With a slow, deliberate grace, the old woman lifted her hands high over her head. As she did, a breeze swept through the room, cooling it, but the walls continued to shimmer. A shadow crept across the room like slow molasses. The walls curved in as if I were seeing them through a fisheye lens, then seemed to drop away into a deep blackness, which gradually enveloped me. Still, I could see Mother Francesca sitting as she was before— except that her rickety wooden stool had become an ornate ivory throne inlaid with gold and studded with rubies and onyx. She stood, took my hand, and bade me stand. Everything seemed strange, new— when I looked at her face, it shone with the pure white light of an angel, flowing out onto the void.

Quietly, a sweet, longing melody more beautiful than even the most sublime note of Mozart's *Requiem*, a song of achingly distant joy, welled up around us, its source invisible. Its musical light bathed me, and I floated, uncomprehending, in it. Gradually, the music and light focused into one glorious, buoyant melody, sweeter than

the sweetest fruit, and I heard in the sound a voice like Francesca's:

"A mentor is a source of light and truth, a guiding Hand of the One."

I felt reawakened. Even after three years of study, my teacher in Williamsburg, who had treated me far better than the Mother did, had never shown me magick like this. This bent, gnarled old woman was awakening me to an essence I had never felt; she was lighting my soul on fire. It was beautiful— all I could think was that this was the teacher I sought. But Mother Francesca was no parlor magician on stage for my amusement.

Suddenly, I was plunging straight into the blazing inferno of a fiery sun.

Its boiling gasses curled around me, blinding me as I flew into it, white flames roared and deafened me, its hurricane winds tossed me like a paper doll— but I felt no heat. Gradually, I slowed to a stop. My vision returned, painfully. Yet my mind still reeled from shock and terror.

I was floating in the calm eye of a gargantuan cyclone of flame that stretched beyond sight above and below me. On all sides, flames raged, whirling upward in a mad dance. The shaft's crackling walls seemed to twist into each other and curve away miles above me. I felt fragile, vulnerable, horribly small. Mother Francesca's magick was my only protection from instant, fiery annihilation.

I squinted in the bright light, trying to look at Mother Francesca—and looked away, my eyes burning even more. She radiated brilliant light, like that of the ocean on a bright, breezy morning, when thousands of tiny waves scintillate in the sunlight. The radiant splendor of the One shone through her, a cool, glorious brilliance amidst the Stygian shadows of the flames.

"Mother Francesca," I cried, "what is this place?"

"This is the power— and danger— of your studies, child."

"Why did you bring me here?"

"To show you why you need a teacher, a true mentor." The Mother's accent had disappeared. She passed a cool hand over my burning eyes, and I could look again at her. Her face shimmered with a benign white light. She seemed tall, angelic.

"What do you mean?"

"I simply mean that you must learn why you are here and not in Williamsburg tinkering on your own with forces beyond your control. You need guidance, both away from dangers and toward your true path. If you are here to learn, I will show you your Avatar, the fragment of the One that resides in your innermost being. The One has chosen you to be consciously united with her, through your Avatar. As you learn more and seek your path with growing commitment, you will need to ask questions. I am honored that the One has chosen me to lead you to the right questions and to help acquaint you with your Avatar. Perhaps I will even learn with you.

She gave me her hand. "At the same time, I will show you the darkness within and outside of yourself. Books and magick do not seem like dangerous things until you learn the consequences of their contents. There are perils beyond your ken, child, but two in particular make your studies more dangerous than you realize."

"What are those?" I asked.

Mother Francesca gently brushed my cheek with her shining hand. "Yourself and others, little one. I am here to guide you through both snares."

I had heard such warnings from earlier teachers, and, of course, I didn't ignore them. Still, they never seemed to be pertinent. Yet there, in the midst of a sun that teemed with more shadows than there should have been, the words seemed somehow different. This time they held meaning.

As if she knew my thoughts, Mother Francesca added, "These snares are insidious: pride—which you know in abundance—Paradox, politics, foes and failure."

"So you're here to teach me about these snares?"

"No. I am here to teach you how to avoid them. If you will learn, I will teach you humility, a great gift that most mentors never bestow upon their unfortunate students. Humility reins back overconfidence, which can and will destroy you if it causes you to wield power you cannot control." She paused, as if to let her words settle in my mind. She continued, "As most mentors do, I will also teach you the power of coincidence, so that another reality does not destroy you. I will teach you what I know of the Traditions, their goals, and the dangers of such goals clashing. I will teach you to avoid your foes, of which you have many."

"What foes?"

"Hidden foes, and obvious foes. Many more than you suspect you have; probably more than I suspect you have." She released my hand and floated a short distance away. "And, last, I will teach you the fear of failure, which will destroy you, but which you can prevent if you are careful."

"I don't understand—"

"You will."

A cool breeze wafted past me, and I shivered pleasantly, incongruous as it seemed in the midst of the giant funnel of flame. Then, very suddenly, Mother Francesca disappeared and the heat of the solar cyclone blasted me mercilessly. I screamed in agony and terrified anger at her utter betrayal. I felt myself blacken and crumble to ash. Then, for one appalling, insane second, I knew nothing except the momentary, absolute horror of becoming utterly no one, the frightened, helpless moment just before the concept of "I" no longer had meaning. The moment passed, and all semblance of consciousness disappeared into void. "I" was no more.

Hours, maybe seconds later, from the dark maze of void that was mind, I heard the faint music of Francesca's voice whispering my name. Longing like instinct filled me, then lightness, and I felt myself floating up towards a bright, watery white light far above me.

My eyelids fluttered open, and I found myself kneeling before Mother Francesca in the little stucco room in the Roman cabal. She rested a warm hand on my cheek. Slowly, the madness dissipated. Gradually, my sense of self, my reality, returned like the flow of the ocean tide.

The wrinkled old woman, dwarfed now even by the low-ceilinged room, covered my hands with her gnarled hands and said, "I ask you now, child: what seems to be the most important aspect of learning magick?"

"Most important?" I meditated on the question. I thought about that moment of astonished horror just before I had ceased to exist. Then the thought struck me— the most obvious answer to the Mother's question—and I grasped to verbalize my newfound knowledge: "Mastery of oneself. The ability to resist the loss of your reality."

Mother Francesca smiled serenely. "Precisely, little one. Willpower, your ability to keep yourself while shaping reality, is most important. It is crucial to learning and to surviving. That, my child, is something no mentor can teach." She paused. "But know this: above all, and according to our own understanding of reality, mentors protect their disciples as a mother protects her child." Gently, she caressed my cheek and smoothed my brow. Slowly, peacefully, as if the Mother's words had soothed some wound deep within me, I slipped deep into slumber.

The Avatar and Essence

We know what we are, but know not what we may be.

— Ophelia, *Hamlet* Act IV, Scene V

One man is equivalent to all Creation. One man is a World in miniature.

— Abot de Rabbi Nathan. Palestine, 2nd century

To: sysop42@myob.org

From: blake@jedi.mit.edu

Subject: avatar & essence

Hope this line's secure, 'cause I'm ready to chat. BTW, when you gonna get me that headgear you've been talking about?

> Well, now that you've proven you won't sell your Avatar for a piece of technology, you'll get the headgear real soon.

>What do you mean "proven"?—Last weekend wasn't another test, was it? I thought you said the testing was over.

> I lied. ;) We had to be absolutely certain that you are who you appear to be. By refusing to give your password in exchange for access to the Technomancer database, you proved your loyalty.

> You know, I got this strange piece of e-mail the day before, warning me to keep my priorities straight. It didn't have any context at the time, and it didn't have a sender. I thought maybe it was one of your practical jokes.

> Interesting. The same thing happened to me when I was an initiate. You'll probably never guess who it turned out to be...

> New World Order?

> No, no, nothing like that...

> Who?

> My Avatar.

> Yeah, right.

> No, seriously. Every now and then, e-mail from an unnamed user appeared in my mailbox, warning me of something or predicting that I would do something I later did. It was eerie, until I realized that my Avatar was guiding me.

> You talk about your Avatar as if it's a real person, with goals & desires.

> It is, just as you're "real".

> You mean people are fooled by the e-mail and think there's really somebody sending it.

> No, I mean that there IS somebody sending it. It's not one of your mechanical MIT lab creations. It's a somebody, and when that somebody feels you're ready, it'll appear right in front of your eyes. In fact, it appears to some as a real, blood-pumping, air-breathing person.

> Yeah, but what about to others? What the hell does an Avatar look like to most of us? An angel with praying hands and feathered wings?

> To some. Others say they see a ghostly spirit or a shadow. Or Elvis. It depends on who you are, what you're like, and, to a small extent, what you expect to see: now and then I received e-mail from this mysterious person. After a while, that correspondence began to evolve into a sort of on-line hide-and-seek, where I'd wait at my mailbox (with my VR gear on) for mail from this stranger and then try to trace the mail back to its source.

> So what does your Avatar look like? I bet it's tall and geeky— taped glasses and a pocket protector, right?

> Hardly. More the strong, mysterious type. : o

I saw it once, a few years ago— fleetingly. It was beckoning to me from a dark alley on the Net. It was shadowy and vague, but it definitely resembled a human being. I walked towards it, but it seemed to drift into the back of the alley, and it disappeared before I could get a good look. A few seconds later, I overheard a conversation between a Virtual Adept from California and a HIT Mark. I was able to sneak away and report the VA as a traitor to some of the guys in L.A.

> Wow. You think your Avatar did that intentionally?

> Probably. Someone once told me that all our Avatars are fragments of an entity known as Prime. These shards, at some point in the hugely distant past, became our souls. Now all these shards want to do is become reunited, which can only happen when we reach Ascension. So our Avatars guide us little by little to global Ascension. Sleepers have Avatars, too, but theirs are such small fragments that most never know they have them. Our Avatars guide us so that we can guide Sleepers to Ascension and reunite Prime.

> What about Einstein and Gates—do they have Avatars?

>Most animals have them, but can't use them. Though if Einstein and Gates really can open beer cans as you claim, maybe we should rethink our theories about animals. Hmm... I wonder how their Avatars would speak to them?

> Doggy dreams, of course. How do they speak to mages?

> Of the Traditions? I met a member of the Cult of Ecstasy a few years ago who claimed that her Avatar spoke to her not in words, but through the "passionate emotions" that her music evoked. I suppose it's possible, but she seemed a little flaky. She called the Avatar her "Muse".

> What did her "Muse" say to her?

> Never told me. I wondered for a long time what it was like to hear your Avatar speak. Later, a friend of mine in the Order of Hermes told me that the Avatar appears to us in

five aspects, each which speaks to us differently: the Monitor, the Guardian, the Mover, the Progenitor, and the Fool.

> What do they mean?

> Well, to be honest, I'm not certain how the OOH views them. But I've come to interpret these aspects in my own way. The Monitor surfaces as our conscience. The Guardian guards the gate to Ascension to prevent pride from overwhelming us. The Mover motivates and guides us toward Ascension. The Progenitor and the Fool are two highly mysterious aspects of the Avatar, but seem to correspond to the birth and lineage of the Avatar and to what the transcendent nature of the Avatar will be when we attain Ascension.

> The lineage of the Avatar? You mean Avatars belong to families?

> Well, the OOH friend I was corresponding with seemed to think so. She said there were two main lineages, each of which had many branches. She termed the lineages "Dianoia" and "Res"—one Greek for "thought from meditation" and the other Latin for "physical thing". Bluntly put, the lineages represent the old mind/matter division.

> I bet she thought the OOH sprang from Dianoia.

> Actually, yes. But she went into more detail than that. She mentioned five branches: Mentem (pure intellect), Aesthetica (taste/aesthetics), Moralis (morality/ethics), Creatus (creative spirit), and Mutatio (shaping spirit). The first three, she said, were branches of Dianoia; the last two, branches of Res. She felt strongly that each Tradition had a governing Avatar lineage, but I've seen too many exceptions to believe it plausible.

> Let me guess: the OOH's lineage was Dianoia and Mentem.

> Right again. She claimed that the Dianoia: Mentem lineage governed the OOH, the Akashic Brotherhood, and the Dreamspeakers. The Dianoia: Aesthetica lineage, she said, governed the Cult of Ecstasy, and the Dianoia: Moralis lineage governed the Euthanatos and Celestial Chorus.

> So who are we?

> Res: Mutatio—us and the Sons of Ether. The only one left, Res: Creatus, governs the Verbena.

> What about the Orphans?

> She ignored them. She doesn't think they're mages at all.

> God, I can't stand those OOH mages. They're so stuck up!

> Actually, she's not that horrible, once you get past all the Latin drills and hocus-pocus numerology.

> Maybe. But the OOH's so set on the rank and file gig. They love the idea that we can be categorized or stuffed into arcane lineages that control our behavior.

> Not exactly. That's simplifying their position—like saying "being a software engineer has made me a software engineer." Chance determined the nature of your Avatar and, since you're in large part your Avatar, your Avatar determined your nature. Think of your Avatar as a being hidden within you that you haven't discovered yet.

> Very comforting. Does that mean I have just as much influence on it as it has on me?

> I don't know. What it does mean, though, is that you have SOME influence on it. Your decisions—moral, ethical, or otherwise— may attract or repulse your Avatar, just as they may attract or repulse other human beings. If you make decisions that you and your Avatar consider unethical or wrong, you may corrupt your Avatar or make it impotent.

> Impotent?

> Yup. A repulsed Avatar may fester and become as corrupt as the mage with whom it's associated and/or it may refuse to lead the mage to Ascension until the source of infection has been purified. Such mages are usually so preoccupied with self-loathing that they have very little energy left to learn about reality and magick. It's thought that the Monitor—that aspect of the Guardian that serves as the conscience— purposefully redirects the mage's energy into morbid self-loathing until the mage corrects his actions.

> That's the negative side... can a mage have a positive influence on his Avatar?

> Of course. The more good decisions a mage makes (by his Avatar's standards), the more secrets the Guardian lets him in on.

> So do you think my Avatar was pleased with me this weekend?

> I'm sure your Avatar is very satisfied with your decision.

> Think so?

> Beyond a doubt. We're holding this conversation, aren't we?

> Yeah, but I thought that this kind of teaching's the domain of the Avatar.

>

> Hello? You there, sysop? Damn it, are you there?

>

>

> exit chat
%who?
blake   ttyq5   Jan 6 3:23
the_mover   ttyq5   Jan 6 3:23

Quintessence and Tass

Great men are they who see that the spiritual is stronger than any material force.

— Ralph Waldo Emerson

To Daria, the sleeping Lupine looked and smelled like a huge flea-bitten mongrel with gigantic claws. Her Clique had come upon it as it slept at the back of the town dump; it was curled up inside a cave of broken furniture and old, soggy newspapers. Now it was frozen in sleep, thanks to Daria's friend Isbelle, who had incapacitated it using Time magick.

Still, Isbelle had posted guards, prepared to soothe the beast's rage if anything went wrong, while Rich, a Virtual Adept along for the ride, readied their getaway. They only had a few hours to steal Quintessence before the werewolf awoke.

"Daria, get your ass over here." Isbelle motioned her closer to the sleeping beast. Reluctantly, Daria approached. "You asked me before about Juice. I want to show you what it feels like to gather it."

"But—*this* is where we're getting it? In the middle of a junkyard?"

Isbelle chuckled. "I think you're afraid of the Pit Bull. Never mind him. C'mon, I'll show you how to get juiced." She slipped around the werewolf and merged into the shadows of its junkyard cave. The damp, musty smell of mouldering newspapers wafted out of the cave. Daria stepped inside, careful to avoid the slumbering beast.

The frail beam of Isbelle's flashlight lit vague shapes and the edges of deeper holes. Daria fervently hoped they were formed by rusting refrigerators and other forgotten furniture. In the darkness, she could hear a steady, hollow plink, like raindrops on metal, and tiny squeaks and rustles issued from the back of the cave.

"Juice," Isbelle whispered, "or Quintessence as some call it, is the condensation of reality. The concentrated raw essence of the universe fuels magick. Some mages believe this 'Quintessence' to be shards of a great, slumbering being called the One; others believe it to be the tangible, spiritual essence of sentient creativity. I think George Lucas almost had it right: Quintessence is a concentrated manifestation of the Force."

Daria scowled. "Oh, come on...."

"No, really," Isbelle continued, "Diluted Quintessence is all around us, within us— it *is* us. Concentrated Juice is the energy that is magick."

Daria squinted to see into the deeper darkness of the cave. "So where's the Juice?"

"Don't bother trying to *see* it; try to *feel* it. It's incredibly strong here."

Daria closed her eyes and tried to empty her mind. Yet thoughts of an awakening Lupine crept back in. She pictured a blank slate. Slowly, the image of a faded black and white photograph, yellowed with age, stole before her mind's eye. Unaccustomed nostalgia washed over her, and more images— a willow dipping its fronds into a shaded pool; her old three-speed bike propped against the chain link fence, its blue paint chipped with years of use; her abandoned cast, colorful with friends' signatures, from when she'd broken her leg; the lilac smell of her favorite aunt's perfume—all drifted over her like a lazy cloud at noon.

Somebody was shaking her shoulder. The images faded. Isbelle was whispering excitedly, "...think you feel it. This is a full-blown Node, Awakened and everything."

"The things I saw —"

"This Node seems to resonate with a feeling of nostalgia. You were probably attuned to it." Isbelle pointed the flashlight into a dark niche, spotlighting a rat which blinked and scurried away. She sat down on an overturned icebox.

Daria remained standing, senses alert. "It was very powerful. Are all Nodes like this one?"

Isbelle shook her head. "No, most of the ones I've raided don't have Juice colored so strongly by emotion. The

Juice in this Node must resonate somehow with him." She tossed her chin in the sleeping werewolf's direction. Putting her hands to her mouth, she hissed, "OK, guys, it's safe. C'mon in." Four of Daria's friends crept into the cave and sat down at opposite ends. The others, she noted, stayed outside to guard them.

Said Isbelle, "I'll teach you how to do what they're doing some other time. Right now, I want you to learn what Juice is, what it feels like—" As she spoke, her flashlight roved from niche to niche. Her eyes went wide.

"What is it? What's wrong?" Daria's heart thumped as she looked around for more wolves.

"I feel something I haven't felt for years," whispered Isbelle.

Daria's throat tightened. "What? What is it?"

"C'mere." Isbelle launched herself from the rusty icebox towards the shadowy rear of the cave, the flashlight beam bouncing haphazardly in all directions. Daria followed more cautiously. "We've always made a habit of peeking into the Umbra when we raid Nodes," continued Isbelle, her voice louder than before, "ever since I found Dram in the form of a SoundBlaster card in a Virtual Adept Node four years ago. It's paid off again!" Isbelle stopped near the back of the cave, light brushing the lips of shadowed nooks and crannies all around her. As Daria ran to catch up, all she could see was Isbelle's silhouette crouching over something, facing away. She ran up to Isbelle and stopped.

"Wait a sec— back up. What's Dram?"

Without turning, Isbelle motioned her closer with an impatient hand. "This. Can't you see it?"

Daria peeked around Isbelle, who had pointed her flashlight at the ground where a tarnished old victrola sat. On its turntable lay a thick, scratched record with no label. The heavy stylus rested on the ground nearby.

"See what? This is a rotting old piece of junk."

Isbelle shook her head, still looking at the victrola. "If that's all you see, then you're blind." She turned to look up at Daria. "Don't believe in physical appearances. Looking past the surface layer makes us mages, after all. Look into the Umbra with your mind."

Daria shut her eyes again and reached out to the victrola with her mind. Blindly, she brushed it with her fingers, touching it, turning it over, running her fingers along its smooth, cold surface. Dimly, an image of the victrola grew in her mind, still an old, abandoned victrola, but now pulsing with a melancholy glow. She could feel its warmth, but also the sadness associated with it.

"Is this Juice?" she asked.

Isbelle's voice seemed to come from far away. "Does it feel like it?"

"No, it feels different somehow. It's— tangible."

"Exactly. It's Dram. Some call it 'Tass.' It's a physical form that Quintessence takes only once in a very great while."

Daria mentally hefted the stylus. It had no needle. "When?"

"I'm not sure, but I've heard it said that Nodes can form Tass when they haven't been tapped for a long time— when Juice builds up quickly, for some reason, and starts to overflow into the physical realm."

Daria opened her eyes and looked again at the victrola. "But why does it look like *that*. I mean, it's junk!"

"Take a look around. What else would you expect it to look like in a dump?" Isbelle took a seat on the cold dirt. "Dram usually takes the form you expect it to take. For example, describe to me what you see." Daria described the victrola to Isbelle. "You know what's funny? I don't see a victrola at all."

"Seriously?"

"Yeah, seriously. I see a broken eight-track tape. Like I said, what Tass looks like will differ from person to person within the range of expected surroundings."

Daria sat down. "You felt the nostalgia, though."

Isbelle nodded. "Yeah, but that's Juice, not Dram. Juice isn't physical—you can feel it with your mind, but you can't pick it up with your hands. This," she picked up the broken stylus, "you can touch and carry." She handed the stylus to

Daria. "Speaking of which, you'll have the responsibility of carrying this Dram back with us when those guys are ready." She gestured towards the other mages in the corners of the cave. They all seemed to be asleep, sitting quietly and concentrating with their eyes closed.

"There's something I don't get, though. Why has Tass formed here, in this dump, at all?"

Isbelle pointed the flashlight at the sleeping lupine. "That's probably why. That and the fact that this dump holds a lot of entropic energy."

Daria's face was blank, and Isbelle nodded as if expecting the response. "Lupines seem to attract ley lines to them. It's an odd phenomenon. Add to that the fact that this dump is a graveyard for a community's memories, an area rich in lost life energy, and you get lots of Juice, maybe even some Dram, especially since it's so out of the way, so untapped."

Daria nodded. "Where else can you gather Juice?"

"Oh, lots of places. Usually we don't go directly into the Node—it's too dangerous. We stay outside and use a form of magick you'll soon learn."

Daria was shaking her head. "But, I mean, what sort of places have Quintessence in them?"

Isbelle thought a moment and said, "I've taken it from all sorts of places — nightclubs, universities, some corporate buildings uptown, churches, malls, a mental institution or two. We even tapped some in a hockey stadium one time."

"Where'd you find the Dram?"

"Corporate building." She grinned. "Actually, I took it from Rich's cabal, but he doesn't know that yet. Don't tell him. I'm going to give it back to him for his birthday."

Daria chuckled. Remembering what she held in her hand, she asked, "What are we going to do with this Dram, anyway?"

Isbelle pointed the flashlight in Daria's eyes. "You ask too many questions!"

Daria shielded her eyes, but persisted, "Oh, come on, tell me!"

"All right, all right." She shut off the light. "Usually, we tap into it as an energy source, in the same way we store Juice in our bodies. I think with this one, though, since it's not so portable, we'll pawn it off to someone in the Glee Club."

"The who?"

"The Cult of Ecstasy." Isbelle settled back against a piece of rusty metal. "Enough talk. Time we got started, or we'll find ourselves dealing with an unhappy doggy." Isbelle winked mischievously.

Daria followed Isbelle's lead as she shut her eyes and concentrated on the Quintessence all around her.

The Nature of Paradox

I had everything within my reach
I had money and stuff
Each and every call
Too much, but never enough.
Tear it up and watch it fall.
— Sisters of Mercy, "Neverland"

Otherworldly voices whispered around them: "She is beautiful, like a chain of lightning," "And fine, like a lotus fiber," "And shines in the minds of the sages." "She is subtle, the Awakener of pure knowledge," "The embodiment of all bliss," "Whose true nature is pure consciousness."

Xiao and Branton floated on air, riding the Wave of Bliss. Branton's thoughts caressed her mind as he slowed time to enjoy their intimacy. Xiao had so much to teach him, the least of which were the Tantric rituals. Though trained of the Cult of Ecstasy, he had so much potential that she was sure he would someday be a great member of the Brotherhood.

Branton sighed. "I never believed it could be this good."

"Believe." Then Xiao tensed— "Wait, does that mean at first you did not believe?"

"No— it's just an expression." He caressed her cheek tenderly. "Really."

"Honestly?"

Branton shifted awkwardly. "Yes, honestly."

"Good." Still, Xiao looked around the room, unsure. Nothing seemed out of place— except a framed photograph that hadn't been there minutes before. Slowly, she withdrew and slipped on a nightshirt.

"Why—" Branton reached for her, but she deftly stepped away.

"You lied. Never lie to yourself or others when questions of reality and belief are involved."

He slammed his fist on the bed. "What do you mean by that? I lied?"

"Isn't it obvious? You entered the Ritual not believing. You've created what we call *yerk dim*—a flaw— in the fabric of the reality we were creating. The design has run amok; it is unbalanced now."

Branton's face flushed hot. "Look, I don't know what you're—"

Xiao shook her head. "I am saddened that you do not wish to learn."

"Learn what? How to make fun of *kwai lun* ? The American guy?" Branton put on his pants and began to gather his belongings.

"Of course not. I speak only of learning how to control your temper and of learning how to make your way out of a Quiet."

Branton shook his head. "I don't know what you're rambling on about."

"Do you want to know?"

Branton paused. Slowly, with some resentment, he met her eyes. "Yes, I guess I do."

Xiao nodded solemnly. "Good. Sit down." Tossing his bag to the floor, Branton sat grudgingly. Xiao continued, undisturbed, "Your disbelief started the fabric running. It created Paradox which—"

"Before you go on, what is this Paradox shit you keep mentioning? I've been told to avoid it, but I've never been told what it is, what it does."

Xiao nodded. "Your undisciplined Cult masters do you a disservice. Paradox is the naturally occurring force that balances Yin and Yang. Too much Yin or Yang, and you violate the reality that World Mind has established— you unbalance it. Paradox simply preserves balance."

Xiao sat down on the bed beside Branton, and the young mage took her outstretched hand. Gently, he rested his head on her lap and stared up into her eyes. "So you're saying that the World Mind, which I presume is consensual reality, is the natural state of things, that we shouldn't violate it?"

Xiao stroked his hair. She shook her head. "No, absolutely not. I made no judgments upon World Mind; just that it is. World Mind is mutable by nature, and its current form is one that all Traditions wish to change."

"So I unbalanced the World Mind, but that's OK, since we want to shape it into a reality of our own making anyway."

"With patience and wisdom."

"Meaning?"

"Do not violate the World Mind too blatantly, or your efforts will be for naught. You see, World Mind is in the employ of the Technocracy now, and, consequently, so is Paradox. If you ignore World Mind, Paradox will destroy you, and you will only have achieved the enemy's goal."

"I'm still not sure I understand what Paradox is. Is it sentient, or is it a force like wind or water? Is it, for instance, capable of mercy? Does it know love?"

Xiao smiled. "Not all things know love. Some know only justice because they are formed only of an impulse for justice." She paused. Could she risk exposing him to the truth? Yes, perhaps she could. They had come this far, and he seemed open enough. "Do you see that photograph?"

Branton sat up and looked at the photo to which Xiao was pointing. "What's that doing there?" The photo, in a gilt lacquered frame, showed Xiao and an older man lying naked on a beach in each other's arms. In the background, the waves of the ocean seemed to sparkle and shift. "Who is that guy?"

Xiao weighed her response. "That, my love, is my father."

"What the fu—" Branton stared at her, disgusted.

Xiao closed her eyes and smiled. "Before you jump to conclusions, let me explain."

"I think you better."

"First, bring that picture to me."

Reluctantly, Branton stood and walked over to the bureau where the photo stood. He put his hand on it, but withdrew it quickly. "Ow! It's hot!"

"That's all right. It won't harm you— just bring it here."

Branton lifted the frame carefully. "It seems heavy. C'mon, tell me what's going on."

Xiao held out her hand, and he placed the framed photo in it. "World Mind is like this ocean, and Paradox is its mobility. The ocean sloshes and sways, but it stays within its basin. It does not fill the sky one day, then disappear into underground caverns the next. Am I right?"

"Yes, but—"

"Listen. World Mind is the same: there are different beliefs— waves and currents in the ocean— but common fundamental beliefs in the nature of reality cause all beliefs to cohere."

Branton sat down next to Xiao. "What about his photo, Xiao?"

"We'll get to that." She pointed to the sparkling waves in the photo. "But what causes these to gather together and crash down in a tidal wave, wash over the land in a monsoon, or form a water spout and fill the sky? Other forces. The forces from you and me—Self Mind contradicting World Mind."

Branton shook his head, confused.

"Paradox occurs when the right mix of forces destabilizes reality, just as a tidal wave crashes onshore when an eruption occurs underwater. If the lava oozes out onto the seafloor slowly, without displacing large quantities of water, there is no tidal wave. If a volcano blasts molten rock into the ocean, suddenly displacing huge quantities of water, there is sure to be a backlash. The tidal wave is like a Paradox Backlash."

"So Paradox is not sentient— it is just a force?"

"Not exactly. That metaphor describes how Paradox works, not what it is."

Branton stood and began to pace back and forth. "Look, I want to know why you have that picture, OK? If it's related to Paradox, explain it. Just stop dancing around the issue!"

Xiao looked down at the floor. "Yes, you are right. I will explain. This picture is related to Paradox, so hear me out. Paradox is all that I have said it is, but it is also more. In a sense, it is sentient: as sentient and merciful as those who punish themselves with it. To put it plainly, Paradox is a manifestation of our own impulse to punish ourselves. Down deep inside, we expect punishment for violating World Mind, and we get it by inflicting it upon ourselves."

"So if we train ourselves not to expect punishment—"

"We do not receive it. But that is very, very difficult, if not impossible. And luck plays a role in it."

"How?"

"If someone who doubts sees magick without coincidental effect, World Mind sends the punishment even before the mage's self-punishing impulse has a chance to."

"Can the two work together?"

"Yes."

"Is that what happened here?" Branton's voice sounded tense.

"Yes."

Tenser still: "But why the picture? Why didn't lightning strike us down or something?"

Xiao smiled. "The nature of Paradox is subtle and often poetic. During our Ritual, we slipped into a Quiet."

Branton stepped closer to Xiao. "Yes, what is that?"

"It is a state of Paradox for which my only clue was this." Xiao held up the photograph.

"So are we dead?"

Xiao chuckled softly. "No, no. We are simply stuck in an altered mental state."

Branton drew up a chair and straddled it. "Like we're on drugs?"

Xiao nodded. "In a way."

"What's the meaning of the photo, then?"

"It's a kind of psychic residue— the imbalanced portion of Yin and Yang. Eventually, it will disappear from our sight, as World Mind rights itself. In the meantime, we are the only ones who can see it."

Branton snorted. "So everyone else would see us carrying nothing in our hands and saying, 'See this?' and, 'Ow! It's hot!', and they'd think we're crazy, is that it?"

Xiao smiled. "Yes."

Branton's smile stiffened. "But why'd it have to show you and your Dad? How does Paradox decide to punish you?"

"That is a wise question. I do not know the answer, but I can guess. Perhaps because of the nature of the ritual and the fact that there was doubt in your mind and worry in mine, the ritual didn't succeed entirely without Paradox. I have, and I am sure you have, accumulated Paradox energy in the past. That energy was channeled into the psychic creation of the photo. It was something that, during a ritual intended to create concord, created discord instead."

"What were the voices, then, if the ritual failed?"

"Part of the Quiet. Part of our own concord, even as our doubt created discord."

Branton took Xiao's hand. "Yin and Yang balancing each other?"

"Yes, Yin and Yang," she replied, letting the photo drop to the carpet.

Branton looked deep into her eyes. "Do you forgive me?"

"I love you and honor you. You require no forgiveness."

"Then I'll take this as a— what do you call it?"

"*Ha job ging yim.*"

"Yes, a learning experience."

Seeking and the Guardian

For the human kingdom, beneath the floor of the comparatively neat little dwelling that we call our consciousness, goes down into unsuspected Aladdin caves. There, not only jewels, but also dangerous jinn abide.

— Joseph Campbell, *The Hero with a Thousand Faces*

Tasha felt the rock beneath her feet tremble slightly as she padded into the caverns. Her skin seemed to hum, tingling with fearful anticipation. A wall of fire crackled across her path. Hot air seared her throat and nostrils and her bare skin had a sheen of sweat. Caught between the clammy fear inside and the dry heat of the cavern, Tasha shivered, steeled herself, then stepped forward through the curtain of fire and into the labyrinth.

The Dancer glided from a niche and drew herself up *en pointe* beside Tasha, resplendent in grace Tasha only wished she could possess. They shared the face and form of a professional, but the Avatar personified the catlike flow that the mage herself lacked. *Back again so soon?* the Dancer asked silently. Tasha nodded assent. *Ambitious, aren't we?* The Dancer smiled, but her eyes clouded with nightmare. Her empath "voice" echoed in Tasha's bones, like a half-felt seismic tremor. *Beyond this point, you go alone; I'll advise, but cannot aid you.*

"I know the drill," Tasha said aloud as the tunnel loomed ahead. It was black, pitch black, and wound endlessly downward. Tasha steadied her breathing as she stared into the earthen void. Far below, she knew, lay the Light, the Ledge, the Pool, and other places… but to reach them, she must pass through darkness. Heart hammering, she entered, leaving light and Dancer behind.

She spread her arms to feel her way along the rough stone walls. Her toes passed lightly across the pebbly dirt floor, searching for trips and pitfalls. Each steady breath expanded into the tunnel, searching for the things eyes could not see. As Tasha crept forward, the walls narrowed. The floor and ceiling tightened. Soon, her hair brushed the tunnel's crumbling top. The air grew thin, stifling, heavy. Still she continued, humming softly to herself.

The tunnel shrunk to crouch-height, then to crawl-size. Darkness was eternal here, and the air was thick with rich earth-scent. Tasha's heart thundered in spite of her comforting hum. Dirt sifted into her hair, worked its way beneath her questing fingernails, gritted in her mouth and nose, plastered itself to sweaty skin. Cold slick— things quested, found her, and withdrew. Stone walls scraped her flesh as she slid deeper downward, towards the Light she knew waited beyond.

Years passed. Eons. Eternities. *Not fair!* she moaned. The tunnel grew longer and tighter each time she entered. *It should get easier!* Tasha wormed her way through a passage

barely wide enough to pull her head through. Her breasts and ribs pressed painfully against the walls with each cautious breath, each heartbeat. Wild panic surged at the trap. *Cave in!* screamed her fear. *They'd never find you!* Was that a light ahead? Or only a wishful vision?

The passage widened from wormhole to crawlspace. Fresh air flowed from the darkness ahead. Then the Light, the blessed Light, warmed the tunnel from black to gray to earthy brown. Tasha paused at last to wipe away the dirt before rounding a final corner and entering the Cavern of Winds.

The air here was goose-bump cold in contrast to the stifling tunnel, and it swept her hair into tangles. The walls glowed green with iridescent fungus and cool light beckoned from the Ledge of Faith. *Not bad*, said the Dancer. "I knew you'd be here," Tasha replied aloud, wrapping her arms to her sides. The two of them walked to the Ledge in silence. *I didn't think you'd get through it the first time*, the Dancer finally admitted.

"Why does it keep getting longer?" Tasha asked testily. *Each new secret ups the stakes. Each new insight ups the cost. Each new power ups the threat. Without discipline comes disaster.*

"You sound like von Dagram," the mage shot back, recalling her preachy mentor. The wind roared through the cavern, biting to the bone. Light blasted through the chinks in the rock walls as they padded to the sunlit Ledge. This part always gave Tasha the creeps.

The ground at the mountain's foot seemed miles away. The mage's stomach dropped away with it. Scouring winds threatened to sweep Tasha and the Dancer from the Ledge into oblivion. Frost sparkled on the Ledge, and Tasha's breath puffed in the icy air. In the distance, another mountain rose, with another Ledge leading to further tests. Between the mountains lay a void bridged by nothing. The mage wavered, clinging to the Ledge's walls, fighting vertigo and the pulling of the wind.

Well? said the Dancer.

"I'm working on it," Tasha snapped. "Give me a minute." A book she'd once read said that the secret to flying was to throw yourself at the ground and miss. The author wasn't far from wrong. It had taken Tasha three tries before she'd mastered the Ledge, and two of them had nearly killed her.

The mage hummed softly, drawing her concentration inward from distractions. Gooseflesh rippled, and hair whipped her closed eyes. The deep chill she felt came only somewhat from the wind. She stepped back into the cavern and gathered her confidence like a blanket against the cold, then rushed out to the Ledge and leaped.

The stomach-lurch of free-fall hit her as she sailed into the void… and then the winds lifted her. *I did it!!* She laughed wildly as she flew, arms and legs spread wide, head thrown back, brown hair trailing behind her. Icy air-fingers caressed her as she swept across the chasm like a naked human kite, the cold forgotten. Her dancer's instincts took over and she spun in flight, pirouetting and twisting as she laughed. The mountain loomed ahead, but Tasha took her time, chasing sparrows high above the snow-covered wastes. Finally, she alighted on the far ledge to continue her quest. *Have fun?* the Dancer asked, but Tasha only nodded, panting and grinning. *Catch your breath*, said the Avatar; *You'll need it.*

The Pool waited at the end of a long spiral passage through the mountain. Inside the mountain, the air grew warmer, though Tasha still shivered with exhilarated chill. Along the way, the mage prepared herself by breathing deeply, expanding her lungs to the limit. The rush from her flight gave way to concentration. "Last time," she said to the Dancer, "I met the Guardian at the Pool and fetched him the pearl before the oyster shut. This is as far as I've gone so far. Where do I go from here?"

You'll know.

"How?"

Look for what is different. Follow it. The Guardian will meet you at the next bridge.

The Guardian was the eternal end of this seemingly endless journey: the Watcher at the Soul's Crossroads, the Gatekeeper of the Inner Self, Granter of Enlightenment, the Miser of Arete. The Guardian, Tasha knew, personifies aspects of conscience, fear, discipline and repression. All the things the mage could not yet handle assumed the form of her Guardian, and she knew she had to take her demands of enlightenment to him. In the past, she'd met him at the end of the tunnel, the far Ledge and the Pool. At the thought of the new test, she shivered. To convince the Guardian of your worth, you had to face symbolic tests of fear, faith, greed, wisdom and other traits. Tasha was still working on simple faith and fear. The caverns glittered with crystal veins and light breezes stirred the sandy floor. The Pool sat in the center of a gigantic chamber. The Guardian was nowhere to be seen.

The mirrored surface was deceptive; the Pool went down farther than Tasha cared to guess, to a rocky bottom strewn with giant oysters and strange crab-like striders. It had been all the mage could do to reach the bottom, claim a pearl from the jaws of an open clam, and surface. Each time, the tests changed slightly. The mage dreaded the variations. She flexed her limbs and filled her lungs. "Same deal as last time?" she asked the Avatar. The Dancer shrugged and handed her a belted leather sack. Tasha slipped it on. "See you on the other side," she said, then gulped a lungful of cool air and dived.

The shock of breaking the icy Pool hit Tasha hard. She kicked downward, feeling the water's weight press in against her eardrums. As her lungs began to protest, Tasha sighted the bottom. To her annoyance, it had changed from last time — now it resembled an ornate Oriental ruin, as if the Pool had swallowed some ancient pagoda. The garden, she noted, seemed intact. Fish darted among the carefully-tended rock

patterns and trimmed flowers. The pagoda, however, was a shambles. *Look for what is different*, the Dancer had said. The mage shrugged and swam into the ruins.

The dim interior glittered with scattered gold and whitened bone. There had been a massacre here, it seemed; the bodies of dozens of long-dead combatants littered the floor, mingling with piles of gems and bright gold coins. Tasha's pulse quickened, thumping in her ears. Greed swelled. *Jesus, look at this haul!* She glided to a pile of treasure. *This must be what the sack is for!* Quickly, she stuffed handfuls of loot into the pouch, watching the bones for some sight of a trap.

The shadow wrapped around her ankle, tight and biting cold. She gasped, and precious air bubbled past her lips. Her lungs hitched as the shadow drew her backwards, away from the doorway and into the ruin. Tasha screamed mental curses as she flailed for a handhold. The light fell away and darkness colder than the windy Ledge enfolded her. *Dancer!* she thought frantically, but there was no reply.

Panic burst forth, bright and crazy. Tasha scrabbled at the darkness, her thoughts flying, her concentration wrecked. To die during Seeking was worse than simple failure. It was a tiny death of the soul, and mages had died physically of the shock. Some Seekers had simply disappeared, and Tasha feared she might become one of them. She could break the trance that bound her here, but didn't want to think of what that might do to her.

The darkness bound her tightly. Its embrace was warm, comforting. The urge to quit fighting and merge with the darkness welled up like fresh-drawn blood. Outside the darkness, the water was cold. The thunder in her heart eased to a steady thump. Each pulse seemed to drain the air from her straining lungs. *Whatever you do*, she thought, *you'd better do it quick!*

Embrace the darkness, said von Dagram, *and darkness is what you'll receive.*

What did I do? Grab a few coins?

You robbed the dead. Was this von Dagram, or the Guardian?

I didn't come to steal. I came to take what was already mine! She nearly spoke the words aloud. Her lips parted, and she tasted water. Her lungs spasmed, and she choked. *Get out!*

Darkness squeezed. Tasha struggled, slipped off the pouch of gold. The darkness would not let go. *To hell with this!* The mage gathered her desperate fury into a core of Prime force and released it. Bright light seared the shadow away. Light spilled in, and cold water. The shadow wavered and Tasha kicked away for the surface. Tendrils clung to her, tugging at her as she pulled for the light above. The shadow drew her down again. The last of her air slipped past her lips. She turned in its grasp and fired a blast of pure Prime into the darkness. The tendrils released her, and she burst upward, into light.

Fresh air exploded into her lungs, burning as she gasped. Tasha's limbs felt like stone as she swam rapidly for the side of the Pool. The rock edge felt good beneath her numbed fingers. She hauled herself up and crouched in the

sand, vomiting water. When the fit passed, she sank, exhausted, to the ground and lay there for a long time.

The Dancer touched her arm with gentle fingers. The Avatar's eyes were bright with concern. "Was that it?" Tasha asked weakly. The Dancer shook her head. "Damn. Well, I'm gonna rest, and the Guardian can go screw himself."

She awoke on stone, heated by the fire of a volcanic chasm. The Dancer still crouched beside her, but the Pool was gone. In its place was a mammoth cavern split by a flaming abyss. Tasha lay on one side, in a sheltered alcove; the Guardian loomed on the other side, impassive in his black robes, taller than her mother's house. As the mage stirred, the Guardian folded his handless sleeves across his chest. As Tasha pulled herself to her feet, the chasm widened and the flames leapt higher. *You have come*, said the Guardian, *but you are not yet ready. Return later.*

"Like hell!" The room reminded her of Hell, a Dante-esque vision of gulfs that could not be bridged. She strode to the edge of the cliff, sweaty from the cavern heat. Primal fear and anger warred with frustration. She could still feel the slippery grasp of darkness. Her belly sickened with terror and Pool-water. "I didn't come all this way for nothing," she roared across the gulf; "Give me what I came for. I'm ready!"

You are not. At her feet, the mage noticed a tightrope, old hemp stretched across the flaming chasm. Splintery pegs anchored the rope at both ends. Wisps of smoke rose where fire singed the tightrope. *You have failed the tests.*

"I survived!" she cried. "I came out on the other side all three times. I've done it before!" the inferno's size and rumble swallowed her words. "I'm ready, dammit! I'm ready!"

Is magick mere survival, then? Is Awakening a means to gain and pleasure? Or is it a means to stave off fear of darkness?

"I'm not afraid!"

You lie.

Tasha shook her head. Hair stuck to her face, and she pulled it aside. "You're right. I am afraid…"

And angry, too.

"And angry," she admitted. "Christ, mages get angry, mages get scared. We're human, we're not perfect, and I've known others who've come this way who still carry anger and fear in their hearts." She extended a foot to the tightrope, tested it, and gingerly stepped onto it. It dipped crazily, but held.

Their way was not your way, the Guardian replied. *Each finds her inner demons here. Each creates her own test.*

Tasha spread her arms, balancing against the sickening pitch of the rope across the fire. Gouts of flame licked at her soles from the lava far below. Live steam burned her nose and throat. Behind her, the Dancer waited, silent. "I faced my fears," said Tasha. "I'm doing it now."

Indeed. The Guardian inclined his head a bit. *And if you fall?* A wave of panic hit Tasha like a blow, teetering her on the rope. She glanced down as a blast of heat seared upward. Her legs wobbled. Her toes clenched the rope. *Falling*, the Guardian intoned, *is death. Worse than death.*

Falling. The fear of twisted ankles and broken bones that haunts the dancers who defy gravity, time and human limitations. Tasha remembered the fear of falling that had paralyzed her after a bad spill in high school. And she remembered how she overcame that fear; she shifted her fears to the music and embraced herself and the music as one.

She took a deep breath and hummed, feeling the hum reverberate down into her bones. She closed her eyes and washed the panic aside with a calming of her Mind. *Don't think of the pain,* her dance instructor said, *don't think of what you're not supposed to be able to do. Think of the music and the dance and flow with it.* The dance! Of course! The dance of creation; the dance of grace and power, art and love and passion, the dynamic rhythm of eternity's pulse, endlessly pumping the lifeblood of existence through form, mind and spirit. Life, she suddenly knew, was more than a test of wills or an act of defiance. *Reality's a dance,* she thought, *and I am the Dancer!*

Her feet stepped lightly across a tightrope gone suddenly strong and taut. Euphoria lifted her above the pains of her trials. Her arms rode the rising fire currents, and her hair swirled in the updrafts. Tasha rope-danced with cat-like perfection, and was nearly disappointed when she reached the other side.

The Guardian towered above her, his black sleeves rippling in the hot breeze. Tasha swallowed, wetting her lips and tongue to speak. The exertion thrill rushed giddyingly to her head. She forced her breathing and heartbeat to slow; "I'm ready," she said, "to advance."

The Guardian appraised her slowly. *The dance is faster, the moves are more complex, the leaps are higher and the risks of falling are greater.*

"I understand," the mage said, "and accept what's mine."

The Guardian swept his arms open, trailing midnight sleeves. His hood flashed open for a brief instant— was it a woman's face in the folds?— then shadowed his (her?) face again. Light flowed from the Guardian, light mixed with darkness like an oil slick, both flowing together and wrapping themselves around the mage. Unlike the darkness in the Pool, this essence held no fear or panic, only fulfillment, as if some missing vital thing had been restored.

When I reach Ascension, she wondered, *does the Guardian disappear?*

Perhaps, said a voice, the Dancer's voice, *and perhaps not. Only then will you know.* The Avatar emerged from the Guardian's cascade and extended her hands to Tasha, then took her in her arms.

Mage and Avatar hugged like sisters, merging into a single whole. A humming like a thousand melding songs settled in Tasha's mind and spirit, and her hands swept upwards to caress the falling essence. *My self and my dance are one,* she thought as she floated from the place of Seeking into wisdom's warm embrace. Cold, anger, fear, all of these would return in time, but for the moment, Tasha had what she needed.

Until next time…

Myth Into Reason: Opposing Views

The Council of Nine

In the beginning
There was the cold and the night
Prophets and angels gave us the fire and the light
Man was triumphant
Armed with the faith and the will
That even the darkest ages couldn't kill.

— Billy Joel, "Two Thousand Years"

"H-a-a-a-rley, you promised me you'd talk about the Traditions tonight. I wanna know." Deathlace smiled and pushed back an unruly lock of her midnight black hair. Harley was perhaps the single bright spot in her recent dark life: he was pretentious, and silly, and funky. Harley was a self-described living stereotype, a 'hard rocker' from New Jersey who spoke 'rock n' rollese' like he was a character from the latest Spinal Tap movie. His fake rocker accent and rocker speech didn't negate his charm. For some reason it fit: he looked like a wizardly version of Meat Loaf and did his best magickal work with his guitar.

Ever since Deathlace left Atlanta in Harley's bus (called, predictably, the 'Magic Bus'), she had a sense of destiny, like she was being drawn across the continent, driving several thousand miles to have her date with fate. She fell in love with the magickal bus, which was bigger on the inside than it was outside. The inside had three staircases, and, when it got up to speed on the highway, it slipped into some strange reality which made the windows into psychedelic lightshows. She wanted to know more about being a mage, more than Sad Willie, her former mentor, could ever teach her. Harley had been putting her off the entire trip.

Harley downed the last of the cheap beer that he was slurping on and threw the can behind him with a belch. Straightening his bulging leather vest and picking up a finely-tuned Gibson ax in the chair next to him, he filled the back of the travelling Chantry-*cum*-tourbus with a light strumming in the manner of a medieval troubadour. Normally, Deathlace would love to listen to him play— she would sit for hours, here in the living room of the bus, listening to him. Now she grew impatient, and her face showed it.

He paused for a moment, picked out a madrigal and looked up at Deathlace, grinning. She was pretty, in a delicate way, and she knew it. Long black strands of hair cascaded haphazardly down her face, and her eye was outlined in black like a comic book character she loved. She thought for a moment that Harley was coming on to her, but it turned out he was just trying to freak her.

"You wanna know about the Trads, do ya? Well, missy, you sure? 'Cause it ain't all that short a story, and it ain't all true, but it's what m'Boss told me, and that's what I gotta believe." Harley said, his fake rocker accent in full swing.

"Oh, Harley, quit foolin' around and just tell it," Deathlace said.

Harley fixed his Ray-Bans and lit up a cigarette — perfectly legitimate except for the brilliant purple smoke it created. To hell with Paradox. He got a wild look in his eyes and grinned wildly at Deathlace. "Okay, sugar, you asked for it…"

"See, once, all these Trads, they weren't nothin' but a buncha prophets, wise men, freaks, weirdoes, hermits, crazies, medicine men, shamans, sorcerers and hedge wizards. Gee, kinda like they are now. Anyway, waaaay back then, the Traditions weren't like they are now. They were just folks who sorta agreed with one another about how things were. They were Awakened, don't get me wrong. They just didn't have any kind of focus— kind of all over the place. Then, well, these really tight-assed dudes who were calling themselves the Order of Hermes…"

"I beg your pardon…" Lady Cullen said from the front of the bus. Turning around, and carefully stepping down from the passenger seat, she made her way back in the cabin to where Harley and Deathlace sat. "I think that you should watch what you say about things Hermetic. I believe I'll just listen in on this travesty of history that you insist is truth."

Harley smiled showing ragged teeth, shook his head once and began again as Lady Cullen sat down opposite them. "Anyway, so the Order went around well, trying to get everyone organized, you know, like it was a college or a pep rally or somethin'. The Cult, well, you know how the Cult likes to be organized. Not an option, baby. A few of us here and there went to check things out, but basically it was serious nilsville."

Deathlace rolled her eyes and looked dubiously at Harley. The slang was getting a bit thick, even for her. She could never tell whether Harley was kidding her or not. There was a bit of silence, and then Lady Cullen interrupted it, placing her hand on Deathlace's silken forearm. "Child, the Order was designed in those days to accept any of the Traditions who wished to join and become part of our great experiment. The Houses of our current-day Order sprang from this widespread acceptance. Many of the other Traditions have been enriched by our knowledge."

Harley looked down over his sunglasses at the Lady, and then back at Deathlace. "Yah. So, anyway, I don't know if you've heard about it, but back then, about the time of the Renaissance, there was a group of anal-retentive reality freaks who decided that their ways were the best ways, and that they were gonna take over. No, I ain't talkin' about the Order of Hermes…" Harley grinned, looking to

Lady Cullen to take the bait. She didn't. "...I'm talkin' about the Order of Reason. They met in secret, it's said, and they created and planned to throw the largest wet blanket in the world on top of the best party in all history. What I'm talkin' about is the Gauntlet, sugar. You see, it wasn't like one day there were faeries and dragons and magick and pretty girls with tiny feet and nothin' on the next."

"There's still pretty girls with tiny feet..." Deathlace said, giggling and wiggling her toes in his face.

Harley grinned, but he was on a roll, "It was slow, gradual, quiet. An idea here, a bit o' lore there. The best thing that the Order did was to not openly attack the Church, even though the Church immediately attacked it. Nope, folks, it immediately went right out and helped the Church with its little Inquisition. I can't prove anything, but I believe that the Cabal of Pure Thought, which would later become the Convention of the New World Order, had long infiltrated the Dominicans. Anyway, the Inquisition turned from searching for heresy to searching for the supernatural. They started checking for vampires, witches, and werewolves. Now, m'Boss told me..."

Lady Cullen nodded slowly, "Yes." She shut her eyes. "Yes, Torquemada was most likely of the Cabal of Pure Thought. He was a horrible man who enjoyed the psychic pain of others."

"Tha's right. So, the Inquisition, the Black Death, the Crusades, the rise of the power of the Syndics all spelled major change for us. But really, what knocked us for a loop was the Gauntlet. Reality started gettin' thick, like Jello congealin' in a fridge. A whole bunch of mages ran off into the Void, like the Marauders do. A whole bunch decided that they would throw in with the Big S himself and went the heavy-metal route. Heh. And then there's us. We weren't too keen about leaving our wonderful Earth, and then there's the Big Flop of the Order of Hermes..."

"Child, your tutor speaks to you lightly of something that was as bad to us as the Holocaust was to your people. When the Gauntlet was finally deployed, the quieting of magick that occurred shattered ancient spells that held our most powerful magicks. It destroyed over a century of magickal learning. Those who had come to depend upon magick to survive were utterly and immediately slain. And, in the worst cases, the Avatar within many of us was ripped asunder, our minds were made into a child's toy of tangled string. We were even denied the utter transcendence of Twilight, then. So much was lost, so many died. It was a dark day for the Traditions then." Lady Cullen said, lips making a thin line, her chin wrinkled, her eyes intense. "Many mortals also died in the resulting struggles. Our people first blamed the Verbena and the Chorus, and they reacted with magickal attack. This caused many unneeded and unnecessary deaths, even among Sleepers— a fact that the Order of Reason used against us. We were doomed as the masses united against us."

Deathlace looked up at Harley, questioningly. A dark pall hung in the air. Harley took a big long swig of his Jack Daniels and ran his hand across his Fender. "But, I thought you guys were mages. Why didn't you just… blast 'em?" Deathlace asked, looking at Lady Cullen.

"Blast 'em? You know better than that, Barbara," came another female voice. It was Heasha. Deathlace hated to be called 'Barbara.' Heasha made a grand entrance, melting out of the shadowy area near the stairs. She couldn't keep her opinions out of any conversation. Harley had been waiting for her Verbena input. "Hell, at least the Order of Reason shook us up and got us to the table, working together…" Heasha muttered under her breath. "Let me show you what happened, child…"

The Verbena knelt down next to her and took off a leather thong-necklace that she was wearing, and slowly eased it around Deathlace's hands. "You see, Barbara, it's very easy to become entranced when someone's quietly easing something around you.."— with a snap, Heasha pulled up, and instantly bound the younger student's wrists together— "… and then closes the snare quickly. As you can see, there's not much you can do with your hands tied." Harley took another long drag on his cigarette as he watched the interplay between his student and his Chantry-mate.

"You done?" He asked, looking Heasha in the eyes. Heasha nodded and let the young girl's arms go. Deathlace shook out her hair, grinning, a little flushed, and just looked at Harley, taking a long pull on the whiskey herself this time. She was still blushing when Heasha finally sat down across from Lady Cullen.

Heasha smiled, briefly noting Deathlace's embarrassment. "The point I'm trying to make, sister, is that if we had known what the Order of Reason was doing, we would've prevented it. It's that simple. But they were utterly subtle, and the changes they made were so slowly and carefully thought out that we were caught unawares."

"Why didn't the Chorus warn you? I mean, weren't they part of the Church back then?" Deathlace said, rubbing her wrists and looking quietly at Heasha, who bent forward and massaged them apologetically.

"The Chorus was too busy searching for the One to listen to the cries of the Traditions. They were off in their abbeys and hermitages, praying and fasting. Boy, were they surprised when they came outta the clouds," Harley said, grinning. He played a riff on his axe, and Deathlace recognized it from "Jesus Christ Superstar."

A fifth voice joined them in the living room of the bus, deep, resonant, and lyrical. "We were indeed. Never has the Chorus been so deeply betrayed. Never have we learned such a harsh lesson." Christopher stepped into the room, from the top of the stairs. Dressed in simple jeans and a white t-shirt, he had just taken a shower. With his lion's mane of hair and his pure face, he looked like an angel in

a 501 commercial. With him came Heasha's familiar, a white Abyssinian named Shella.

Lady Cullen turned and addressed him, "Well, Christopher, that's all very well and good. What about the covenfolk and custos that were slaughtered in the name of the Crusades and the Inquisition? How were we supposed to respond when we believed it was the Chorus behind these attacks?"

Christopher bowed his head. "Yes. Well. If you had but come to us sooner, you would have learned the truth…" He sat down next to Deathlace on the couch.

Harley swore and took a long drag on his cig. "The whole damn Chantry's in th' living room! Ain't there anybody *drivin'* this thing??"

Heasha nodded as her familiar jumped up into her lap. She petted the white Abyssinian. "The Doctor. Or perhaps one of his driving programs?"

The whole Magic Bus Chantry lurched as it changed lanes, and even the internal reality was affected. Harley shook his head. "Let's just hope it ain't the formula-one program he did the other week. Sheesh. I don't want to get stopped by the cops for speedin'."

Deathlace sat down and crossed her arms, pouting. "Hey, folks, Harley was telling me a story and…"

"And, obviously, being a wise soul, you want the Truth. Or do you?" Heasha said, her eyes challenging the young woman's resolve. Looking up, Heasha patted the seat next to her. "Come over and sit down, Christopher. Besides, Shella wants to see you." Christopher took the beautiful cat into his lap and began scritching her favorite spot.

"Anyway, so, basically, the story goes that Baldric of the Order of Hermes, on the good word of a Cultist of Ecstacy named Sh'zar, took a group o' grogs and went lookin' for someone of the Verbena and someone of the Chorus who'd talk to 'm, because they were the easiest to find. Now, mind you, as our good companions have said already, those groups were already up to their ears in trouble and meaner than a dog on Ex-Lax."

"There was no Cultist involved. He went alone, based on a divination he did for himself." Lady Cullen said.

Heasha shook her mane of flame-red hair. "No, Lady, I'm sorry. The Goddess Herself came to the man, and he had the good sense to listen to Her for once."

Christopher sighed, "I don't supposed mentioning the Archangel Gabriel would help at this point, would it?"

"Would y'all please shut up? Y'all know there's more versions of this tale than there are versions of 'Louie, Louie,' so give me a friggin' break. I'm tellin' it, so it's a Cultist, okay." Harley said, taking the bottle back from Deathlace and swigging down another shot.

"Anyway, he lucked out. He happened to find a mage named Nightshade of the Verbena, and an old follower of St. Nerius named Valoran from the Chorus, both of whom happened to have a good solid head on their shoulders, a rarity among their Traditions at that time."

Heasha snorted. "Nightshade is my name-mother, and you better be nice to her, or I'll make all that lovely whiskey in your system go away. Hard."

Harley shuddered and grinned, "Don't worry 'bout me, Heash. I'm jus' havin' some fun. Anyway, so; they actually, all three, got together in the ruins of an old Hermetic Chantry called Mistridge that had gotten slammed in the Albigensian Crusade, in the south of France. You see, Nightshade was a bi... I mean, was a very, ahh, strong-willed woman with closely-held opinions. Baldric was from House Tytalus, and had a hard time letting someone else get a word in edgewise, let alone make peace with them. And Valoran, well, he was the holiest of the holier-than-thou's, 'cause he used to be a Hermes and had spent a lot of time preachin' to the Verbena's Heathen in the Moorish South. Well, after a lot of finger-pointin' and wailin' and yellin' and a visit from some faeries, they finally got down to business. And they talked, sat down and got to know each other. Partied. Jammed. You know, just sat down and hashed everything out. They went round and round and round, and when they were done they weren't sure whether they should off each other or get married. Luckily for us, they decided ta get hitched."

Lady Cullen looked indignant "I'd hardly call the Traditions Tribunal a marriage!"

"That's because you'd rather call it a 'Tribunal'. Heck, what do *you* call somethin' that puts together folks so totally and completely different from each other, makes 'em agree on stuff, and keeps them stuck together for their own good?"

"Only, I guess, this was a group marriage. Where did the other Traditions come from?" Deathlace asked, trying to learn something from the diatribe.

"All over the place. They really didn't have names like they do today. Basically, Nightshade went roamin' all over the place and brought Star-of-Eagles, the Dreamspeaker mage, and the Ahl-i-Batin mage..."

"Ahl-i-Batin? What's that?" Deathlace asked, weaving her fingers together.

"Arabian mages. They dropped out later, to be replaced by the Virtually Inept. I mean, the Virtual Adepts. Let me finish. Baldric from the Order of Hermes brought with him Chalech, the Euthanatos mage, and Sh'Zar, his friend and prophet from the Cult of Ecstasy, and Valoran brought Wu Jin, the first Akashic Brother, and a former follower of the artificer-mage Verdi named Diplomate Luis, a learned scholar who would later be called the first Son of Ether."

"Like the Doc?" Deathlace said, borrowing Harley's purple cig before it burned his hand.

"Like Herr Doctor Geronimo himself. Most of these folks wouldn't have set foot in the same room together. You

see, they all felt like they were the A-number-one authority on magick and all that it entailed."

"Nightshade was the greatest enchantress of her time." Heasha said.

"Valoran was a very pious man, the One's tool in his time." countered Christopher.

"Baldric was a pompous ass. But he was well respected. And well learned," finished Lady Cullen.

Harley grinned. "Sh'Zar was almost too cool for the party, you know what I mean? But he stuck it out, and I guess we should be grateful. Otherwise there wouldn't be any mages at all."

"Why's that?"

"Haven't you been listenin'?? I mean, jeez-o-pizza, girl. The Order of Reason was out for our ass and our reality. And they had already won! It wasn't like this was the ninth inning an' we still had some at-bats. Nopers. It was 'game over,' man. We had no choice, really, I mean, there was a lot of gnashin' o' teeth, but in the end, what else could we do? Give up and go live full-time in those greyfaces' cookie-cutter reality, where the sun rises and sets on the ho-hum Yawn Clock? I think perhaps maybe friggin' not."

"Indeed not. We had to come to some kind of consensus, and perhaps it was only in that time and in that place that we could have," Heasha said as the familiar Shella stretched out her paws in Christopher's lap.

"What place?" Deathlace asked, opening a bag of pretzels.

"They called the place 'Horizon'. I'll have to take ya there sometime. Nice place. Kinda weird, though. Each Primus— Primus, that's the name they gave ya if you showed up to the meetin'. Literally means 'first one.' So, I guess the Traditions were first-come, first-served. Heh— each Primus donated access to one of his or her Nodes, and we weaved us a place where even the Order of Reason would have trouble finding us," Harley said, reaching over and nabbing a pretzel.

"Baldric was a student of Shallowing Effects and of Regio, and it just so happened that Valoran, Star-of-Eagles and Wu Jin learned how to work well together in a very short time. Soon the Chantry was formed, and one of the first intentional Horizon Realms was flown," Lady Cullen interrupted.

"Yes, that's where the name comes from, from Horizon Chantry. After that little bit of business, making a little reality all your own, everything else was relatively easy. I mean, I imagine the first five minutes of the meeting were the most dangerous, and after that had passed, and no one got killed, shifted or devolved, I imagine things would go easily from there," Christopher said in his wonderfully warm voice.

"Indeed, Christopher. The power of the Nine." Heasha said with certainty.

"What's Nine got to do with it?" Deathlace asked.

"Numba Nine, Numba Nine… McCartney had a hold on it, babe. It's old numerology. Nine represents a purity of purpose, an epitome. The fact that nine mages turned out for a meeting to make peace with each other and attempt to do something about this whole Order of Reason thing was a heavy portent back then. Anyway, just like Chrissie says, the rest was easy compared to the first fifteen minutes. I mean, this was like, the ultimate leave-your-politics-at-the-door gig. Of course there were scrabbles here and there, most notably between Valoran and Ali-beh-shaar, who was a Moor. Still a lot of bad blood about Jerusalem, I bet…"

"It was nothing of the sort! The man was a known consorter-with-demons!" Christopher exclaimed, his voice rising an octave.

"Demon, schemons. They were hot little lust-spirits conjured up for his own amusement. Just because he offered Valoran one doesn't mean that he meant anything by it… certainly wasn't trying to convert him… or corrupt him." Heasha began, a smile on her face. "Valoran was a virgin; that's why it was such a big deal, Barbara."

With a chuckle, Harley continued. "Anyway, so there were a few squabbles, but nothing major. Everyone still mistrusted the Chorus, because of the Inquisition, but for the most part, a lot of positive work got done. People decided to work together, decided they would meet again at each Equinox and Solstice, and that they would each bring a gift to the group as a whole the next time they came. That was it, but that little bit was enough. Throughout the winter, Valoran and Baldric and Nightshade hammered out a plan to formalize magick in a way that the Primi would accept. Using something of the Hermetic system of magick-management, they decided to categorize magick into Spheres of power, and do it in such a way that they didn't offend anyone. Too much, that is. When the Spring Equinox came, and everyone gathered back together bringing gifts, it was a really good vibe, like a really good Dead concert, you know?"

"Humph. If it weren't for Nightshade selling every single Primus on the Spheres, we'd be Sleepers at home watching our MTV right now," Heasha said, snagging the bag of pretzels as Shella poked her nose into it.

"The Spheres, the Traditions, the ranking of knowledge, the Protocols, everything was hammered out and agreed upon at Horizon Chantry, the Council of the Nine. For nine years they met, four times a year, the word spreading and members of the fledgling Traditions joining at each meeting of the Council. And Heasha, what you said is right: except that if it weren't for the Primi of the Traditions, none of us would be Awake. They put their necks and their reputations on the line. Not everyone in their affiliated magickal associations agreed with the concepts of the Spheres and the Traditions. They wanted to go their own way, and like lone wolves, they usually met with an untimely end," Christopher said, waving aside the pretzels when they were offered to him.

"That's pretty much it, then…" Harley said, looking longingly at his Fender, wanting to touch it, wanting to buzz off all the chatter with a heavy riff.

"What about the Arabian guys?" Deathlace said, crunching on a pretzel. Shella jumped from Christopher's lap into hers, and she laughed when her tail brushed her nose.

"The Ahl-i-Batin were not suited for the Traditions. They kept to themselves," Christopher said, quietly.

"I beg to differ, Christopher," said Lady Cullen, " I believe their reasons for leaving had to do with the changes in their native homeland. When the spirituality of their homeland began to be twisted for the Technocracy's purposes, and the power of oil began to be more important, they blamed the Traditions for not doing enough to stop the Technocracy's advance. So, they retreated to their private reality. In the end, I think it is best." She sipped a cup of hot tea that she must've gotten for herself.

Heasha shook her head no. "Ah, I think we missed out on a lot. Look what kind of spiritual wasteland we got into in the years that followed. The imbalance…"

"You're just superstitious about the Nine thing. There were only Eight Trads for a while, Deathie, and everyone got all bent out of shape about it. Luckily the Virtual Idiots, I mean, the Adepts, dropped in when they did. I believe that '67 was the last big meeting of the Council." Harley said, pulling out a set of picks and looking for a fresh pair of batteries for his tuner in the big leather bag he always carried.

"How often do they meet?" Deathlace asked, scritching Shella.

"They were supposed to meet every nine years, but you know mages— we're busy folks. It kinda got overlooked, and now they only meet when they absolutely hafta. Besides, the Traditions are so intermixed and intertwined now that you can't spit without hitting other Trads in a Chantry, regardless of where the Chantry is. Not too many are Tradition-specific any more.

"What about mages like Blackrose, in San Fran?" Deathlace said, putting Shella on the floor. The familiar sniffed and bounded off into the cockpit. Deathlace felt a twinge in her gut. Blackrose was a good friend of hers.

The sunlight flashed through the window, suddenly the world was coming into focus. The psychedelic lightshow was dying down, and the bus was slowing down.

Harley held up a dead battery and crooked an eyebrow at Lady Cullen. She rolled her eyes and held out her hand, like a mother keeping her son from throwing something rather than gently handing it over. Harley coughed and looked down at his frets, running a soft cloth over the finish of his beauty. Deathlace stared hard at Harley, sensing his subterfuge, feeling his unwillingness to discuss this particular topic.

"They're… not one of us, babe. Hollow Ones. Orphans." Harley said, not looking up.

"Like me?" Deathlace said, her tone and face daring Harley. He knew she had Awakened on the street, with no master to guide her. No Tradition had claimed her yet.

He didn't even look up. "Like you, babe. Only you're gonna be in the Cult of Ecstacy, like we talked about."

"Or the Verbena, if you so wish, child. We would be able to teach you much. And I think you'd prefer being among my coven-sisters back home in Boston," Heasha said, her tone friendly and warm.

Lady Cullen smiled. "Listen to them, Barbara. You'd think they were coaches of a football team recruiting you. I'm sure it's because of your particularly potent Avatar. Never fear. But do keep in mind the Order. We could teach you much, if you are willing to learn."

Christopher just smiled.

"Well, Chris, you gonna give her a sales pitch, too?" Heasha said, laughing.

His mane of blonde hair was like a halo around him. "No, if she doesn't wish to hear the music of the Chorus, then I will sit quietly. She will ask if she feels like joining with us, joining with the One."

"What's wrong with the Hollow Ones?" Deathlace asked, quietly. The things Blackrose had said about travelling with the Chantry started to come back. *Am I really not one of them?* she said to herself.

Heasha didn't even pause. "They don't give a damn about Ascension for one thing. For another, they're just plain selfish and stuck on themselves. I mean, I could see them revelling in their pitiful state if they did it for pleasure, or for enlightenment, but they do it out sheer apathy. They just don't care. They're lost souls, as far as I'm concerned. Most of them are a waste of good skin." The venom in her voice was like a splash of ice water on Deathlace's face.

"The Orphans must be led, too, Sister." Lady Cullen said, a touch patronizing. The older woman seemed oblivious to the rage that was building up inside of Barbara. "They will come to see the Truth, just as the Traditions did." She took a pendant with a Seal of Solomon on it and touched the symbol to both ends of the batteries. There was a crackling noise, and a few sparks, and then she handed them back to Harley.

"Maybe they would, if they had a place on the Council." Deathlace said, looking down at her feet, remembering what Blackrose had told her now. All of it finally came into place.

Harley tucked the batteries into his guitar tuner and began to correct its tone, smiling at Lady Cullen. "Thanks, Lady. You're better than that bunny with the drums on TV." Deathlace hated to be ignored, and Harley was doing a pretty good job of it.

Heasha spoke in response, trying to break the heavy silence. "They wouldn't accept a seat on the Council, even

if it were offered to them. They're just like the Disparate in the early days, those who refused to join the Traditions, but instead went deep into hiding. They are too caught up in their own views to accept the ideas of others."

Deathlace looked up at Heasha. "Oh really? Well, what would you say if I told you I was already a Hollow One? Inside me, that's what I am. Hollow inside. Hollow like the Council of the Nine, because you don't know the whole story. You know what I think? I think it's time you grew up and entered the twentieth century. Who cares about numerology? Who cares about stupid superstitions? I'm a Cancer— does that mean I can't be a mage? You're just hung up on this damn Nine thing, all of you."

The other mages were surprised by Deathlace's tone, the vehemence in her voice. Even Harley stared at her, dumbfounded, for once not having a snappy comeback for the situation.

Her eyes flashing, Deathlace held up a single finger. "Get used to another number, how about it? Not 10. Zero. The end, the beginning, all in one circle. Hollow. Like this…" Harley watched as her nail grew long and sharp and diamond-hard. She cut a circle in the glass coffee table and didn't even blink when the glass circle shattered on the floor beneath it.

"Get over it. We're the end, we're the beginning. Get over it. And until you accept us… warts and all… well, you can just hang up Ascension ."

There was an echo in the living room, an echo of the shattered circle, something that spoke to every Avatar in every mage in the room. It was an unmistakable sound to those gathered there. It was the ring of truth.

As Deathlace climbed the stairs, the tears of rage starting to flow, she couldn't help but smile to herself.

Downstairs, there was some serious quiet.

A Brief History of the Technocracy

… if moral judgments are essentially assertions of value, and if value is the fundamental ground-stuff of the world, then moral judgments are the fundamental ground-stuff of the world.

— Robert Pirsig, *Lila*

Notes of Professor Terrance Whyte
Collegium of History
"A Brief History of Technocracy," Lesson One

The war has brought suffering to all of us. As we work to bring humanity into the next millennium, there are those who reject us and blindly rebel against reality. Their guerrilla tactics strike at us repeatedly, despite the efforts of a brave few who try to offer the rebellious mages a place within our Union. Many of the Tradition mages seek to remake the world in their own image. They've done that before.

Most Tradition mages know very little about the history of the Technocracy. Each Tradition has its own history of what happened, but each Tradition has added its own bias. As I am so fond of saying, history is not an absolute science, it is an interpretation. The mages have interpreted history to support their own beliefs, and in each version they advance, their portrayal of us is grossly distorted.

The Technocracy has its own reasons for fighting the War for Ascension. Individuals within the "Collective" have their own views on the potential of the Technocracy and their own personal visions of how to "heal" the growing Schism within it. Our enemies see us as monsters—faceless conformists, ruthless dictators or evil overlords. They will not accept that we are human beings, struggling against powerful odds to bring the light of reason to a dark world.

Mages who wish to leave the separatism and the bitterness of the failed Traditions behind should consider some of the historical accounts commonly related within the Technocracy. As new members of the Technocracy, you must remember that truth can be the most powerful weapon of all. We must examine the truths behind the War. Although the early efforts of our Union can be traced to the birth of civilization, the real story of the Technomancers' role in the Ascension War begins in the Mythic Age.

The Mythic Age

Everything in the history books about the Middle Ages is wrong. The Masses will never know the truth, and they do not want to remember. Only We know the real story of the Mythic Age. The Order of Hermes has forgotten what really happened. They have relied on archaic methods of preserving data, and their data is corrupted.

Before the Age of Reason, the first mages claimed to live in a Utopia. It was a Utopia… for them. They claimed to benevolently watch over their vassals from the safety of their covenants, but for many, their only true interest was in pursuing their arcane studies. The peasants often suffered, regardless of what the Tradition mages say. Perhaps a few covenants properly tended their flocks, but in many areas, the Masses slowly died as the forces of the supernatural world grew stronger.

As many of the magi began to slowly go insane, the peasants in the field began to wonder if they should really rely on them...

The Mythic Age was a time when superstition and ignorance were the foundations of civilization. After the Fall of Rome, most of Europe needed a system to protect the people who worked the land. The result was a system of feudalism. The most powerful organization in this structure was a group of individuals Gifted with the talent of magic: the magi.

The magi established Hermetic Orders to perfect their skills. To find the freedom to practice their craft, many made arrangements with the populace of their regions. The practitioners of magic offered to assist the populace in caring for their community. They offered to protect the land from danger, deal with the threat of supernatural forces, and employ the most talented members of the populace as part of their retinues. In exchange for this, the people would help the magi maintain fortresses in which magic could be studied. These places were known as *covenants*. The system was simple, and it worked... for a while.

While the vampires controlled the largest cities and the werewolves cared for the untamed wild, the magi led a double life: they pursued intellectual perfection while they oversaw their land and their people. Many balanced the two aspects of their life well. Many of the magi, however, did not.

Some magi neglected their part of the bargain. Some went slowly insane or disappeared entirely as they reached the higher levels of their discipline. Others simply failed to protect their lands from the forces that threatened to destroy them. For every mage that neglected the needs of the Masses, trust in the covenants began to falter.

I would like to focus on a classic example of a once thriving covenant that betrayed that trust: a covenant known as Mistridge. As the decades wore on, the people living near Mistridge grew increasingly dissatisfied with their protectors. Attacks by supernatural creatures, the loss of a few members of the convenant to the effects of creeping insanity, and the betrayal of the Tremere magus named Grimgroth were are all part of the gradual disintegration of a once respected covenant.

At the same time, an obscure Order of mages who lived secretly in a region near Mistridge were exploring radical new theories of magic. Although their Order was not large in this area, many practitioners of this group were minor members of a larger group of radicals called House Ex Miscellania. They had their origins in many movements, and they have been referred to by many names. Many

Technomancer accounts identify this group as simply "The Craftmasons."

There has been ample speculation concerning their original philosophy. One common account is that the Craftmasons wanted to find a way for the Masses to hold their own power and live independently of the covenants. By creating items of power that anyone could use, they worked to undermine the system of feudalism. Furthermore, they saw the supernatural activity near the covenants as threats to everyone's survival. By shutting off the power of the spirit world, by draining the land of magic, the threat of these forces to the mages and the Masses would be reduced.

To expand their domain, assist the Masses, and test their recent innovations in magical theory, they made their move on a winter day in the early 13th century. They began the liberation of Mistridge.

The War for Ascension had begun.

The Revolution of Mistridge is a classic example of how to handle a Chantry. First, a few Ex Miscellania mages raised the Spirit Gauntlet around the building and lowered the magical power within. Then the shock troops— consisting of irate peasants—kept everyone inside the covenant. Of course, a few spies within had already taken out a few key magi, but the real soldiers arrived later to lay into them with their greatest weapon.

Hey, all those ideals about chivalry and single combat were useful in the Mythic Age, but the protectors of the land couldn't do their job. That's why we invented the tools of liberation. That's why the cannon was invented. That's why Mistridge was reduced to rubble.

— Field Commander Davis, Instructor of Iteration X HIT Marks

Terrance Whyte, Collegium of History

Excerpts from Lesson One

...and although Sleepers were not able to use the cannon in battle until the Siege of Metz in 1324, it made for an outstanding magically-enhanced weapon for the Craftmasons of the 13th century. Mathematicians and engineers transported several of the devices to support revolutions in other parts of Europe...

After the destruction of Mistridge, the Craftmasons taught their Gifted apprentices the basics of their techniques. This included erecting Spirit Gauntlets to isolate covenants, methods of draining these covenants of their magical energy, and skills for manufacturing devices to bring prosperity to the people. The Masses no longer needed to rely on magic to protect themselves from the unknown. They relied instead on the devices of the Craftmasons to improve their lives. Better farming techniques, medicine, sanitation and education are but a few examples. The most effective weapon against the Traditions was the idea that an elite group of mages was no longer needed to rule the world. Society no longer existed to serve the magi. It existed to allow the Masses to thrive.

The first Craftmason "community" at Mistridge was a success. Others heard of this unbelievable event. They heard of the courage of a group of peasants who asserted their will and helped destroy a corrupt covenant. Similar revolutions were occurring throughout Europe.

The belief in magic as a form of protection waned. Belief in the *need* for magic began to wane as well. A different paradigm of reality was born: a system where superstition did not hide solutions to one's problems, where mysticism did not leave true knowledge to the few. The idea itself was quite old, but the Craftmasons helped spread it throughout Europe. Reason and order began to replace fear and superstition. The new leaders who emerged were not practitioners of the magical arts. They were Sleepers.

Another movement in the 13th century also fueled the fires of dissent. The Inquisition strengthened the power of the Church and assaulted the forces of the supernatural. The Craftmasons and their allies were not the only ones to recognize the threat of the supernatural world; they merely handled the situation differently. Some segments of the Inquisition declared the mages to be "evil" and added to the bloodshed of the first Pogroms.

The death and misery was compounded by the greatest failure of the covenants: the Black Plague, a scourge of unknown origin that destroyed magi and Sleepers alike. Many Sleepers who formerly trusted the covenants had no choice but to turn to alternatives.

As the support of magic lessened, the forces of Dominion and Reason were strengthened by belief. Magic had always been predicated on belief. The Faith of a holy man could enrich the spirituality of a church, a belief in the fey could help someone enter a regio of the faerie world, and the belief of a mage in his own power assisted him in exerting his will. This entire system was supported by the belief of everyone that the power of magic was real. Reality shifted. The Church's power of Dominion and the growing power of Reason eclipsed the powers of magic.

Magic died because humanity wanted it to die. The spirituality of the land still existed in some places, but hatred towards the mages and the memory of their failures raised other forces in its place.

Science did not begin with the Age of Reason. There was always science— the rules were merely different back then. People were willing to believe in just about anything: ghosts, faeries, giants, even the philosopher's stone.

But there were still things that were too far from reality to be believed. They hid in the realms of Arcadia or other worlds waiting nearby. They were held at bay by a spiritual force that mankind never knew existed. Now we have a name for it.

"Paradox."

—Ashton, defector from the Order of Hermes

The Masses swarmed the continent hunting mages as well, and the force of Paradox aided them. The people vowed never to be at the mercy of mages again. The Craftmasons hid and watched, leaving more of human

history to the Sleepers. Their powerful spirit magics, in the meantime, helped guide the forces of Paradox. A renaissance was underway.

The revolution of Sleepers, the campaigns of the Craftmasons, the Black Plague and the Inquisition were major forces in ending the failure known as the Mythic Age. A few evasive mages escaped into the "spirit world" as they abandoned their covenants. One Order, the Tremere, even joined with the vampires to escape retribution. As the Pogrom raged, the Craftmasons continued their researches. The items they crafted became more and more fantastic.

Excerpt from Lesson Three

...soon the surviving magi protected themselves by secretly forming the Order of Hermes. They allied with the so-called "Traditions," many of which were no older than the origins of the Conventions. The real magical power was vested in a rapidly growing society of Awakened philosophers and inventors who held many of the beliefs of the original Craftmasons. The Order of Reason was larger, stronger, and held the support of a growing consensual reality.

The origins of the Conventions existed long before the Order of Reason. The scholars who first gave the world mathematics began the long path towards the programming of Iteration X. The healers of Ancient Greece and Rome were the humble beginnings of the Progenitors. Ancient astronomers laid the foundations for the twentieth century Void Engineers. Of course, these discoveries came from throughout the world. Enlightened men and women pursued science throughout the world, from the inventors of China to the navigators of the Phoenicians. Once the Order of Reason gained strength, these disparate historical elements came together, and the Order changed the course of history.

Behind the scenes, however, the Craftmasons kept their existence secret. They were the hoarders of wealth, the makers of kings, the architects of reality, and the most powerful of the mages. They were also human, with human frailties. A few became corrupt in their power, and the first seeds of the Schism were sown.

The Age of Reason

Even in the Age of Reason, science was just a way of proving that anything was possible. Science used to be a tool for dreaming. Yes, there was Paradox then, but people were so enraptured by the possibilities of science that its forces were weak.

If only we could build Da Vinci's inventions again. They really worked then...

—Dr. Horatio Baldridge, Son of Ether, currently living in the Cloud Realm of Montgolfier

Excerpt from Lesson Four

The hidden leaders continued their agenda while many members of the Order of Reason found methods of perfecting their magic. They were inventors, explorers, dreamers and innovators. It was a Golden Age, especially for one rapidly growing secret society— the Parmenideans.

Their name began as a joke, for the Greek philosopher Parmenides rigidly believed in the power of stasis. The mages of this secret order sought to defy this stasis whenever possible. As a result, early science was just as outlandish as magic. However, the illusion of stasis was maintained while the dynamism of magic was explored. The practice of their craft, the perfection of invention and creation, was something they knew they had to do secretly. This movement refined many of the early ideas of coincidental magic. Furthermore, by altering the boundaries of reality, by performing coincidental acts that could later be replicated by actual inventions, science advanced.

The Parmenideans understood the practice of magic in the presence of Sleepers. The Inner Circle gained its power by carefully directing and orchestrating their efforts. They formed organizations to oversee the efforts of the Outer Circle and organized august bodies to debate the consequences of their actions. These were the first formal Symposiums.

With the passage of time, the names of various subgroups came and went. The word "Craftmason" fell out of use, although the word "Parmenidean" remained throughout this period. The name remained in use throughout the Renaissance, an era that allowed for the building of a more egalitarian civilization. Since the Parmenideans established the foundation for the Sons of Ether, the Traditions are quick to claim their achievements as Tradition ideas. This is, of course, foolish. The Parmenideans followed the dictates of the Inner Circle…

Excerpt from Lesson Five

As they continued this exploration, a few noted Parmenideans broke the boundaries of reality. The parameters of possibility shifted. By overcoming the force of Paradox, they redefined the nature of society. One example was Gutenberg, a Technomancer who found a brilliant coincidental application of the powers of the Mind to disseminate information— under the guise of the printing press.

Copernicus was, undoubtedly, one of the greatest members of the Order of Reason. By drawing upon the assistance of a group of scientists, he performed one the most powerful communal rotes the world had seen. The Traditions have stated that because of Copernicus, the Sun actually ceased to revolve around the Earth. The Traditions expect its recruits to believe that the power of Correspondence moved the Sun and the Earth. This is yet another one of their lies. The Earth has always revolved around the sun.

Publicly, Copernicus disproved erroneous beliefs concerning the nature of the solar system. Privately, Copernicus had been watching events in the depths of space. His cabal succeeded in further strengthening the Gauntlet around the Earth, shutting out malefic forces he had seen waiting

beyond the Horizon. His supporters, following the precepts of earlier astronomers, advanced his Convention, one that would later become part of the Void Engineers.

The Victorian Age

Hell, the word 'Technocracy' started in the Symposiums of the Victorian Era. We almost won the war right then. When this VR program is finished, it's gonna show a lot of the new recruits what Victorian London was really like...

—Lightspeed, VR programmer, former Virtual Adept

Excerpts from Lesson Six

One of the most productive time periods for the Technocracy was the Victorian Age. Several Conventions grew more visible. One was the result of a few Awakened secret society members who had formed a Lodge hidden within Scotland Yard...

December 18th, 1886

The screaming will not stop. I have tried repeatedly to purge the neighborhood of those horrific spirits, but my efforts are not enough. If sorcery can raise them, then sorcery can dispel them. I have organized my assistants from Scotland Yard, and we will drive this horror from our midst. We will act as one to purify this neighborhood for the safety of all.

—Diary of Inspector Rathbone

This well-orchestrated team of hunters who used their magickal abilities to safeguard England against the encroaching horrors of the unknown formed the foundation of what would later become the Men in Black...

London grows each day. If our production is to properly meet the demands of the populace, we must increase our efforts to meet the demands of the machines. Otherwise, the Masses will starve.

— Augustus Fortinbras, Executive Director of the Guild

Industry also flourished. A few Enlightened magi were able to capitalize on the possibility of using magick to speed production and predict the success of companies. The idea of using business to assist the Masses began in the late Middle Ages with a society known as The Guild. This Convention evolved in the Victorian Age with the advent of the Industrial Revolution, and the Guild later became the Syndicate.

The descendants of the apprentices who assisted Copernicus and Kepler still labored towards their exploration of the heavens. The fringe Convention of the Celestial Masters— who later merged with the "Seekers of the Void"— continued to collect their data.

The Parmenideans became enthralled with the idea that the Earth was bathing in a spiritual mist. Data collected from magical experiments lead to the discovery of the Deep Umbra, although two of the leading mages in this secret investigation, Michaelson and Morley, insisted on calling it the "Etheric Continuum." The discovery so alarmed this Convention of mages that the name "Sons of Ether" came into vogue. The name stuck.

The "Corruption" of Technology

Do you really think the Technomancers shaped reality? You really believe that? It's the same old question: does mankind reshape history, or does history reshape mankind? I think the events of this century got out of control, and that destroyed the Order of Reason. I am free from blame. My only fault was trying to describe things as they really are. Now I'm glad you're going to kill me, because now I can really be free.

—Xerxes, former agent of the New World Order, Euthanatos spy

As technology continued to advance, so did the Conventions. Inventions in communications led to further development of the Correspondence Sphere, and a group of Sons of Ether began to split off to pursue this study. The Void Engineers, looking out upon the endless reaches of space, also set out to master Correspondence, pushing into new frontiers.

The Symposiums, still led by the Inner Circle of the long occulted Craftmasons, had other agenda. By extrapolating upon the data of the Sons of Ether, they found a way to explore the further reaches of the ether. Vehicles were constructed to carry Symposiums beyond the Horizon, establishing research installations in the Deep Umbra.

Beyond the Horizon, the Symposiums were able to establish their bases of operations. The Technomancers were able to fully pursue research without fear of Paradox. With this advantage at their disposal, their science grew by leaps and bounds. In fact, their knowledge grew too quickly…

The Cutting Edge

If a man's reach can't exceed his grasp, then what's a heaven for?

—Robert Browning

Freed from the constraints of Earthly reality, the Technocracy soon advanced far beyond the technology of Earth. Some of the Technomancers of the Deep Umbra lost touch with the reality, and morality, they left behind. By the '80s, some Technomancer innovations were estimated to be approximately 50 years ahead of the technology of the Masses.

Eighty years of unrestrained research had a deleterious effect on what once began as a fringe revolution against the covenants. Some analysts of the Collegiums have boldly stated that this was the result of improper leadership in the Inner Circle. I find such radical beliefs disturbing. Our leaders deep in the Great Beyond still hold the original ideas of "helping" the Masses. However, I will advance this qualification: some leaders of the research installations, including some of my former colleagues, have adjusted the concept. They see themselves as infallible, removed from the imperfections of the Earth. They claim to know what is best for humanity. Our victory has been predicted, and in turn, this has given them the fortitude to do anything in the name of progress. This, however, is only one segment of the Technocracy. Forgive me. I digress.

Countless discoveries in Technomancer technology occurred during the twentieth century. The first secretive spacecraft began exploring the solar system, venturing beyond the Gauntlet strengthened by the Craftmasons, Copernicus, Kepler and others. Bases were established on the Horizon, in the Deep Umbra and on other worlds.

One Deep Umbral journey led to the discovery of Autochthonia, a Machine Realm located in Earth's orbit on the far side of the Sun. Conjecture continues as to whether this world is merely a parallel Earth, the result of the communal magick of Copernicus and Kepler, or actually a "spirit realm" of the Technocracy. Some call it Utopia; others call it a fringe religion.

Fuelled by our variants of magick, we have perfected artificial intelligence, cloning, cyborg technology, fantastic methods of transportation, mind-shattering innovations in artificial life, and other breakthroughs. We are waiting to slowly introduce them into the world. Never again will our influence be hurried.

The Schism

Technology is a tool to empower individuals. We just wanted to empower people with the tools to control their own lives. The Technocracy has forgotten that goal. They see technology as a force to enslave the Masses, not liberate them. They're fanatics. That's why I'd do anything to destroy them.

— Zarathustra, Virtual Adept, From issue #136 of the *webslinger.spys-demise* samizine

…despite the ongoing debates, many of the Symposiums and research labs had already retreated to the Horizon and were oblivious to the criticisms of individual Technomancers. Many analysts of the academic Collegiums, for instance, were discounted by the more "elite" practitioners of the Executive Orders. They obtained the freedom to critique and analyze, yet our greatest chance to offer our insight to the Technocracy always came from our task as educators…

There are two Conventions that have not concurred with the new Technocratic agenda. They could not pursue their goals through civilized discourse, and they have been disenfranchised from the Collective. Whether they defected or were cast out is a matter of some conjecture. The Sons of Ether, seeing the results of their research, no longer fit within the rigid hierarchy that was being established. Many left during the Victorian Age rather than attempt to heal the Technocracy. Decades later, the Virtual Adepts, a Convention based around the discovery of Virtual Reality, also fled, divorcing themselves from responsibility in favor of escapism…

After the defections, we have examined our Union with greater scrutiny. Some members of the New World

Order have spoken of a growing Schism in our ranks. Our leaders beyond the Horizon do not always have direct contact with our agents in the field. Those who bring innovations through research do not always listen to warnings from the theorists and academicians. Different views of Ascension, different opinions on our future, different opinions on how we must handle the Tradition mages—although we stand United, the debate we pursue over these issues is rigorous.

There is, however, a great deal of common ground. We care for the future of humanity. We bring progress, innovation, security and enlightenment. We are the advocates of technology and, as such, the protectors of humanity.

The Future of Technocracy

…both sides are becoming identical. What, in fact, is being created: an international community, a perfect blueprint for World Order. When the sides facing each other realize that they're looking into a mirror, they will see that THIS is the pattern for the future.

—#2, The Prisoner, "Chimes of Big Ben"

Do the actions of the Technomancers in this millennium demonstrate that all technology is "evil?" Far from it. Medicine, communications, sanitation, education, transportation… all these breakthroughs for mankind resulted from the explorations of the Technomancers.

The Traditions, who once failed to lead the world, rejected their opportunity to join our future. Self-delusion, escapism and fantasies of Ascension help them to pronounce all Technomancers as "evil." Anachronists, cultists, primitives, hedonists, worshipers of death— some of these misfits of reality label all *technology* as "evil," despite the many advances it has given civilization.

The clock cannot be reversed. The magi once controlled the Mythic Age, but they have failed. The Tradition leaders strive to shift the parameters of reality to serve themselves, but they do not understand humanity. Now we offer the Tradition mages two choices. They can take the challenge of joining the lowest levels of the Technocracy and help to heal reality or they can continue to defy us and become extinct. If they do not join us, if they directly oppose the dictates of the Inner Circle, they will die. They can choose to end this war. Their choice is a simple one: life or death.

We must never forget the importance of our cause. We must never forget what history has shown us. Our Union has brought humanity out of the Dark Ages and into the light of Reason. Now we must gather together to heal the growing Schism in our ranks. For the sake of humanity and the stability of reality, there is only one option for us: overwhelming victory.

Book Six: Guiding Words
Council

The measure of wisdom is a hard look in the mirror.
The measure of maturity is the ability to act on what you see.
— Heasha Morninglade, Verbena Adept

Mage covers a lot of ground, but at a basic level, it's a game about choices; if you had the power to mold reality, what would you do with it? How would it change you? And how would you cope with the obstacles and temptations that would come with such a realization?

The following essays offer some guidance to **Mage** players and Storytellers. Some address the game itself, while others compare the World of Darkness with our own "real world." These essays are meditations on the game and our thoughts about it, not gospel handed down from on high. We're all players here... players of one game or another.

The Hero's Handbook

By John Robey

The mythological hero, setting forth from his common-day hut or castle, is lured, carried away, or else voluntarily proceeds, to the threshold of adventure. There he encounters a shadow presence that guards the passage. The hero may defeat or conciliate this power and go alive into the kingdom of the dark… or be slain by the opponent and descend in death… Beyond the threshold… the hero journeys through unfamiliar yet strangely intimate forces, some of which severely threaten him (tests), some of which give him magical aid (helpers). When he arrives at the nadir of the mythological round, he undergoes a supreme ordeal and gains his reward. The triumph may be represented as the hero's sexual union with the goddess-mother of the world…, his recognition by the father-creator…, his own divinization…, or, again—if the powers have remained unfriendly to him— his theft of the boon he came to gain…; intrinsically, it is an expansion of consciousness and therewith of being…. The final work is that of the return. If the powers have blessed the hero, he now sets forth under their protection…; if not, he flees and is pursued… At the return threshold the transcendental powers must remain behind; the hero re-emerges from the kingdom of dread… The boon that he brings restores the world…

— Joseph Campbell's capsule definition of the Monomyth, from *The Hero with a Thousand Faces*,

The *Random House College Dictionary, Revised Edition* defines a hero as "a man of distinguished courage or ability, admired for his brave deeds and noble qualities," "a man who is regarded as having heroic qualities and is considered a model or ideal," or "a small loaf of Italian bread." However, Joseph Campbell Fanatics (like me) tend to prefer the Campbellian definition of a Hero, which is simply anyone (man, woman, child, spirit) who is dedicated to something other than himself — another person a relationship, a cause, and so on. In **Mage**, the player characters are Heroes who have dedicated themselves to making the world better by unraveling the intricate grid of the Technocracy — or who will make the world better when they discover what the Technocracy plans to achieve.

In order to achieve this goal, the heroes must first undergo the long and difficult process of making themselves better people; this is the archetypal Hero's Journey, wherein the Hero improves the world by improving herself. This essay is designed to identify steps in this journey, to help players think of directions for the characters, and to provide Storytellers with tools to add meaning to their stories. Keep in mind that these are only the major points; plenty of minor motifs inevitably fall through the cracks. Interested parties are referred to *The Hero with a Thousand Faces* or *Joseph Campbell and the Power of Myth* as good starting places for more detailed discussions.

The basic motifs of the Journey are contained in the Monomyth, quoted at the beginning of this essay. The

Monomyth is nothing more than the reduction of the many and varied stories of the different cultures of the world to the most basic elements that they have in common. The stories that endure for centuries or millennia (Ancient Greek mythology, the mytho-religious stories of the Judeo-Christian tradition, Buddhism, Islam, Shakespeare, Arthurian legends, fairy tales and so on) all contain elements of the Monomyth, as do the best stories in popular culture. Some modern storytellers consciously emulate the Monomyth (George Lucas is the obvious example, but there are hundreds of others), while others simply tap into the "collective unconscious." The Storyteller Games have all been written with an eye towards linking them to the Monomyth, but **Mage** provides the most hope of breaking through the darkness and getting to the light beyond. The Storyteller must remember the Hero's Journey so that players may descend and ascend over and over again.

Keep in mind that the motifs of the Hero's Journey, while archetypal, should not be clichés. Unimaginatively following the quest formula will only give you an unimaginative game. One way to do this is to avoid the obvious; the Hero's Journey to the Underworld could certainly be a trip into a deep sewer or a Wyrm-infested section of the Umbra, but a far more unique trip to the Underworld might be a foray into the uppermost levels of a Technocratic corporation's skyscraper or a vampire's downtown haven. These motifs should be obscured whenever possible, preferably only discovered when the player thinks back. If everyone in the group shouts, "Hey, look, we're going to the Underworld!", the Storyteller needs to be more subtle.

Elements of the Hero's Journey

The archetypal Hero is unusual in some way, but is still "incomplete". That is, there is something that sets him apart from his peers. Even Jack (of "The Beanstalk" fame), one of the least characterized Heroes of all time, is unusual: his father is dead, slain by a giant, and Jack and his mother live far away from town. This difference is necessary: ordinary people don't have adventures. If they did, they wouldn't be ordinary any more! Obviously, the mage is "Awakened" and can perform magick. His "heroic" stature goes deeper than that. Player characters represent the hope for the future, and, as such, should be unusual even among mages.

Orphans make excellent player characters for just this reason. Because they haven't been indoctrinated into the dogma of any one Tradition, they have an all-encompassing perspective which allows them to see the seeds of truth in each Tradition's creed without being snared by the Tradition's particular blind spots.

The Hero leaves home; he either goes voluntarily or is thrown out by her peers or superiors. Prior adventures can't take place at home: they must occur in the wilderness, or on a frontier of some kind. Just as the Hero has been elevated beyond ordinary experience by being "different,"

his experiences must be elevated to be worthy of him. The Hero's adventure is the one the Hero is ready for. In the best stories, only *that* hero could have *that* adventure. Eddie Murphy as a streetwise cop in Detroit is just another streetwise cop. Put him in Beverly Hills, on the other hand, and he stands out. His brand of street-smarts is not only a quirk, it's a liability, though one that ultimately makes victory possible.

The Hero acquires a helper or mentor. Arthur had Merlin; Bilbo had Gandalf; Jason had Medea; Bond had Q. The helper is very often an older kind of "ex-hero" who can no longer complete an adventure herself, but wishes to pass her experience on (e.g. Obi-Wan Kenobi). This helper often puts herself into considerable danger, and may even sacrifice her life to protect the Hero at his most vulnerable time. This not only protects the Hero, but instills a sense of duty and an ideal that will carry the Hero through in later times of trouble. Eventually, the Hero must see through the ideal and see the person in the helper — Ben tells Luke a pretty whopping lie, after all — but he will hopefully have enough wisdom to eventually understand why the helper did this.

The Hero must confront The Enemy, usually in open combat. The Enemy can be a powerful entity (a Technomancer near the top of the hierarchy with an Arete 10 and a kerjillion minions) or can be an idea or a situation (racism and prejudice). The Hero's earliest victories are likely to be small ones (beating up a security guard in a Technocratic Construct), and there will be defeats.

One of the most common defeats is being captured, but since captured heroes are usually taken into the Enemy's stronghold, this only leads to (eventually) bigger and better victories. Another common defeat is the loss of friends and loved ones. This is often the direct or indirect result of the Hero's actions (thus giving him something to feel guilty for later) though it need not be.

Entering the Underworld: The hero eventually gets to the Underworld, usually by choice, in an effort to gain something or achieve a goal (gain information, rescue a person, destroy the Evil King's rule over the land, find Prince Charming, etc.). Sometimes, however, the Hero is taken to the Underworld as a prisoner of The Enemy. The Underworld is usually where the Hero's most significant victories (and defeats) will occur.

Obviously the Underworld doesn't have to be underground; it's simply someplace dangerous and/or mysterious. Very often, it forms the heart of The Enemy's domain. In **Mage**, the most common Underworlds might be Technocratic Constructs, Nephandus Labyrinths, Shard Realms, or (best of all) personal Quiet.

The Underworld is a rotten place to visit, but you really wouldn't want to live there. It is a source of primal knowledge and power, but it also confronts the Hero with all of the pain and sorrow of existence, and his existence in particular. The Underworld should be frightening, painful and just plain nasty.

The Hero's toughest battles will always be those in which the Hero is confronting something within himself— a weakness, or a crime (often unconfessed) for which he must atone, or his own inner capacity for evil. Sometimes, the character fails these tests (King Arthur's marital problems come to mind), but these failures are only temporary setbacks.

Once in a very great while, a character may not only fail the test, but be nearly destroyed by it, such as Darth Vader's fall or Faust's selling of his soul. This can be a traumatic thing to play, and will cause large shifts in the structure of the chronicle. Very often, the character will die or find herself forced from her cabal. Running such a fall should be set up between the players and the Storyteller, but the character should ultimately choose between an attempt at redemption, eventual death or resignation to the Land of Recurring NPCs.

The Hero cannot leave the Underworld until she is redeemed— which isn't to say that she's held prisoner, although she may be. More often, a Hero fallen from grace carries the Underworld with her wherever she may go. Oedipus, Jason and a double-handful of other tragic heroes spent the latter halves of their lives wandering the world in torment and never managed to gain redemption. King Arthur and Lancelot could only be redeemed by the recovery of the Grail, and England withered and became a wasteland in the meantime...

Eventually, the victorious (or redeemed) Hero escapes from the Underworld. It isn't easy; the Hero has to get through great difficulty and/or sacrifice. George Lucas' film *Return of the Jedi*, from the moment Luke Skywalker surrenders to Darth Vader until the removal of Darth Vader's mask, is simply one long trip into the Underworld. Luke undergoes one of the oldest of quests — to bring his father back up from the abyss. Luke's trials, in this one film, include despair in the face of the Emperor's power, rage at the Emperor's treachery, and self-discovery when he is goaded into nearly killing his father. Even though Luke successfully passes all these trials, successfully redeeming his father, a sacrifice is still made — Vader's death at the end. Any **Mage** character's trials can be just as difficult.

The Hero has his final confrontation with, and ultimately defeats, The Enemy, even if The Enemy is nothing more than the character's own personal bugbear. This often comes late in the character's career, for obvious reasons. If the players and the Storyteller want to wrap up the chronicle, then a climactic end-game in which all of the characters get a chance to wipe out their personal Enemy and score a major victory against the Technocracy is in order. If the tale simply concludes one character's Journey, that character can either stay in the game or retire, depending on the wishes of the player and the Storyteller. Players shouldn't assume that a Hero's journey ends with the conquest of The Enemy. Life goes on; the world still turns. If nothing else, the Hero can act as the guide/helper for others in the chronicle still undergoing their own Journeys.

Once the Hero has finished his Journey and defeated The Enemy, the Hero returns home (or settles down in whatever new home he's adopted), changed and matured by his adventures, in order to (attempt to) bring his experience hard-won wisdom back to ordinary people. The fruits of the Hero's labor thus feed the common good. Eventually, continuing the cycle, the Hero will be the mentor for younger Heroes going through the same cycle.

And so it goes...

Roleplaying the Awakening

By Beth Fischi

Therefore, trust to thy heart, and to what the world calls illusions.

— Henry Wadsworth Longfellow

We don't see things as they are; we see them as we are.

— Anaïs Nin

It's often difficult to identify with characters who have undergone something totally foreign to our own experiences. This becomes particularly problematic when we try to roleplay an Awakening; since we (probably) haven't experienced such a thing, we require an "in" into the mind, background, and experiences of the mage-to-be who is just beginning to grasp what reality's all about. A number of factors give us that "in": the character's emotions, her Tradition, her Essence and her personality.

EMOTION

Think of the Awakening as a cousin to the kind of dreams that Walter de la Mare once wrote of: "A lost but happy dream may shed its light upon our waking hours, and the whole day may be infected with the gloom of a dreary or sorrowful one, yet of neither may we be able to recover a trace." The mage cannot forget an Awakening, as such dreams are soon forgotten, but she may experience the similar thrill of having touched a profound reality. The excitement of pursuit and discovery, of intense new understanding, is what the Awakening is all about; it's about the electric moment when conscious, everyday existence confronts a dream reality that is somehow more substantial.

TRADITION

Your character's Tradition largely determines the plot of the Awakening. Once you've chosen a Tradition for your character, think about its unique view of reality. The types of mages it attracts, the attitudes it fosters and the enemies it has earned will shape your character's Awakening. Remember that, with the exception of Orphans, the members of your adopted Tradition usually take the initiative in Awakening your character. Consider how these mages view the Awakening: is it their duty to help you? Is it a

sacred responsibility? Do they guide you out of love, fear, hope for the future, necessity or some other reason? How long have they been watching you? Must you pass an informal or formal trial period first? Is the Tradition like an exclusive club whose members must have "credentials," or is anyone with potential brought into the fold? Finally, who are your Tradition's arch-nemeses, and will they emerge during the Awakening to prevent the Tradition's induction of yet another soldier into its ranks?

The Order of Hermes, for instance, might require the potential mage to make a small breakthrough in numerology or astrology before being considered. The Akashic Brotherhood might ease your character into the concepts of dynamic reality and magick through a philosophy she has already begun to practice. Euthanatos mages might attempt to assassinate the character to teach her the meaning of death and the value of fleeting life.

ESSENCE

A character's Essence also influences the Awakening, but more subtly and pervasively than her Tradition. The Essence that you choose for your character now becomes the foundation for the many Seekings that she undergoes later. Arguably the most important Seeking, the Awakening, should be the character's first step toward the discovery of her Avatar; it can set the pattern and the mood for her later discoveries as she gains more points in Arete.

A Sleeper having a Dynamic Essence may find herself longing to make a difference in the world, but feel a lack of power and focus. During the Awakening, her Essence helps her embrace the strange, new reality she's encountering. Through the Awakening, such a person would see magick's potential to change the world for the better.

A Sleeper with a Pattern Essence may be disturbed by the pace of life today, feeling that technological advancement has become divorced from ethical understanding, or fearing that unfettered materialism has eroded the human spirit. Such a character is likely to experience an Awakening whose theme revolves around preserving ethical responsibility while discovering one's self. Through it, she may discover that her role is to slow the pace of a chaotically changing world.

Unlike a character with a Dynamic Essence, a character with a Questing Essence probably knows precisely how he would like to change the world, but doesn't have the power to do it. The Awakening enables such a character to pursue his goals. For pessimistic or cynical characters, the Awakening may even restore her hope in the feasibility of her task. The Awakening session can give characters of this Essence a tantalizing taste of the magick that will help them achieve their deep, inner quests, and it can make them hunger for more.

A character with a Primordial Essence may initially be estranged from her own feelings as a result of some deeply disturbing event in her past. She may unconsciously long for a time when her emotions were still untouched by the

obsessive, alienated and alienating society that has demoralized her. The Awakening, for such a character, reunites her mind with her heart. Through it, she relives that pivotal, debasing event and defeats it, at the same time she finds a new hope, one that she can shape with each advance she makes towards comprehending it.

PERSONALITY

Personality adds emotional depth to the prelude and externalizes the profound metamorphosis that has caused the Sleeper to Awaken. When your character undergoes such an experience, ask yourself what has happened to him—what changes have occurred in his psychology, his outlook? Then think about what it takes to get a sense of the emotional magnitude of the Awakening:

Discovering you have AIDS?

Or that you've found the cure for cancer?

Before you play an Awakening prelude, consider how your character will react to a world in which magick really exists. The character might shiver with the knowledge that creatures of unspeakable evil corrupt scores daily. He might fear a world in which malevolent organizations hunt him and his friends to extinction. He might cry for a world in which everyone for whom he fights is too blind to see the dangers, and the potentials, surrounding them. And he might savor a world that is fundamentally foreign to our own, in which anything from myth and anything from the dark or forbidden recesses of the unconscious might emerge.

Also consider what sort of a personality progression, if any, would make sense. A Sleeper with a Jester nature might become a Caregiver when she confronts and defeats her sorrow and pain; a Bon Vivant who realizes that Ascension exists and is attainable might become a Fanatic or a Visionary. A Curmudgeon who gains an imagination might even become an Architect while remaining hidden behind his habitually churlish demeanor. On the other hand, there are good reasons for a Curmudgeon to remain a Curmudgeon and a Jester to remain a Jester. It's up to you.

Remember that a successful Awakening story lets you explore the themes of change and discovery. Much of the work of setting up this exploration lies in the Storyteller's hands, but as a player, you have the challenge of devising the focus around which the Awakening revolves: your character. The Awakening session should be a vehicle through which you explore your character. With a little preparation, your character can ascend to that electric moment of comparison and feel the dream come alive, not fleetingly, but forever.

Magick & Belief in Mage

by Donald H. Frew

If you ask most players of fantasy roleplaying games about magick, you'll get an enthusiastic description of fireball spells, levitation spells, shapeshifting spells and the like in response. You could easily get the impression that magick in roleplaying games consists basically of impersonal lists of spells that are learned and cast with mechanical efficiency. Well, maybe that's how magick works in some fantasy roleplaying games, but not in **Mage**, and not in real life. That's right— real life.

Whether or not you or your fellow players believe in magick, the fact is that the vast majority of the world's population does believe in it. For them, magick is an integral part of everyday life. In the world of **Mage**, it is this widespread belief that makes magick possible. The **Mage** rulebook refers to the Paradigm, the dominant belief about the nature of reality. It is easy for Western readers to equate the Paradigm with the Western scientific world-view, but this is not the case. Everyone across the world may believe that dropped objects fall, but that does not mean that they all believe in gravity. They may all believe in illness, but comparatively few believe in germs.

In **Mage**, when a sorcerer performs coincidental or static magick, she is operating within the confines of the Paradigm of her own culture, in most cases, that of Western society. When a magician performs dynamic or vulgar magick, she is trying to break those confines to produce spectacular and dramatic displays of power. Even with an Awakened Avatar, it hardly seems possible that *any* individual could overcome the "momentum" of the Paradigm of an entire culture. But a mage has at her disposal alternate Paradigms, ways of understanding the world that allow for magick. These ways are believed in by sufficient numbers of people to overcome the beliefs of the local culture, at least temporarily, and at the direction of an accomplished magician.

These alternate Paradigms, the world-views of other cultures, are represented, in part, by the Traditions. A magician's training in the beliefs of her Tradition is what allows her to perform dynamic or vulgar magick. A player and a player character must both come to terms with the idea of multiple Paradigms existing as part of a spectrum from the global to the personal, with the cultural Paradigms and those of the Traditions lying somewhere in between.

The global Paradigm is concerned with the common human experiences of the world, largely as perceived by the five senses, e.g. things fall, the sun rises in the morning, hunger is alleviated by food, etc. The cultural Paradigms try to explain why things happen, whether through cause and effect, by the action of spirits, or whatever. The Paradigms of the Traditions (and of human imagination)

theoretically make magick possible. Personal Paradigms guide the magician's actions in life and explain her relationship to her world.

Our contemporary Western cultural Paradigm incorporates two attitudes towards magick: either it is ignored completely or it is seen as a kind of proto-science. Roleplaying games often tend to take the same approach — either ignoring magick or taking Clarke's Law to heart, treating it as a technology virtually indistinguishable from science. What does it matter if your magician casts a fireball spell or fires a laser pistol? In most games, very little. Magick and science are both treated as predictable and impersonal.

In the real world, and in the world of **Mage**, magick is only somewhat predictable and is *never* impersonal. Magick is the process by which we and our characters make contact with and interact with a reality that underlies the everyday world. In some sense, this is a reality understood as being more fundamental, more "true," than the everyday world. As limited physical beings, we and our characters understand this reality by means of various personal symbol sets. What a Christian adept may encounter as angels, a Pagan sorcerer may encounter as Gods or a Hermetic magus as impersonal planetary forces. A magician cannot have such an encounter and remain unchanged.

As a result of our magickal experiences, we develop beliefs about that fundamental reality, as well as beliefs about the everyday world, our personal Paradigm. These beliefs take the form of conceptions of divinity, ideas of the afterlife and spirit world, morals and ethics governing day-to-day behavior and more. Such beliefs in turn, shape our future practice of magick.

Indeed, magick in the real world and in **Mage** can be seen as belief focused by will and skill. In **Mage**, belief becomes Arete, will is represented by Willpower and skill is represented by the Spheres. It is up to each Player and Storyteller to determine the way belief comes into play, weaving it into the storytelling aspect of the **Mage** magick system. Players and Storytellers should consider the following questions, both as conditions for magick use in the game and as factors shaping the development of a character throughout a chronicle.

• What does the character, based on previous magickal experience, believe is possible? Self-imposed conceptual limitations should limit magick as much as the game rules do. A beginning **Mage** character, new to the ways of magick, may still reject the spectacular effects of dynamic magick out of hand as patently impossible. Until she is confronted with the reality of such effects, she should not be able to create them. They are outside of her personal Paradigm.

• What does the character believe is moral and ethical? For some characters, this may just be an innate sense of right and wrong; for others, this could be a fear of divine retribution. A belief that certain magickal acts are immoral or unethical may cause a character's magick to backfire upon her, not through any outside force, but through the intent that her own subconscious imposes upon the magick. A character may invoke her own Paradox Spirits, not through vulgar magick, but solely through her own expectation of punishment for unethical magick.

• How does each use of magick add to or change the character's beliefs? Few things can engender, support, question or shatter religious beliefs like magick. Dramatic conversions and crises of faith should not be uncommon for mages. A character who routinely calls upon a particular deity for aid, and receives that aid, may come to think of herself as a representative of that deity upon earth and suffer from delusions of grandeur. Another character may see magick as an impersonal force, only to have a vulgar fireball manifest as a 15-foot Agni, Hindu god of fire, who smites the intended victim. Or a character may call upon her god(s) in a moment of crisis and get no assistance or response at all. Either of these situations could and should lead to a radical rethinking of the character's personal Paradigm. In fact, it should not be all *that* rare for mages to change their Tradition after one or more such experiences. As a character's Paradigm changes, so might her Tradition.

Belief is an integral part of the practice of magick. It is both the expression of the incorporation of one's magickal experiences into one's life and the context out of which further such experiences arise. This is true in both the real world and the world of **Mage**. The beliefs of mages will always be fluid, changing with each new magickal experi-ence and, in turn, changing the way in which the mage experiences magick. This aspect of the life and practice of a mage may be more difficult to roleplay, requiring more care, thought, and time from players and Storytellers alike. It can, however, lend a new dimension of depth and realism to any **Mage** character.

Alienation of the Savior

By William Spencer-Hale

Around me, the world whirls about its ludicrous business. It doesn't even realize what it owes me. Jesus, I'm talking like a pratt, a paranoid, lonely, pratt.

— Jamie Delano, *John Constantine, Hellblazer*

Loneliness. Hollow footsteps echoing down darkened streets; whispers in the shadows heard only by you. This is the life of the mage, a reality that no one else can see, a world that can be shared with no other for fear of what may befall the confessor. It is an existence of silent frustration and anger where one has the power to alter reality, but cannot hold rein on the fragile strings of one's own life.

The Gothic-Punk world of the Storyteller system is dark and lonely; a world of violence, corruption, betrayal and sudden death. This is perhaps more true for mages than for any other inhabitants.

Playing a mage, you pursue a lonely existence re-moved, to a large extent, from the world of the mundane.

You go about your business as normal, hiding behind the facade that you have created to blend in to your surroundings, but there is more to you than those around you can see. You hold the fabric of reality in the palm of your hand— the reality of Sleepers, daydreamers who circle about you so involved in their daily routine that they remain ignorant to the truth right before their eyes. It's a truth that you know all too well.

Like the vampire, who can call upon her clan in times of need, or the werewolf, who shares close bonds with the pack as well as the tribe, the mage can call upon members of his Chantry when necessary. What separates a mage from the other inhabitants of the World of Darkness is his uniquely mortal and painfully human point of view.

Indeed, the mage is human, made of flesh and blood. Her profession separates her from the world around her, but human nature and emotions still bind her to this world. Thus, the mage lives life in a paradox, forever cursed to protect a world she can never truly embrace.

As a player in **Mage: The Ascension**, you must embrace all the conflicting emotions of the world around you and mold them into your own reality. In your world, nothing is black and white. There are no absolutes. Everything is awash in varying shades of gray, and good and evil are nothing more than points on an invisible compass created by the ignorant fools who whirl blindly around you. You have no time to ponder what is evil and what is not, only what is right for the moment, what needs to be done. Will using "the end" to justify "the means" be enough of an excuse when your conscience burns your soul and you just can't seem to quiet the screams that echo through your head?

The world has no care or understanding of your struggle. You act as a shield against forces attempting to destroy the fabric of Sleeper reality. This can be a thankless duty; few believe in your world, and fewer still would care if you lived or died there. This ingratitude sometimes awakens bitter resentment in you and your kind, and this resentment can be poison in the Ascension War.

You are their true savior; the one who allows Sleepers to continue their peaceful, ignorant existence in safety. Yet they do not acknowledge you as anything more than another sheep when, in reality, you are the shepherd that guides them along their path.

Instead, they help create a reality that serves others who they believe are the saviors of humanity. They forge these messiahs in their own image and believe them to be the saviors who will bless them and lead them away from the evils that they are too weak to combat themselves. Yet it is necessary that you maintain your secrets, keep them well hidden from those who would not understand. They are infamous for their fear of the unknown and, historically speaking, often take violent measures to eliminate anything that they cannot fathom.

Your loneliness, your misery is your own, and it must remain that way. The only people you can turn to are those of your own kind, and they suffer from the same torments that you do; alienation from the world that they live in. You can pretend to be like them, but you will be an outcast forever.

Remember, there is a balance to your tragedy— the power that you wield. You hold the forces of reality in the palm of your hand. Time, Spirits, the very fabric of reality are mere toys for your entertainment. Only you can decide if it is worth the price that you must pay.

The Chains of Reason

By Teeuwynn

Each one of us, without exception,... is somewhere attached to, colored by, or even undermined by the spirit which goes through the mass. Freedom stretches only as far as the limits of our consciousness.

— Carl Gustav Jung

Mages love knowledge; they crave it like the drug it is. They are— let's face it— knowledge junkies. The search for more knowledge, more power, one more ancient tome of magick, can cause mages to lose sight of the big picture. Big picture? But the more hard knowledge you possess, the closer you *are* to grasping the big picture, right? Wrong— to a degree.

Knowledge and learning taken out of context can provide an entirely skewed view of reality. Knowledge without balance of some kind can be more dangerous than total ignorance. Just ask some poor teenage Einstein-wannabe who blows off his finger in a home chemistry experiment. Yeah, he possessed the knowledge to make the formula, but he didn't have a handle on the consequences of creating that not-so-nifty potion.

Metaphysically, mages can be seen as being in the same boat as Einstein Junior. There is a grave danger for mages toying with Reality. They have the power, yes. Paradox spirits are there to spank them if they flaunt their power too blatantly, true. However, Paradox spirits care little about any other ways the mage might screw up.

The world is made up of more than hard facts. Actions do not occur in a vacuum. In **Mage**, there is a great temptation to manipulate Reality and gather knowledge without any true contemplation of the spiritual and ethical consequences of such manipulations. Sure, you can play **Mage** without a moment's thought to spirituality or emotion, but you may be missing out on some of the more intriguing aspects of the game. There is a Yang to every Yin, and often, spirituality, faith and emotions are considered anathema to detached observation and the sorting of fact from fiction. But facts cannot truly be divorced from their emotional and spiritual associations, lest they become less important, less vital to Reality. A flag without meaning to the people standing beneath it is merely a piece of colored cloth, but a flag that stirs up powerful emotions in the people observing it flutter in the breeze is something more than its physical essence. It becomes a symbol, and thus has the power to inspire. Many have died for such symbols and the ideals they represent to their observers. The face of Reality itself has been altered by the actions the flag inspires.

In a similar manner, the mage who reaches out emotionally and spiritually to the world around her is something more than just another wizard. Her connections heighten her understanding, and thus, her power. A scientist who studies a pool of water from the outside (noting its composition, color, salt content, etc.) does not truly understand the water as much as a scientist who plunges into the water and feels it wash over his head, feels that instant of panic as he leaves the surface world behind. Perhaps he feels joy as gravity loosens its implacable hold on him for just a little while, or perhaps he feels fascination observing the odd beauty of a dolphin. The latter scientist has a greater understanding of water because he has felt some of its emotional impact, not just the facts of its existence.

Mages who view Reality as a pool to be studied and manipulated, something from which they themselves are detached, can never have a full understanding of Reality. They have locked themselves out of the party and, as Jung points out, they are not truly free. In order to stay detached and clinical, one can never be free to plunge into the pool and make one's own splash.

This is not to say that learning and reason are not important to **Mage**, but if you limit yourself to just that half of Reality, to just the surface of the pool, the deeper meanings and interconnections of Reality will never be yours to understand... or command.

Of course, opening one's mind and senses to the spiritual rhythms of the universe necessitates one's seeing the ramifications of actions as more than just any obvious, factual results. Mages are responsible for their actions and the consequences of those actions. No one else holds responsibility for another. In plunging into the pool, in opening one's mind and heart to the universe, one cannot deny this responsibility; there is no one else to blame.

It has been observed that chains can be comforting because a person chained is a person without responsibilities. Someone else is in control; someone else understands. Such ethical slavery can indeed be comforting, but it ultimately keeps a mage from ever having any meaningful impact of her own upon Reality. Clawing for detached, dry knowledge and reason, the mage only blinds herself.

In order to open her eyes and shake off the chains of reason, a mage must be willing to let the waves of uncertainty and instinct wash over her. She must recognize that she holds the keys to Reality and that, in freeing herself, she accepts all that implies. There are no more parents, no more jailers. The responsibility of freedom rests squarely on the mage... and on you.

Enjoy.

Turning Vampires into Lawn Chairs and Other works of "High" Magick

By Stephan Wieck

"So, can we at least agree that reality in the World of Darkness is subjective?" someone said.

It was January of 1993, and Mark Rein•Hagen, Chris Early, my brother Stewart and I were in the middle of fusing our brains together to create the basis for **Mage**.

"Yes," said Mark.

"Yes," said Chris.

"Yes!" said I.

"Yes, for now, but remember *Lila*," said Stewart (whose equivocal response branched into a discussion that shaped a future for the metaphysics of **Mage**, but that's a story for another time).

So, in designing the metaphysics, and thereby the magick system of **Mage**, we began with the basic premise that reality is subjective and built a system of metaphysics which grew to include such oddities as Quintessence, Paradox and Patterns. In the end, we had a system that was certainly not perfect (what system of metaphysics is?), but was complete enough to be a good foundation for a system of magick, and for a mage's concept of the universe itself. From the metaphysics, it was a natural progression into defining the Spheres, and then finally, the game mechanics evolved.

The problem we had was that the original magick system rarely bowed to the altar of game balance or playability if it meant sacrificing its adherence to metaphysical concepts. I had always felt that such a sacrifice was analogous to killing story to preserve rules, which the Storyteller series of games has always abhorred. But, as the developers at White Wolf patiently (well, pointedly) reminded me, **Mage** is still a game. In the end, there were rotes and rules and flowcharts so that players and Storytellers would at least have a snowball's chance in hell of navigating the magick system without losing their minds.

Nevertheless, the system is still incredibly open, diverse, and, like the metaphysics it is based upon, subjective. It is open to interpretation by each person playing the game. For some storytelling groups, this will be a curse that fulfills a power-mad player's fondest dream; for others, it can open up what I see as an evolutionary step the storytelling experience, because in **Mage**, the players inevitably become assistant Storytellers.

Mages truly believe that anything is possible using some combination of the Spheres. Storytellers will quickly discover that the players will be capable of an incredible assortment of effects even at low Sphere levels. This alone makes it nigh-impossible to plan a firm plot line for a **Mage** adventure. It is impossible for a Storyteller to predict every use of magick the players might concoct over the course of an adventure, and then plan a plotline around it. Just try to imagine keeping **Mage** players onto a linear plotline where the Storyteller wants events X, Y and Z to happen in order right after one another. The players will inevitably get to scene X and then perform some magickal feat that make scenes Y and Z meaningless and catapults the storyline in an entirely new direction.

One **Mage** player wrote to us and said (I'm paraphrasing here), "Since my mage has rank such-and-such in Sphere so-and-so, doesn't that mean he could walk up to a vampire and turn her into a lawn chair?" Now imagine the poor Storyteller who has planned a vampire enemy to be central to the evening storyline, and when the characters first meet the vampire, a player announces that his mage will turn the vampire into a lawn chair, summon up a margarita and start a lawn party. Thus endeth the story.

Well, I certainly won't deny that it is possible to turn vampires into lawn chairs at some rank of Spheres. But is this good for the story? Some argue that **Mage's** magick system is inherently flawed by being so open to interpretation that **Mage** game sessions will inevitably break down into arguments between players and Storytellers over what it says on page 123 versus what it implies on page 243, etc., etc., etc. Who's having fun in that situation?

Ultimately, the folks holding this book, the players, determine the quality of any **Mage** story. I argue that the magick system's openness is not a flaw, but rather its primary strength. It allows the players to participate in telling a good story. I cannot think of any other storytelling game that requires as much creativity, self-discipline and storytelling ability from its players as **Mage** does. Everything from thinking of when and what type of magick to use, to combining Spheres for new effects or the appearance of coincidental magick, requires the player to be creative.

More important than a creative player, however, is player self-discipline. Does turning a vampire into a patio set contribute to the mood or theme of the story? Does the story become more meaningful or entertaining by your character's action? There will be plenty of opportunities for you to blow big holes in your Storyteller's plotline. Don't. This is not a commandment to artificially restrain your character— your creativity determines how successfully your character will survive the harsh world of **Mage**. But if you must disrupt the storyline, do it in such a way that the story is taken in a new and even more exciting or suspenseful direction. In **Mage**, you are not so much a player as an assistant Storyteller. Most of a **Mage** story's excitement must come from the players helping to create the saga.

If your Storyteller claims to have trouble designing a **Mage** story, then you and the other players aren't doing enough. What motivates your character? What does she strive for? How does she pursue it? Don't wait to be led into an adventure— tell your Storyteller that in the next game session, your character plans to quest after the knowledge of the Oracles, or go into the Chimerae, or whatever else you desire. The Storyteller might concoct something that will cancel or delay your character's plans, but at least you've set a character's goal. As the Storyteller's story progresses, you can weave in your character's own story.

So, that's the message. In **Mage**, you aren't just a player, you're an assistant Storyteller (amazing what a change in title can do to your outlook on something). Use your character's versatility and raw power to further the story, not to destroy it.

Prisoners in Eden

By Steven Brown

The face gazed up at him, heavy, calm, protecting, but what kind of smile was hidden beneath the dark mustache? Like a leaden knell the words came back to him:

WAR IS PEACE
FREEDOM IS SLAVERY
IGNORANCE IS STRENGTH
—George Orwell, *1984*

I am a media whore, just like the rest of you (even you "tragically-hip" Goths who are manipulated into buying White Wolf products. Hey, nobody's innocent). We just cannot live in the modern world without suffering some psychological manipulation. Still, despite Madison Avenue's attacks, I believe I spend my money on what I really want to spend it on.

I am a name and number in the databases of corporations and the government just like the rest of you. We use numbers for practically all dealings with each other. But I still believe in individuality.

I watch the news on television and read it in the newspaper, and I usually accept it as fact, just like most everyone else, without ever questioning it. Still, I know that the news media manipulates the information to suit its sponsors and others who hold power.

I know my country is the greatest country on Earth and that it stands for freedom and justice for all, just like . . . well, a lot of you might think. Still, I know the government caters to special interest groups, takes part in illegal activities, and that virtually all the higher positions are held by the wealthy. (Have we ever had a poor president? How about a poor senator?)

I am entertained by violence. I watch Beavis and Butthead, play Mortal Kombat and read plenty of violent books and comic books. Still, I know that violence is plaguing our society and that we must stop it from happening before it is too late.

I love those commercials with all those half-naked beautiful, hard-bodied women who tell me to buy certain companies' products. Why not? But hey, I know women shouldn't be treated as sex objects. Right?

I drive a car and buy countless non-recyclable products because I accept that it's okay for me to do so. Still, I think it's awful that the environment is being destroyed at such a rate that it probably can never be mended.

I am registered with social security, the draft, the U.S. census and so on. I use a credit card, even though I know that I give those who keep up with it a description of my purchasing habits. I have also filled out countless forms for jobs and loans. Still, I know that much of the information can, and probably does, reach the wrong people.

I buy products tested on animals, and also eat meat. There's nothing wrong with that, right? However, I hate cruelty to animals more than just about anything, and I love my dog as if he were a person.

Different "truths," but I accept them. We, as a society, accept them. As Orwell put it, we are "double-thinking": holding two incongruent "truths" in our heads without realizing how insane it is doing so. We don't really believe them, we really don't know what to believe. "Double-thinking" just makes life easier, and isn't that what life is all about?

We seem to be willing victims. Like drug addicts, we think we are in control of our own lives, although we're not. The mental programming we are bombarded with each day instills in us delusions of a somewhat perfect world where we are free-willed individuals living in a democratic society. When we do belly-ache about all our ills, as soon as we finish, we turn around again and continue behaving as they have trained us to behave. The only problems we have are the ones the media chooses to focus on.

Is this progress? Are we even the slightest bit aware of how much we are manipulated by the powers that be? Are we unaware of how many of us have given up hope? We have embraced this wondrous age with all the miracles it has to offer us: longer life, sanitation, super-technology and convenience, along with mass-marketed products and services. And the cost? You say, "Oh, not much, just our individuality, sense of identity, freedom, energy, beliefs and money." But don't worry, you'll never know it, or at least never care (because they won't tell you to care).

So what if our technology can create machines to work and function as human workers, only better? So what if businesses want to turn their employees into machine-like conformists? So what if we spend billions of dollars each year consuming tasteless, mass-produced, fast-foods that are bad for our health? So what if we spend hour after hour in front of the television watching situation-comedies and police shows designed for viewers with an I.Q. of 3? So what if we give strangers all sorts of information concerning our lives when we fill out forms for this or that? So what if we don't know what they do with all that information, or if we believe everything the media tells us, or if we rush out and buy products because we've seen a dozen commercials about them this week alone?

So what? That's progress. Right? Isn't life so much better this way? After all, aren't we taught that it is? Maybe we do live in a cold, impersonal age where we choose convenience and conformity over free will. The question is, what are we willing to do about it? What *can* we do about it?

How does this relate to Mage? That's the question you've been asking yourself, right? Well, if the Technocracy were to exist, would the world around us "Sleepers" really look any different than the way it looks to us now?

Yes, **Mage** is a game of make-believe. But we know that groups just as conspiratorial, manipulative and self-serving as the Technocracy could be out there watching over us, guiding our lives. Therein lies the real horror we "Sleepers" should consider.

Suggested Reading

A book is a participatory adventure. It involves a creative act at its inception and a creative act when its purpose is fulfilled. The writer dreams the dream and sets it down; the reader reinterprets the dream in personal terms, with personal vision, when he or she reads it. Each creates a world. The template is the book.

— Harlan Ellison, Intro to *Strange Wine*

There are so many good books— *great* books— of interest to the **Mage** player that it's hard to compile any sort of list. For what it's worth, however, the books below have all offered something useful to the writers of this book. **Mage** players and Storytellers may want to check them out themselves.

• Arrien, Angeles. *The Tarot Handbook: Practical Applications of Ancient Visual Symbols*

— Introduces the Tarot deck as a portal to understanding Tarot symbols from a Jungian psychological, mythological and cross-cultural perspectives.

• Campbell, Joseph. *The Hero with a Thousand Faces; Joseph Campbell and the Power of Myth*

— Invaluable books, not only for **Mage**, but for any player seriously interested in the universal roots of all myths, faiths and folklore. Unlike many philosophers or mythologists, Campbell is quite accessible; his greatest flaw is elaborating so extensively that the reader's thoughts become derailed. *The Power of Myth* is also available on audio cassettes and videotape and comes highly recommended.

• Cunningham, Scott. *The Truth About Witchcraft Today*

— Describes folk magic and Wiccan beliefs in the context of modern culture. While the book is a bit too guarded, in that Cunningham includes repeated reminders that Wiccans are not evil, human-sacrificing Satan-worshippers, it is nevertheless a good, basic introduction to folk magic and Wiccan beliefs.

• Ellison, Harlan. Strange *Wine; Paingod and Other Delusions; Deathbird Stories*

— Ellison is the most decorated fantasist of our time, and many of his intriguing, disturbing and often hilarious tales tie in well with the themes of **Mage**. The books above are particularly suited for fans of the World of Darkness, but any book of his is worth reading.

• Fraiser, Sir James George, *The Golden Bough*

— The quintessential work on anthropology and folk traditions and beliefs. A ponderous read, but very informative.

• Guiley, Rosemary Ellen. *The Encyclopedia of Witches and Witchcraft*

— A good resource for those seeking information not only on historical and modern witchcraft, but on the personalities involved as well. Also includes an extensive bibliography covering a variety of sources.

• Halevi, Z'ev ben Shimon. *Kabbalah: Tradition of Hidden Knowledge*

— Describes the kabbalah's beliefs and traditions in detail, providing diagrams and color plates to illustrate points. Also provides a 38-item bibliography for further reading. Very useful to anyone playing Order of Hermes characters.

• Hawk, Simon, *The Wizard of Fourth Street*

— An especially entertaining look at magick, technology and the mixing of the two in a wiseass neo-Gothic setting. The first sequel, *The Wizard of Whitechapel*, is decent, but the other books in Hawk's "Wizard" series go downhill fast.

• Kieckhefer, Richard. *Magic in the Middle Ages*.

— An academic approach to the magical traditions in medieval Europe and the Middle East. Less theoretical than detail-oriented. Very useful for players running chronicles in the Middle Ages.

• Lackey, Mercedes, Burning *Water; Children of the Night*

— Though the magic is a bit flashier than our own Paradox-bound world, the heroine of these books, Diana Tregarde, could be a Mage character! The situations and setting of Lackey's Tregarde books are quite appropriate for Mage players, and fun as well. The third book, Jinx High, is fairly lame (sorry, Misty!), but the first two are more than worthwhile.

• Starhawk, *The Spiral Dance*,

— A bit New-Agey, but certainly worth reading. This book is a developer's favorite and explores the relations of faith and belief to magick and personal fulfillment. Starhawk herself supplies the salt to take with this (or any other) book of personal truth — "… all the material in this book is presented so that you can take it and make it your own, adapt it to fit your inclinations and circumstances, add what works and discard what doesn't. I consider this a book of tools, not dogma." The same could be said for this so-called **Book of Shadows: The Mage Players Guide**.

Index